LAND AND LEASING

by
Judith Eubank

Edited by Jodie Leecraft

Published by

Petroleum Extension Service
Division of Continuing Education
The University of Texas at Austin
Austin, Texas

in cooperation with
Association of Desk and Derrick Clubs
Tulsa, Oklahoma

1984

© 1984 by The University of Texas at Austin
All rights reserved
Third Impression 2011
Printed in the United States of America

Catalog No.1.00110
ISBN 0-88698-094-1

The University of Texas at Austin is an equal opportunity institution. No state tax funds were used to print or mail this publication.

CONTENTS

FOREWORD

The Association of Desk and Derrick Clubs is an educational organization with some 10,000 members employed in the petroleum and allied industries who are convinced that, by acquiring greater knowledge of their multifaceted industry, they can enlarge their interests and improve their job performance. To further their goals, Desk and Derrick developed, in conjunction with the Petroleum Extension Service of The University of Texas at Austin (PETEX), a popular textbook, *Fundamentals of Petroleum,* an overview of the basic aspects of the petroleum industry, which is now in its third printing.

To expand this line of publications to cover each strategic portion of the industry in more depth, this volume encompassing land and leasing was compiled from the ideas and guidelines presented to PETEX by Desk and Derrick. It is designed to present to the nonprofessional the complexities of land and leasing in broader scope and greater detail than *Fundamentals of Petroleum* in order to provide comprehensive background and practical information for reference, yet it is written in concise and readable style. Other similar segments are planned for future publication.

Nonshareholding, noncommercial, nonprofit, nonpartisan, and nonbargaining in its policies, the Association of Desk and Derrick Clubs has very positive concepts on the value of education for women.

Association of Desk and Derrick Clubs
315 Silvey Building
Tulsa, Oklahoma 74119

PREFACE

Using Desk and Derrick's proposal for scope, organization, and audience, PETEX obtained the services of Judith Eubank to do the research and writing of *Land and Leasing*. Cinda Cyrus of the PETEX staff coordinated the constant communication between writer, Desk and Derrick members who were assigned to the project, content consultants, and manuscript reviewers. Each section of the manuscript, as soon as it was written, was sent to project members of Desk and Derrick, who, in turn, each forwarded it to a reviewer involved in the field, selected on the basis of experience and expertise. Reviewers' suggestions were then incorporated into the manuscript. When the entire manuscript was completed, along with tables, illustrations, and forms, it was reviewed by two lawyers experienced in land and leasing work — James Chandler and Ivan Geddie.

It should be apparent that the material in *Land and Leasing* received careful scrutiny from many knowledgeable readers; in spite of this fact, some errors, especially of omission, may have crept in, and PETEX would be grateful to readers for pointing these out so that they may be rectified in future editions.

The book attempts to cover as comprehensively as possible those aspects of land ownership, transfer, and leasing that are necessary to a basic understanding for those interested in the petroleum industry. *Fundamentals of Petroleum,* its forerunner, provides the overview of the subject of petroleum, and *Land and Leasing* dips further into it by concentrating on one area.

Land and Leasing is arranged around the broad subjects of land ownership, the leasing process, and arrangements for exploitation of leased minerals. Appendixes deal with specific leasing provisions in the top ten oil-producing states, lease filing systems, calculation of interests, and filing of legal instruments for record.

It is hoped that *Land and Leasing* will take its place alongside *Fundamentals of Petroleum* as a useful and practical source of information for those interested in its subject matter.

Jodie Leecraft
Editor

ACKNOWLEDGMENTS

Gathering information for the writing of *Land and Leasing* required not only the reading of pertinent written materials but also the interviewing of persons experienced and knowledgeable in the field. Sincere thanks for their generous gift of time and expertise is extended to Clem Ware of Fluor Oil and Gas Corporation, Midland, Texas, and William Parmeter, Zenith Petroleum, Houston, Texas. Others who were most helpful were —

Scott Anderson, TIPRO, Austin, Texas
Mary Badgett, CPA, Lubbock, Texas
Katherine S. Boyd, API, Washington, D. C.
Jim Caples, abstractor, Georgetown, Texas
Robert Lewis Chandler, attorney, Dallas, Texas
Gwynne Gazzaway, independent producer/royalty owner, Dallas, Texas
Kim Kunkel, energy consultant, Austin, Texas
Charles Liles, API, Dallas, Texas
Michael McElroy, attorney, Austin, Texas
Judy Orme, abstractor, Austin, Texas
Ernest Smith, dean, UT School of Law, Austin, Texas
Mrs. James Stafford, NARO, Ada, Oklahoma
Philip Whitworth, attorney, Austin, Texas
Keith Williams, attorney, Austin, Texas

Much gratitude is also due the following persons who performed the invaluable service of reviewing the manuscript for accuracy and usefulness of content:

Patricia H. Booker, Columbia Gas Transmission Corporation, Charleston, West Virginia
Sharon S. Butand, American Exploration Company, Bixby, Oklahoma
Kay Capps, Moncrief Oil, Fort Worth, Texas
Calvin Ellis, Amarillo, Texas
Eva Franklin, Phillips Petroleum, Houston, Texas
Sue Gilmore, Graham, Texas
C. R. Kourt, Phillips Petroleum, Bartlesville, Oklahoma
R. F. Maul, Phillips Petroleum, Bartlesville, Oklahoma
James McCommons, McCommons Oil Company, Dallas, Texas
James Read, Black Eagle Petroleum, Billings, Montana
W. Roy Rice, Sr., Columbia Gas Transmission Corporation, Charleston, West Virginia
Charles W. Sartain, attorney, Baton Rouge, Louisiana
J. E. Williams, Phillips Petroleum, Bartlesville, Oklahoma

Final review of the complete and edited manuscript was done by James H. Chandler, attorney, Midland, Texas, and Ivan G. Geddie, attorney, Kerr-McGee Corporation, Oklahoma City, Oklahoma. Their help was considerable and is much appreciated.

Desk and Derrick members deserving acknowledgment for their conscientious efforts in guiding the project from start to finish, reviewing the manuscript for organization and tone, and providing content reviewers are —

Joyce O'Bannon, ADDC coordinator for the project
ADDC Education Committee members for 1983
Dottie Faust, ADDC immediate past president
Loretta Owens, ADDC second vice-president
Barbara Rollinson, Puget Sound Club

Dr. Keith Carter, Petroleum Land Management Coordinator of The University of Texas College of Business Administration, gave much helpful guidance in the selection of leasing forms to be used in the book. And Mark Longley of the PETEX staff performed the task of acquiring information, maps, and leasing forms with the greatest possible efficiency.

Sincere thanks are due the American Association of Petroleum Landmen for permission to reproduce material from its book *The AAPL Guide for Landmen*. Other associations, agencies, and companies who furnished forms and illustrative material for the book deserve thanks also.

Alberta Department of Energy and Natural Resources, Edmonton, Alberta
Canadian Association of Petroleum Landmen, Calgary, Alberta
Continental Oil Company, Houston, Texas
Exxon Company USA, Houston, Texas
Willard C. Kimball, Midland, Texas
K. Kunkel Resources, Austin, Texas
Kraftbilt Products, Tulsa, Oklahoma
McMoran Offshore Exploration Company, Metairie, Louisiana
M. L. Bath Company, Shreveport, Louisiana
Petroleum Industry Training Service, Calgary, Alberta (especially Les J. Evans and Wayne Wetmore for gathering together many Canadian forms)
Pound Printing and Stationery Company, Houston, Texas
Stephens County Mineral Owners Association, Duncan, Oklahoma
Texas General Land Office, Austin, Texas
U. S. Department of the Interior, Bureau of Land Management
U. S. Department of the Interior, Geological Survey, Denver, Colorado
U. S. Department of the Interior, Minerals Management Service, Anchorage, Alaska

INTRODUCTION

Before a petroleum corporation can develop oil or gas reserves, it must acquire the legal rights to explore, drill, and produce. How these rights are acquired and from whom will differ from country to country. In most oil-producing nations, mineral resources are owned by the national government, and petroleum corporations must negotiate with government representatives in order to secure contracts for mineral development. The complexity, cost, and, in some cases, the instability of these arrangements can be very great.

In the United States, too, much of the land and mineral wealth are publicly owned. But, in addition to the resources belonging to state and federal governments, vast amounts of land (about two-thirds of our onshore territory) belong to private persons. The mineral rights to this privately owned land are also commonly in private hands. Very often, then, corporations that wish to exploit domestic oil and gas reserves must acquire the rights to do so from private citizens. The legal instrument used to transfer these rights from both private and public ownership to a petroleum corporation is the oil and gas lease. The term *oil and gas lease* is a generic term and as used herein includes "oil, gas, and minerals lease," as well as "oil, gas, and associated liquid hydrocarbons lease."

The legal obligations established by an oil and gas lease differ markedly from those set up by an ordinary commercial lease. Landowners and leasing corporations are connected, economically and legally, in ways that require regular monitoring and occasional renegotiation to ensure that all the lease provisions are satisfactorily met. The personnel involved in acquiring and handling company relations with landowners differ, of course, in their numbers and functions as the companies they work for differ in size, policies, and procedures. More and more such personnel, however, have at least some legal training. Many are attorneys. Private owners, for their part, realize increasingly how valuable their mineral resources are and how complicated the arrangements that allow for effective development of those resources. They, too, often employ specialists—attorneys, accountants, financial analysts, and estate planners—to help them make decisions about leasing their mineral rights. State and federal governments use their own specialists to assess the value of publicly owned mineral wealth.

A grasp of the basic legal issues and terms, as well as some attention to the economic and social complexities, is essential to understanding how the petroleum industry leases and develops mineral reserves in this country. To facilitate that understanding, the discussion that follows is divided into three major sections. The first section deals with land ownership: who owns land and minerals, who may lease and under what conditions. The second section describes the leasing process: how oil and gas leases are acquired and by whom. The final section discusses a number of related arrangements often needed to exploit leased minerals effectively—for example, operating

1

agreements, joint ventures, and unitization. These last arrangements frequently involve the same company personnel who help to secure leases.

Since one of the distinctive features of mineral ownership in the United States is the widespread occurrence of private holdings, the discussion will begin with the private land-owner. Starting with private or fee lands has the additional advantage of allowing the discussion to move from the more general and theoretical to the more concrete and specific.

Privately Owned Land

PRIVATE OWNERSHIP

The word *landowner* describes a person who holds the title to a specific piece of property. Some people think a property owner can do almost anything with the land he or she owns—sell or lease it, build on it or dig into it, plant it, or leave it to anyone in a last will and testament. A variety of laws affects what the landowner may do with his property, however. Besides federal and state laws and regulations, city ordinances may also influence the owner's actions. Zoning ordinances, for example, may prohibit an owner from drilling a well in his back yard. It would seem that a rural landowner would have fewer restrictions and could explore, develop, and profit from his property without hindrance. But can he? And does his property include anything that may be found beneath the surface of the land as well as whatever is standing or growing on top?

The answer to such questions may be yes or no, depending on a wide variety of circumstances. American property law is complex, and much of it is *case,* or *common, law.*

Such law is composed of many court decisions made over the years on many individual cases. Common law is fundamental to land ownership in all of our states, with the exception of Louisiana. There, the French Napoleonic Code serves as the basis of *statute,* or *civil, law* that governs real estate ownership. Statute law, unlike common law, originates in the laws established by a legislative or other governing body. Both of these types of law—common law and civil law—have long histories and are full of numerous statutory additions and variations. Statutes often vary from state to state, and common law itself is full of many confusing terms.

One common-law term very frequently applied to the private ownership of land is *fee.* A property owner might be told that he holds his land in *fee simple,* that the oil and gas lease he has just signed constitutes a *determinable fee* in that same land, and that the lawyer who has just explained the lease will certainly expect a handsome *fee* for his services. All of these *fees* seem to be connected,

3

yet they are clearly not the same. The various usages, in fact, can all be traced back to the Middle Ages when a *fee,* or *fief,* meant land held from one's feudal lord. Such an estate could be inherited and passed from generation to generation, but the original grant was for services (often military) rendered to an overlord. By extension, a fee came to mean almost any service or payment rightly due to a superior. Eventually, the term was applied to the remuneration for professional services, to the sum charged for a license or an admission ticket, and even to a tip or gratuity. In common usage these days a fee can be almost any sort of payment, but in common law, a *fee* still means, basically, an *estate or interest in land.* The landowner is a fee holder; the land is the fee, and he owns — or holds — it in fee.

Types of Ownership

Subject to state and federal laws, a twentieth-century American fee holder still enjoys considerable freedom in the use and disposal of his property. One important freedom is the right to inherit and devise, or will, the fee. (An owner is said, legally, to *devise* real estate and to *bequeath* personal property to his heirs.) *Fee simple* means that no restrictions exist on the privileges of inheritance. In nearly all states, a modern American holder of fee simple property can leave his estate to his wife, his sons, his daughters, or a stranger met once on the road. Sometimes, though, property is entailed; that is, there are restrictions on how the owner may devise it. If, for example, he holds his land in *fee tail,* he can leave it only to "heirs of his body," and property held in *fee tail male* can descend only to a male heir. Should the family stop producing male heirs, even distant cousins, the fee would revert to the original grantor or his successors. Entailed property is

rare in this country; fee simple holdings are far more usual. For that reason, references to the *landowner* in the following pages can be understood to mean *the free holder of fee simple property,* unless the term is qualified in some way.

Rights of Mineral Ownership

The unqualified landowner holds title to the surface of the land, the space above it, and the subsoil below it (all the way down, in a narrowing pie-shaped wedge, to the center of the earth). He also owns any minerals contained in the land. To him alone belong the rights to explore, dig, drill, produce, and benefit from minerals on his estate. He can prevent other people from coming onto his property and doing or trying to do any of these things.

The owner of a fee simple estate may sell his entire interest (all his legal rights) in the land, sell only the surface and retain the minerals for himself, or sell only the minerals and keep the surface (in which case he becomes owner of the "fee in surface"). If he does *sever* or separate his interests, he creates a *surface estate* and a *mineral estate.* These are then considered to be separate estates, legally speaking. They may be sold to separate owners, leased to separate companies or individuals, and divided again and again as they are *conveyed* (transferred) for various purposes. Mineral estates especially are subject to complicated divisions. An owner, for example, can sell all or a specified portion of his interest in the minerals or all or a specified portion of his interest in the proceeds from the minerals.

The legal instrument that gives an organization or individual the right to enter someone else's property, search for oil and gas, produce them when found, and profit from them when produced is the *oil and gas lease.* Its legal definition varies from state to state, and even within a given state no· actual document or lease form can be regarded as standard. While there are various legal instruments by which such sales, or conveyances, are made, it is important first to look at some of the limitations placed by the law and by economic considerations upon the mineral estate owner.

Limitations on Mineral Ownership

Any sales or leasing agreements the owner of a mineral estate may wish to make are limited by legal and economic considerations. Legal limitations may arise from the concept of mineral ownership held by the state in which the minerals are located and from decisions that the courts have handed down in settling disputes in accordance with that concept. Other legal limitations come from statutory (civil) law, especially from the rules enforced by the regulatory commissions created for that purpose by legislatures of particular states. These rules vary from one state to the next, but, in general, they concern such matters as well spacing, each well's allowable daily production, and field rules for production practices. Economic considerations— especially the tremendous amounts of money required to drill for and produce hydrocarbons—also influence the owner's decision to sell or to lease his mineral estate. These legal and economic limitations influence what the owner of a mineral estate can do and what he may wish to do, and both the owner and any person or company with whom he enters into an agreement concerning the mineral estate must have a clear understanding of the constraints on that estate.

Legal limitations. Many of the legal constraints on the use and disposal of subsurface

minerals have their origins in early confusion about what minerals were, legally, and how they could be owned when they were invisible (hidden in the depths of the earth). English common law, though it said some useful things about mining hard minerals, offered little guidance on the subjects of oil and natural gas. American courts realized that petroleum was not a stationary resource like a coal seam and thought, in fact, that oil wandered around rather freely, migrating across property lines and behaving very much like an underground river or a free-ranging wild animal. Since oil and gas were thus migratory and (until produced) invisible, the courts in some states decided that such minerals could not actually be *owned* until they had been "captured" and reduced to possession. This concept has been referred to as the *rule of capture.* In states that adopted this view (variously called *nonabsolute ownership* or *nonownership* or *nonownership in place*), the person who owns a fee simple estate cannot own subsurface oil and gas until these minerals have been separated from their natural habitat and reduced to possession. Instead, he owns the land's surface, the exclusive right to drill for minerals, and the right to retain any minerals produced. The rule of capture, as first enunciated by courts in nonownership states, gave a landowner title to all the oil and gas he could produce from wells on his estate—even if it could be proved that some of these minerals had been drained from under a neighbor's land. The unlucky neighbor had no recourse except to drill his own wells and capture his own oil as fast as he could, as suggested by the offset drilling rule.

The courts in other states took a different view, one that affirmed the ownership of minerals *in place*—that is, under the surface of the land. This is called *absolute ownership,* and this theory declares that oil and gas are part of the land and can be fully owned even before they are produced and visibly flowing from a well. Even states with an *absolute,* or *ownership-in-place,* view of minerals, however, acknowledge that oil and gas can move around under the surface in ways impossible to control. So, oil that travels across a property line and moves to a well on the other side leaves its owner, and he loses title to it. The new owner acquires title until someone adjacent to him drills a well and drains away his property in turn.

In practice, then, neither theory of mineral ownership prevented neighbors from draining each other's property. So long as the rule of capture was applied in disputed cases—as it was in nearly all states—a landowner's only real protection for his mineral estate was what might be called retaliatory drilling. When it finally became apparent that the rule of capture and the offset drilling rule were leading to recklessly wasteful practices, as they did in the East Texas oil field, state legislatures were forced to pass conservation laws to regulate production and to create agencies to enforce such laws. The kinds of laws enacted again varied from state to state. For example, Texas found it advisable to pass fairly strict laws about well spacing. West Virginia, on the other hand, left the spacing of shallow wells relatively unregulated. Many of these conservation laws were challenged in the courts, but most were upheld. State regulatory agencies like the Texas Railroad Commission or the Oklahoma Corporation Commission were charged with the responsibility for enforcing sound conservation rules, preventing waste of valuable resources, and protecting landowners' correlative rights. (*Correlative rights* are those rights afforded the owner of each property in a pool to produce without waste his just and equitable share of the oil and gas in such a pool. If both Smith and Jones own land over Big Money Reservoir, both should

enjoy benefits from it, in justly proportionate measure.)

Though the rule of capture and the offset drilling rule are less liberally invoked these days, they are still included in many large-acreage leases, and the theory of ownership that prevails in a given state can still make a difference to the landowner. Ownership or nonownership of minerals in place can, for example, affect the way that interests in oil and gas can be conveyed (and by whom), how severed oil and gas interests are taxed, and the legal remedies available to owners who feel that their interests are being threatened. Only an attorney needs to be well versed in the intricacies of his state's ownership theory, but any landowner would be prudent to find out which theory applies in his state and what practical differences it may make to him. Examples of ownership-in-place states are Texas, Mississippi, Tennessee, and West Virginia; examples of nonownership states are California, Louisiana, New Mexico, and Oklahoma.

Federal agencies also involve themselves in regulatory questions. Though the landowner may never deal directly with the Environmental Protection Agency or the Bureau of Land Management, these agencies can certainly affect his life and legal transactions. Oil and gas production are now among the most heavily regulated of American industries.

Economic constraints. The other constraints upon a mineral estate owner are chiefly economic. No matter how potentially valuable the minerals under his land, a private individual often lacks the money required to explore that land, drill it, and capture his own minerals. Even if he could raise the money, he would still be dependent upon the highly specialized technical knowledge and skills of geologists, engineers, drilling and production crews, and (in most cases) marketing and legal personnel. In the face of dwindling resources and foreign competition, all of these people must use increasingly sophisticated techniques and equipment in order to produce oil and gas at a profit. Small wonder that the landowner generally allows someone else to search for and produce the minerals beneath his property.

TYPES OF LANDOWNERS

Once a landowner has decided to lease, can he in fact do so? Can he execute a valid oil and gas lease? The answer to that question is usually yes if the landowner holds his land in fee simple. Conditions that would prevent him from executing a valid lease include his having already granted a lease on the property, having already disposed of any of the minerals covered by the proposed lease, or having incurred a legal disability that would invalidate any contract he might make—if he had been adjudged incompetent or insane, for example.

Property can be held, however, by other types of ownership than fee simple, and even that straightforward arrangement can be complicated if the owner severs the surface from the mineral estate. Each of the several kinds of private ownership directly affects petroleum leasing and what must be done to execute a valid lease. The types of landowners most commonly encountered are surface owners and mineral owners, life tenants and remaindermen, cotenants, married persons, illiterates, owners who are agents of the state, and fiduciaries.

Surface Owners and Mineral Owners

The owner of a surface estate has little to say about the leasing and production of subsurface minerals. The mineral estate owner, subject to the limitations of his deed, can enter the property, use as much of the surface as is reasonable to explore for oil and gas, then produce the minerals for his own profit.

The owner of the mineral interest may also have the right to execute an oil and gas lease (thereby becoming the *lessor*). His *lessee* (an oil company, for example) in turn receives the right to enter the property and the exclusive right to explore; conduct drilling and operating activities; and build roads, gathering lines, tanks, and other aids to the reasonable development of the mineral estate.

Whether or not there is any cooperation and consultation between surface and mineral estate owners, the courts usually uphold a lessee's rights to enter and develop leased property. Though a surface owner has not, in law, much to say about these rights, some irate owners have expressed themselves on the subject with the help of a shotgun. Any surface owner who turns back the drilling trucks at his gate risks a court judgment that may allow damages to a lessee denied access. These damages can include the increased costs of drilling and any loss of oil and gas from drainage to production on adjoining land. If, on the other hand, surface and mineral owners *are* on good terms that they wish to maintain, the mineral estate owner may do his best to provide preagreed surface damage compensation to the surface owner. In some areas (parts of Utah and North Dakota, for example), lessees may even give surface owners small royalty payments to which they have no legal claim but which offer some compensation for damaged surface property.

The surface owner in all states is normally entitled, as a minimum, to compensation for damages to growing crops that are the result of drilling operations. Some states, such as Oklahoma, have also passed statutes that affect the relationship between the mineral estate owner or his lessee and the surface owner. Therefore, the laws of the state where the well to be drilled is located must be reviewed to determine whether unusual requirements exist before operations are begun.

Life Tenants and Remaindermen

A life tenant does not have full legal title to property but only the exclusive right to possess and use it during his lifetime, and cannot leave the property to his heirs. The remainderman does have an interest in the property and will come into possession upon the death of the tenant. Because they share interests in the land, both the life tenant and the remainderman should, under ordinary circumstances, execute an oil and gas lease together. If the remainderman does not execute the lease or ratify it, the lease will expire when the life tenant does. This possibility could become, for the lessee in the middle of production, an unpleasant and expensive reality.

With all the needed signatures available, the lessee's only problem is how to pay rentals, royalties, and bonuses to the parties concerned. These payments should, ideally, be specified in the lease itself, or, failing agreement among life tenants and remaindermen, the matter should be referred to an attorney for his advice.

Cotenants

Cotenants (also known as *co-owners* or *tenants in common*) are people who own land together. They are entitled to equal use of the land and may also—if their co-ownership is

the kind known as *joint tenancy*—inherit one another's interest in the land. Whether one cotenant can lease the land without the consent of his fellow owners is a disputed point. Some states, like Louisiana and West Virginia, do not permit a co-owner to lease without such consent. A number of states do so permit, while stipulating that a lease obtained from a single co-owner applies only to that owner's interest and cannot be held to bind anyone else. A lessee then becomes, legally, a tenant in common with the other owners and as such may enter the land and search, drill, produce, and so on.

In a majority of states, cotenants who did not sign the lease cannot be held responsible for the costs of exploring and drilling a well that proves to be dry. Should a well prove productive, nonjoining co-owners *do* receive a share in the profits after the drilling party has recouped the costs of drilling, development, production, and marketing that can be attributed to the nonjoiners' shares.

Once a lease has been signed, nonjoining cotenants may later decide to *ratify* (that is, approve and confirm) the lease rather than share the ongoing costs of producing wells and additional development. (Such ratification would entitle them to cost-free royalties.) It is also fairly common, especially when many cotenants are involved, to have one cotenant sign a base lease and all the others sign a lease ratification. Finally, some states have *forced pooling* statutes that require unleased cotenants to join in drilling a well on pooled land or to lease their interests to the lessee. The terms of such leases are set down by the relevant governmental authority.

Married Persons

The old common-law disabilities that once prevented married women from disposing of their own property without their husbands being party to the contract have been greatly reduced by changes in state and federal law. Nonetheless, anyone seeking an oil and gas lease from a married person would be prudent to have both spouses sign the lease. There are still situations—and states—that require both signatures. Some community property states, like California, and most noncommunity property states require both spouses to sign. (*Community property* is property acquired after the marital community has been formed; what each spouse owned before marriage remains his or her separate property.) When the husband is legally head of the marital community, as he is in Texas, he may execute a lease without his wife's signature on the document. If, however, the land to be leased is part of the homestead, both husband and wife are required to sign any instrument that encumbers the homestead. *Homestead property,* it may be noted, consists of the land, house, outbuildings, and sometimes other things (tools, for instance) that are occupied or used by the owner and his family. Where homestead property is recognized, it cannot be seized or forfeited to pay general debts. Finally, if a lease involves property that forms part of the wife's dower or the husband's curtesy rights, both spouses usually need to sign. *Dower property* is that part of a husband's estate that his widow inherits for life, and *curtesy rights* refer to a widower's interest in his dead wife's lands when the spouses have had children capable of inheriting.

Illiterates

The inability to read and write does not constitute a legal disability. The illiterate person has full power to execute an oil and gas lease on his property. It is a wise precaution, though, for the lessee or his agent to read the lease aloud to the landowner in the presence of witnesses before the instrument is signed.

State statutes vary on the correct procedure for an illiterate person's execution of a legal agreement. The need for witnesses and the way in which the mark should be made also vary. The relevant rules should, therefore, be made clear to all parties and, of course, be carefully followed.

Owners as Agents of the State

In many countries, the government is the sole owner of all subsurface minerals, and anyone wishing to produce those minerals must deal directly with the government concerned. In Texas, rather oddly, the same situation once existed. In its first constitution, Texas followed the legal examples of Spain and Mexico that declared all minerals under the land to be crown or state property. Somewhat later, Texas changed its laws to conform to the English model of private and fee ownership. Later still, the state gave to its land commissioner the power to classify land at the time of patenting. (A *patent* is simply a grant of land conveyed by the sovereign, that is, by the state or other public entity that holds the title.) The land commissioner classified property according to its use, and those tracts that were *minerally classified* remained, so far as their minerals were concerned, the property of the state of Texas. A citizen might obtain the patent to a minerally classified tract, fence it, farm it, and enjoy all the rights of fee ownership except the right to lease and profit from its minerals.

Certain lands patented between 1895 and 1931 were minerally classified; the state of Texas still has the title to any minerals found under those lands. In 1919, however, Texas passed the Relinquishment Act that was interpreted by the court (in *Greene v. Robinson,* 1928) to mean that the surface owner of a minerally classified tract is—for leasing

TABLE 1.1
Descent and Distribution for the Top Eight Oil-Producing States

(For up-to-the-minute changes or additions, consult the relevant state probate code or other pertinent statutes.)

ALASKA (subject to dower and other rights of the surviving spouse)

1. To children and descendants of deceased children by representation;
2. If no children survive, to other lineal descendants, equally if in the same degree, otherwise by representation;
3. To the surviving spouse;
4. To parents equally or the survivor of them;
5. To brothers and sisters and descendants of deceased brothers and sisters by representation.

CALIFORNIA

1. To child or children and descendants of a deceased child or children, in equal amounts if all are of the same degree, otherwise by right of representation;
2. To parents or surviving parent;
3. To brothers and sisters and issue of deceased brothers and sisters, such issue taking always by rights of representation.

KANSAS

1. If the decedent leaves a surviving spouse and child or children, ½ to the surviving spouse and ½ to the child or children surviving and the living issue, if any, of prior deceased children, but such issue inherits per stirpes; if no surviving spouse, then all to the children;
2. If the decedent leaves no issue, the whole of the estate to the surviving spouse;
3. If the decedent leaves no surviving spouse or issue, the whole of the estate to the parents or all to the surviving parent.

LOUISIANA (subject to community property)

1. Surviving spouse and children (or their descendants):
   a. Spouse takes ½ community property plus usufruct of the other ½ until death or remarriage.
   b. Children or their descendants take ½ community property (subject to the mother's usufruct) and all separate property.

2. Children and their descendants but no surviving spouse: children and descendants take all.
3. Surviving spouse and parent or parents but no children:
   a. Surviving spouse takes ¾ community property.
   b. Parent or parents take ¼ community and all separate property.
4. Surviving spouse with no ascendants or descendants:
   a. Surviving spouse takes all community property.
   b. Brothers and sisters or their ascendants take all separate property.
5. No spouse or descendants, but brothers and sisters and one parent:
   a. Brothers and sisters take ¾.
   b. Parent takes ¼.
6. Brothers and sisters and two parents:
   a. Brothers and sisters take ½.
   b. Parent takes ½.
7. No descendants, surviving spouse, brothers, or sisters: parents or survivors take all.

NEW MEXICO

1. To surviving spouse, ¼ of estate; the remainder in equal shares to children;
2. If no issue, entire estate to surviving spouse, or, if none, to parents.

OKLAHOMA

1. If there is a surviving spouse but no descendants, father, mother, brother, or sister of the decedent, and the property was acquired during coverture by joint industry of the husband and wife, surviving spouse takes all.
2. With a surviving spouse and one child (or its descendants), each takes ½.
3. With a surviving spouse and more than one child (or their descendants), the spouse takes ⅓, and the children take ⅔.
4. With a surviving spouse and parents, brothers and sisters, but no descendants, spouse takes ½ and parents, brothers, and sisters take ½.

TABLE 1.1—*Continued*

TEXAS

1. With a surviving spouse and children, the surviving spouse takes ½ of the community property, ⅓ of the personal estate (separate property), and a life estate of ⅓ the separate property. The children (or their descendants) take ½ of the community property, ⅔ of the personal estate, and a fee in ⅔ of the separate property.
2. With surviving spouse but no children, the surviving spouse takes all community property and personal estate and a fee in ½ of the real estate. Decedent's parents, brothers, and sisters (or their descendants) take fee in ½ of the real estate. If there are no surviving parents, brothers, and sisters (or their descendants), the surviving spouse takes fee in all real estate.
3. With children (or their descendants) but no surviving spouse, the children (or their descendants) take all community property and all separate property.

WYOMING

1. To children equally, descendants of a deceased child taking the share to which such child, if living, would be entitled;
2. To parents, brothers, and sisters equally, descendants of a deceased brother or sister taking the share to which such brother or sister, if living, would be entitled, except that if the decedent leaves a surviving spouse, parents, or surviving parent, they take to the exclusion of the brothers and sisters.

purposes—the agent of the state. The surface owner can execute an oil and gas lease on his land and receive 50 percent of all the economic benefits from that lease. The other 50 percent goes to the state. If a Texas landowner is in any doubt as to whether his land is minerally classified, the Commissioner of the General Land Office in Austin, Texas, can inform him of the facts. Oil and gas leases on such property must be executed on official forms supplied by and filed in and approved by the General Land Office.

Fiduciaries

A *fiduciary* is a person who serves, with or without bond, to act for the benefit of another in all matters connected with a specified undertaking. He may represent an estate to its best legal, financial, or other interest. Fiduciaries are often lawyers, bankers, executors, or administrators who work on behalf of an estate entrusted to their care by a will or other legal instrument (for example, by a trust agreement or a power of attorney). Whether a fiduciary can execute a valid oil and gas lease depends upon the laws of the state in which the property is located and the specific provisions of the empowering instrument. Among the more common fiduciaries are executors and administrators, guardians, trustees, persons acting under powers of attorney, and representatives of unknown or missing heirs.

Executors and administrators. When a landowner dies *intestate,* or without leaving a will, the court appoints an *administrator* to oversee the deceased owner's estate. Such an administrator can generally, with the authority of the court, execute oil and gas leases. Gaining the court's approval depends upon procedures that vary from state to state. When the deceased landowner's heirs take possession—according to the state's *laws of descent and distribution*—they may then execute valid leases on their inherited property. (See table 1.1 for descent and distribution laws in the major oil-producing states.)

Independent *executors,* on the other hand, are named in wills to carry out the provisions of those wills. They are not usually able to execute mineral leases unless the will under which they act expressly allows them to. In some states, an independent executor cannot execute an oil and gas lease even *with* court authority if the will does not explicitly empower him to do so.

Guardians. Guardians manage property for persons legally unable to manage for themselves — for minor children, for example, or the mentally incompetent. Whether appointed by the court or named in a will, guardians have the power — when acting under court order — to execute oil and gas leases. They need to be familiar, however, with the state statutes that regulate leases granted on behalf of persons in special legal categories. Many states have enacted laws that make leasing the property of minors and incompetents considerably easier than it once was, but the prospective lessee — as well as the guardian — should examine these laws carefully for special procedures and provisions.

Minors or incompetent persons who attempt to execute their own leases may or may not be legally able to do so. Some states do not recognize as valid any contracts signed by minors under the age of majority or those signed by the mentally incompetent. Other states allow such contracts to be voided — by the minor, for example, when he reaches legal age or by the appointed guardian of a person formally judged incompetent or insane or certified as a drunkard. Once again, the lessee should carefully familiarize himself with the relevant state laws or risk signing and paying for an invalid lease.

Trustees. A *trust* conveys property to a person (who may be, legally, an individual, partnership, or corporation) for the benefit of a third party. The *trustee* holds legal title to the property, and the third party receives benefits and owns the equitable or beneficial title. *Equity,* it should be mentioned, is a system of rules and doctrines that supplements and can — in the interests of justice and fairness — supersede both common and statute law.

It is always desirable that a trust instrument specifically empower trustees to execute oil and gas leases. If a trust agreement is silent on this point, state law may still permit a trustee to grant leases, particularly if he is authorized to sell the property. (If the trust merely allows him to mortgage the property, the power to lease is *not* automatically carried as an additional right.) In Texas, for instance, a trust instrument that explicitly invokes the Texas Trust Act gives trustees quite liberal powers to execute leases. In other states, the appropriate language can similarly empower trustees to grant mineral leases.

Persons acting under powers of attorney. A lawyer or other agent acting under a general *power of attorney* (written authority to act for another) cannot, in most instances, execute oil and gas leases. Other powers — to bargain, sell, grant, and convey property — do not carry the right to grant mineral leases unless that additional authority is explicitly set out in the instrument. State statutes govern such matters as the proper execution of a power of attorney and how it must be recorded. Finally, a power of attorney is revoked by the death of the person who executed it unless it is drawn so as to survive disability, which can include death. Before accepting a lease from anyone acting under such a power, the lessee should examine the instrument's specific provisions, its execution, and its recording (if recording is required). The lessee will also wish to know the current status of the holder.

Representatives of unknown or missing heirs. It sometimes happens that landowners or heirs remain unknown or simply cannot be located even after diligent efforts to find them. In such a case, the court can effect a *judicial transfer* or *judicial determination* of ownership by appointing a receiver to represent the missing owner and to execute oil and gas leases on the property. This procedure can also be used after tax sales or mortgage foreclosures.

State and Federal Lands

While much of our nation's oil and gas is located on privately owned land, large amounts of both are to be found on state and federal lands. (Extensive private ownership of mineral resources is the exception, not the rule, among nations. For example, see Appendix A on mineral ownership in Canada.) The various state legislatures, as well as the United States Congress, have made provision for the leasing of some (though by no means all) of this publicly held land to the petroleum industry. Already noted is one set of conditions, in Texas, in which a mineral estate—severed from the surface estate—can be leased by the surface owner acting as agent for the state. On such minerally classified lands, the government and the private citizen may share the economic rewards of successful mineral development. When the government owns both surface and mineral estates, leasing may still be possible if the appropriate procedures are carefully followed.

STATE LANDS

The leasing of state lands is a matter of separate, rather piecemeal legislation, instead of a uniformly applicable code. Each state has a board or an agency to handle applications for mineral leases. Competitive bidding, done on state-supplied forms, is the common method; but specific procedures, lease terms, and expected payments for a successful venture vary widely among the states. So does the maximum acreage that any individual or corporation may lease. Table 2.1 lists the leasing agencies for all the states, along with other pertinent facts like the leasing method and customary terms. The prospective lessee should realize, though, that all these details are subject to changes in state law. Anyone planning to lease from a state agency should study its notices of sales for particular details. For general requirements, he should request information from the agency itself.

In Texas, for example, a bidder can read the state's leasing regulations in the *Texas Register,* which is kept in the secretary of state's office. For help in interpreting what he reads, he can contact the state's General Land Office (which also supplies forms of the kind

TABLE 2.1
Leasing Agencies for State Lands, with Leasing Methods and Customary Terms

FEDERAL, STATE AND FEE LEASES
APPENDIX "A"—STATE LANDS

State	State Leasing Agency	Method of Leasing Proven	Method of Leasing Wildcat	Average Royalty Proven	Average Royalty Wildcat	Average Rental Proven	Average Rental Wildcat	Term	Maximum Acreage
Alaska	Commissioner of Public Lands	Sealed Bid Oral	Sealed Bid Oral	(6)	(6)	$1-$3 (6)	$1-$3 (6)	5-10	5760
Arizona	State Land Commissioner	Sealed Bid	Application	1/8th	1/8th	25c	25c	5 years	2560
Arkansas	Department of Commerce	Upon Application		1/8th	1/8th	$1	$1	5 years	1000
California	State Land Commissioner	Sealed Bids	Sealed Bids	Varies	1/6-1/ 8	$1 Minimum for both		3-5 years	No limit
Colorado	Board of Land Commissioner	Public Auction	Public Auction	1/8	1/8	50c 1st 5 years; $1 2nd 5 years	50c 1st 5 years; $1 2nd 5 years	5 plus 5	640
Idaho	Board of Land Commissioners			1/8th Minimum	1/8th Minimum	25c	25c	10 years	640
Illinois	Dept. of Mines & Minerals	Bid or Auction	Application	1/8	1/8	$1	$1	10 years	640
Indiana	Oil and Gas Division Department of Conservation	Bid or Auction	Application	1/8	1/8	$1	None	10 years	proven no limit, wildcat 3 sq. mile
Kansas	Department of Interior	Sealed Bids	Sealed Bids	1/8	1/8	$1	$1	5 years	640
Kentucky									
Louisiana	State Mineral Board	Sealed Bids	Sealed Bids	1/8 to 1/6th	1/8 to 1/6th	Half of the Bonus	Half of the Bonus	3 years	5000
Michigan	Department of Mineral Resources	Competitive Bids	Competitive Bids	1/8	1/8	50c 1st year, then $1	50c 1st year, then $1	10 years	
Mississippi	Mineral Lease Commission	Competitive Bids	Competitive Bids	1/8	1/8	$1 Minimum	$1 Minimum	5 years	
Montana	Board of Land Commissioners	Auction	Auction	Oil, see note 1, gas, 1/8	Oil, see note 1, gas, 1/8	$1.50	$1.50	10 years	640
Nebraska	Board of Education, Lands & Funds	Oral Bids	Oral Bids	1/8th	1/8th	50c	50c	3 years	640
New Mexico	Commissioner of Public Lands	Sealed Bids	Sealed Bids	1/8th-1/ 6th	1/8th-/ 6th	25c to $2	5c to $1	10 years	6400
New York	Bureau of Surplus Real Property	Competitive oral and sealed bids		1/8th	1/8th				
North Dakota	State Land Department	Public Auction	Public Auction	1/8th	1/8th	25c	25c	5 years	640
Ohio	Department of Natural Resources	Bids	Bids	1/8th	1/8th	$1	$1	5 years	No limit
Oklahoma	Commissioner of Land Office	Bids	Bids	Minimum of 1/8th		$1	$1	5 years	160
Pennsylvania	Department of Forests, etc.	Bids	Bids	14½% Minimum		$1 to $26	$1 to $26	5 years	300/3000
South Dakota	Comm. of School and Public Lands	Oral Bids	Oral Bids	1/8th	1/8th	10c 1st 5 years, 25c 2nd	10c 1st 5 years, 25c 2nd	10 years	2560
Texas	General Land Office	Sealed Bids (3)	Sealed Bids (3)	1/6th	1/6th	$5 to $15	$5 to $15	5 years	By tract
Utah	State Land Board	Bids	Application or Bids (4)	1/8th	1/8th	$1	$1	10 years	2560 (5)
West Virginia	Dept. of Natural Resources	Sealed Bids	Sealed Bids						
Wyoming	State Land Commissioner	By Application	By Application	1/8th	1/8th	$1	$1	10 years	1280

(1) Oil formula based upon monthly production per well.
(2) Additional delay rental penalty may be assessed in 7 to 10 years.
(3) Certain types of State lands are leased by Public Auction. CHECK. State Land Commission sets rules regarding bids (cash or royalty), minimum bonus and rentals.
(4) Newly acquired land or recently expired leases are acquired by sealed bids. Unleased land available to 1st applicant.
(5) Leases must have land in reasonably compact form, within 6 mile square.
(6) Royalty: not less than 1/8, or 1/8 plus net profits of not less than 30% from lease, or combination bid. Rental: $1-1st year, $1.50-2nd year; $2nd-3rd year; $2.50-4th year; $3-5th and following years.

SOURCE: *The AAPL Guide for Landmen*, 33-34.

shown in fig. 2.1 at the end of this chapter). A truly thorny legal question may best be put to the Texas attorney general's office. These same sources can provide information on how to lease from cities, counties, school districts, and other political units with the state. Veterans land tracts are governed by special rules, and these rules—along with lease forms—may be obtained from the Veterans Land Board in the state capital.

FEDERAL LANDS

Lands administered by federal, civil, and defense agencies amount to roughly one-third of our country's gross area. This fact makes the federal government a landholder of astonishing size. Much federal land is, of course, unavailable for oil and gas production. Land set aside for military uses or for national parks, wildlife refuges, and so on is not, ordinarily, leased to the petroleum industry. (Exceptions in the form of *protective* leases are sometimes granted where such land is being drained of its minerals by nearby producing wells.) Many tracts are available for lease, though, particularly in the western United States. The federal government, as landholder, leases in accordance with its specified goals of care for the environment, orderly development of national resources, and a fair market price for use of the federal estate. Those tracts that are leased may fall into one of several categories including public domain land, acquired land, Indian land, and offshore land.

Public Domain Lands

Land in the public domain is land originally owned by the United States and not subsequently disposed of. Both the surface and the mineral estates belong to the nation. The federal government has also reserved the mineral rights to some property patented to individual citizens (just as the state of Texas has with its minerally classified lands).

When oil and gas leases were first obtained for public lands, back in the nineteenth century, existing mining laws were applied to the transactions. These laws proved so unsatisfactory, though, that in 1920 Congress passed the Mineral Leasing Act specifically to authorize petroleum leasing of federal lands. As amended (the act has been amended a number of times to keep it relevant to new problems), this piece of legislation still governs the leasing of onshore federal lands in the public domain. Leasing procedures are controlled by the U.S. Department of the Interior and by the Bureau of Land Management. The BLM will supply copies of its regulations upon request; questions should be sent to the appropriate state office. Most federal lands in Texas, New Mexico, and Oklahoma, for example, are supervised by the New Mexico Bureau of Land Management in Santa Fe, New Mexico, although some fall under the jurisdiction of the BLM in Cheyenne, Wyoming. The full rules for onshore leasing can also be found in part 3100 of Title 43, *Code of Federal Regulations,* available in law libraries and in many large public libraries. Onshore public domain lands are leased by two methods—competitive and noncompetitive—and a prospective lessee should take care always to consult the *latest* regulations that apply to the kind of lease he plans to bid for.

Competitive Leasing. Competitive leases are granted for lands within known producing areas. Such acreage is leased at government lease sales held periodically by the Bureau of Land Management. Available units are posted in the appropriate state BLM office. Sales are also widely advertised, and descriptions of the units—together with any special terms or stipulations—are sent to prospective bidders. Bidders then submit sealed bids on the correct BLM forms. (See fig. 2.2 at the end of this chapter for sample forms.) When the bids on a given tract are publicly opened, the highest qualified bid receives the lease. The government can, however, exercise its right to reject *all* bids.

Qualified bidders are adult U.S. citizens— whether bidding as individuals or in groups—and those corporations formed under federal or state laws. Corporations whose stockholders include a specific percentage of aliens must furnish the BLM with special information as outlined in that agency's regulations. Aliens may not themselves hold leases on federal lands, and no person may hold leases, whether competitively or noncompetitively acquired, on more than 246,080 acres in any state, with the exception of Alaska. The Alaska limit is 300,000 acres in each of its two leasing districts. (See Appendix B for information on leasing in Alaska.)

Competitive leases have a 5-year primary term. The annual rental is $2 per acre, and royalties range from 12½ percent to 25 percent, depending on production volume. Successful commercial production extends the life of a lease; once production ends or the lease is given up, all leased mineral rights, of course, revert to the federal government.

Noncompetitive leasing. By far the greater number of federal leases (around 90 percent) are acquired noncompetitively. This procedure applies to lands *not* located within a known geologic structure. Such leases are often bought as speculative investments;

lessees usually hope to sell their leases at a profit to oil companies or independent producers.

In the case of public lands *never before leased,* the prospective lessee must learn for himself which tracts are available. He can do so by looking at the official records of a state BLM office. He then simply asks for the tract that interests him, pays the $75 filing fee, and submits the necessary forms. The first qualified offer receives the lease, normally granted for a 10-year primary term at a rental of $1 per acre for the first 5 years; succeeding years carry a rental of $3 per acre and a royalty rate of 12½ percent. Fees and forms can be submitted by mail or over the counter at a BLM office.

Lands that *have been leased before* and that have become available for re-lease are publicly listed in BLM offices on the first working day of each odd month, beginning with January. Interested persons may come to the office to inspect the lists or pay a small fee to have a copy mailed to them. These tracts are handled by what is known as a *simultaneous filing procedure.* In a simultaneous filing, all interested persons must file their $75 fees and forms within a specified number of days after the list is posted. Tracts receiving more than one offer are awarded by means of a drawing held once a month at the BLM office. A successful applicant has 30 days from his official notification to pay the first year's rental and so confirm his lease. (Terms, rentals, and royalties are similar to those in competitive leases.) This lottery method has replaced the earlier first-come, first-served procedure to re-leased lands; the older method frequently resulted in long lines, fist fights, and injured applicants.

Since many of the leases acquired at a simultaneous filing are later sold, lessees should be aware that all assignments of federal leases must be approved by the BLM.

No one who wins at a government drawing may sell or otherwise assign his lease (or even agree to sell it) before the lease is actually issued. Failure to comply fully with federal regulations can cause considerable difficulty for the lessee. Since ignorance of the law is no excuse, all applicants should take care to learn—and follow—the pertinent rules if their filings, assignments, and other transactions are to be valid.

Acquired Lands

Acquired federal lands, as their name indicates, were acquired by deed from earlier owners. In 1947, the Mineral Leasing Act for Acquired Lands gave to the secretary of the interior the authority to lease acquired lands in much the same ways that he can lease public domain lands. However, acquired lands have an additional safeguard against possible damage: the government agency with jurisdiction over a particular piece of property must consent to the leasing of that property's minerals. The agency can also set up special rules to protect the land's primary purpose. Finally, lands located within national parks and monuments—or inside incorporated cities, towns, or villages—are excluded from the Mineral Leasing Act for Acquired Lands.

Indian Lands

Leasing Indian lands can present special problems and, once again, requires that the lessee thoroughly familiarize himself with federal regulations. The procedures involved differ somewhat, depending on whether the land in question is *tribal land* or *allotted land*. Tribal land is land within a reservation or that owned by an Indian tribe, group, or band. Allotted land has been designated for use by a specific individual, but the United States retains control over leases and conveyances affecting the property. In either case, anyone

proposing to request a mineral lease on Indian land needs to conduct a very careful title check before proceeding with his application. The records he needs may be found in one or all of the following offices: the Commissioner of Indian Affairs in Washington, the area director of the Bureau of Land Management (both in Washington and the state where the land is located), and the county clerk for the relevant county. All of these sources should be checked. If the land has a leasing history, it, too, should be carefully examined to make sure that all federal regulations have been followed and that no question about title is likely to cloud a new application.

Whether the prospective lessee wishes to bid on tribal or on allotted land, the rules that he must follow can be found in Title 25 of the *Code of Federal Regulations*. For tribal lands, permission to lease must be sought from the tribal council; for allotted lands, requests go to the Bureau of Indian Affairs. Notice of lease sales for both kinds of land is published well in advance of the sale. Bids are made according to guidelines set out by the secretary of the interior, and successful bidders must furnish certain prescribed bonds with each lease.

There are some reservations in Oklahoma, Wyoming, and Montana that have their own separate rules for mineral leasing. A bidder planning to deal with one of these reservations should consult Title 25, Chapter 12 of the *Code of Federal Regulations*.

Offshore Lands

The Outer Continental Shelf can be defined, for practical purposes, as the submerged land seaward from state-owned areas to a depth of 8,000 feet or so. Beyond that water depth, mineral development reaches its present technological limits. Offshore lands stretching from the shoreline seaward for 3 nautical miles belong to the coastal states. (Texas and Florida—on its west coast—own the land 9 nautical miles from their shores.) Between that 3-mile line and the 8,000-foot depth line lie the federally controlled areas of the Outer Continental Shelf. These federal offshore lands are leased according to the terms set out in the OCS Lands Act of 1953-1954, as amended in 1978. The guidelines for opening OCS lands to exploration and development are given by the Bureau of Land Management. The bureau tries to follow those governmental aims mentioned earlier: orderly development of resources, a fair price, and environmental protection. With the amending of the OCS Lands Act in 1978, it is the responsibility of the secretary of the interior to set up a tentative leasing schedule for a 5-year period. The current proposed schedule would hold 42 lease sales in the 1982–1986 interval; an elaborate series of preleasing steps must be followed before a sale is actually held. The steps include environmental impact studies, public hearings, governmental review, public notice of sales, input from the affected states, and the secretary's final decision to proceed or not to proceed.

If a sale is held, companies make their sealed bids based on their best estimates of the value of the offered tracts. Bids can vary considerably, and the BLM reviews all bids in order to compare them with government estimates of the potential of each tract. Results are announced after this review; if no bids meet the government's expectations, the BLM is not bound to accept even the highest bids.

In accordance with the amendment to the OCS Lands Act (which gave the secretary of the interior increased latitude in offering leases under a variety of bidding systems), lease sales for offshore lands can differ considerably from one location to another and from one sale to another. No interested bidder should assume that the terms and regulations that applied to the last sale will also apply to a future sale. Bidders should always get up-to-date instructions from the BLM. Since offshore lands are extremely expensive to explore and develop, major oil companies make heavy investments when they decide to bid on OCS tracts. Often, such bids represent joint undertakings; two or more companies will combine information and funds to make a bid that they hope will be high enough to win a desired tract. (But not so high, compared to competitors' bids, as to suggest an embarrassing and costly miscalculation.) When the stakes are high and success, or error, is immediately visible to one's peers at a lease sale, no company wants its high bid invalidated because of a failure to follow all the leasing rules.

Figure 2.1. Sample oil and gas lease provided by the Texas General Land Office

Revised
Lease Form 9-81

The State of Texas
General Land Office
Austin, Texas

OIL AND GAS LEASE
No.

WHEREAS, pursuant to Chapter 32 and Subchapters A-E, G and H of Chapter 52 of the Natural Resources Code (hereinafter called N.R.C.), and subject to all rules and regulations promulgated by the Commissioner of the General Land Office and/or the School Land Board pursuant thereto, and all other applicable statutes and amendments to said N.R.C., the following area, to-wit:

SAMPLE

was, after being duly advertised, offered for lease on the _____ day of _____, 19_____, at 10:00 o'clock A.M., by the Commissioner of the General Land Office of the State of Texas and the School Land Board of the State of Texas, for the sole and only purpose of prospecting and drilling for, and producing oil and/or gas that may be found and produced from the above described area; and

WHEREAS, after all bids and remittances which were received up to said time have been duly considered by the Commissioner of the General

Land Office and the School Land Board at a regular meeting thereof in the General Land Office, on the _____ day of

_____, 19_____, and it was found and determined that _____
_____

whose address is _____
had offered the highest and best bid for a lease of the area above described and is, therefore, entitled to receive a lease thereon:

NOW, THEREFORE, I, BOB ARMSTRONG, Commissioner of the General Land Office of the State of Texas, hereinafter sometimes referred to as "Lessor", whose address is Austin, Texas, by virtue of the authority vested in me and in consideration of the payment by the hereinafter

designated Lessee, the sum of _____ Dollars

($_____), receipt of which is hereby acknowledged and of the royalties, covenants, stipulations and conditions contained and hereby

Figure 2.1. — *Continued*

agreed to be paid, observed and performed by Lessee, do hereby demise, grant, lease and let unto _____

_____

the exclusive right to prospect for, produce and take oil and/or gas from the aforesaid area upon the following terms and conditions, to-wit:

    1. TERM: Subject to the other provisions hereof, this lease shall be for a term of _____ years from this date (herein called "primary term") and as long thereafter as oil or gas is produced in paying quantities from said area. ·

    2. DELAY RENTALS: If no well be commenced on the land hereby leased on or before the _____ day of _____ ,

19_____ , this lease shall terminate as to both parties unless the Lessee on or before said date shall pay or tender to the Commissioner of the

General Land Office of the State of Texas at Austin, Texas, the sum of _____ Dollars

($_____), per acre, which shall operate as rental and cover the privilege of deferring the commencement of a well for twelve (12) months from said date. In like manner, and upon like payments or tenders the commencement of a well may be further deferred for like periods of the same number of months successively during the primary term hereof.

    3. PRODUCTION ROYALTIES: When production of oil and/or gas is secured, the Lessee agrees to pay or cause to be paid to the Commissioner of the General Land Office in Austin, Texas, for the use and benefit of the State of Texas, during the term hereof:

    (A) OIL: As a royalty on oil, which is defined as including all hydrocarbons produced in a liquid form at the mouth of the well and also all condensate, distillate, and other liquid hydrocarbons recovered from oil or gas run through a separator or other equipment, as hereinafter provided,

_____

part of the gross production or the market value thereof, at the option of the Lessor, such value to be determined by 1) the highest posted price, plus premium, if any, offered or paid for oil, condensate, distillate, or other liquid hydrocarbons, respectively, of a like type and gravity in the general area where produced and when run, or 2) the highest market price thereof offered or paid in the general area where produced and when run, or 3) the gross proceeds of the sale thereof, whichever is the greater. Lessee agrees that before any gas produced from the land hereby leased is sold, used or processed in a plant, it will be run free of cost to Lessor through an adequate oil and gas separator of conventional type or other equipment at least as efficient to the end that all liquid hydrocarbons recoverable from the gas by such means will be recovered. Upon written consent of Lessor, the requirement that such gas be run through such a separator or other equipment may be waived upon such terms and conditions as prescribed by Lessor.

    (B) NON-PROCESSED GAS: As a royalty on any gas (including flared gas), which is defined as all hydrocarbons and gaseous substances not defined as oil in subparagraph (A) above, produced from any well on said land (except as provided herein with respect to gas processed in a plant for

the extraction of gasoline, liquid hydrocarbons or other products) _____
part of the gross production or the market value thereof, at the option of the Lessor, such value to be based on the highest market price paid or offered for gas of comparable quality in the general area where produced and when run, or the gross price paid or offered to the producer, whichever is the greater; provided that the maximum pressure base in measuring the gas under this lease contract shall not at any time exceed 14.65 pounds per square inch absolute, and the standard base temperature shall be sixty (60) degrees Fahrenheit, correction to be made for pressure according to Boyle's Law, and for specific gravity according to test made by the Balance Method or by the most approved method of testing being used by the industry at the time of testing.

    (C) PROCESSED GAS: As a royalty on any gas processed in a gasoline plant or other plant for the recovery of gasoline or other liquid

hydrocarbons, _____ part of
the residue gas and the liquid hydrocarbons extracted or the market value thereof, at the option of the Lessor. All royalties due herein shall be based on one hundred percent (100%) of the total plant production of residue gas attributable to gas produced from this lease, and on fifty percent (50%) or that percent accruing to Lessee, whichever is the greater, of the total plant production of liquid hydrocarbons, attributable to the gas produced from this lease; provided that if liquid hydrocarbons are recovered from gas processed in a plant in which Lessee (or its parent, subsidiary or affiliate) owns an interest, then the percentage applicable to liquid hydrocarbons shall be fifty percent (50%) or the highest percent accruing to a third party processing gas through such plant under a processing agreement negotiated at arms' length (or if there is no such third party, the highest percent then being specified in processing agreements or contracts in the industry), whichever is the greater. The respective royalties on residue gas and on liquid hydrocarbons shall be determined by 1) the highest market price paid or offered for any gas (or liquid hydrocarbons) of comparable quality in the general area or 2) the gross price paid or offered for such residue gas (or the weighted average gross selling price for the respective grades of liquid hydrocarbons), whichever is the greater. In no event, however, shall the royalties payable under this paragraph be less than the royalties which would have been due had the gas not been processed.

    (D) OTHER PRODUCTS: As a royalty on carbon black, sulphur or any other products produced or manufactured from gas (excepting liquid

hydrocarbons) whether said gas be "casinghead", "dry" or any other gas, by fractionating, burning or any other processing, _____

_____ part of the gross production of such products, or the market value thereof, at the option of Lessor, such market value to be determined as follows:

(1) On the basis of the highest market price of each product, during the same month in which such product is produced, or
(2) On the basis of the average gross sale price for each of the products for the same month in which such products are produced; whichever is the greater.

(E) NO DEDUCTIONS: Lessee agrees that all royalties accruing to Lessor under this lease shall be without deduction for the cost of producing, gathering, storing, separating, treating, dehydrating, compressing, processing, transporting, and otherwise making the oil, gas and other products produced hereunder ready for sale or use.

(F) ROYALTY IN KIND: Notwithstanding anything contained herein to the contrary, Lessor may, at its option, upon not less than 60 days notice to Lessee, require at any time or from time to time that payment of all or any royalties accruing to Lessor under this lease be made in kind without deduction for the cost of producing, gathering, storing, separating, treating, dehydrating, compressing, processing, transporting and otherwise making the oil, gas and other products produced hereunder ready for sale or use.

(G) PLANT FUEL AND RECYCLED GAS: No royalty shall be payable on any gas as may represent this lease's proportionate share of any fuel used to process gas produced hereunder in any processing plant. Notwithstanding anything contained herein to the contrary, and subject to the consent in writing of the Commissioner of the General Land Office, Lessee may recycle gas for gas lift purposes on the leased premises or for injection into any oil or gas producing formation underlying the leased premises after the liquid hydrocarbons contained in the gas have been removed and no royalties shall be payable on the gas so recycled until such time as the same may thereafter be produced and sold or used by Lessee in such manner as to entitle Lessor to a royalty thereon under the royalty provisions of this lease.

(H) MINIMUM ROYALTY: During any year after the expiration of the primary term of this lease, if this lease is maintained by production, the royalties paid to Lessor in no event shall be less than an amount equal to the total annual delay rental herein provided; otherwise, there shall be due and payable on or before the last day of the month succeeding the anniversary date of this lease a sum equal to the total annual rental less the amount of royalties paid during the preceding year.

4. ROYALTY PAYMENTS AND REPORTS: All royalties not taken in kind shall be paid to the Commissioner of the General Land Office at Austin, Texas in the following manner:

Royalty on oil is due and must be received in the General Land Office on or before the 5th day of the second month succeeding the month of production, and royalty on gas is due and must be received in the General Land Office on or before the 15th day of the second month succeeding the month of production, accompanied by the affidavit of the owner, manager or other authorized agent, completed in the form and manner prescribed by the General Land Office and showing the gross amount and disposition of all oil and gas produced and the market value of the oil and gas, together with a copy of all documents, records or reports confirming the gross production, disposition and market value including gas meter readings, pipeline receipts, gas line receipts, and other checks or memoranda of amount produced and put into pipelines, tanks, or pools and gas lines or gas storage, and any other reports or records which the General Land Office may require to verify the gross production, disposition and market value. In all cases the authority of a manager or agent to act for the Lessee herein must be filed in the General Land Office. Each royalty payment shall be accompanied by a check stub, schedule, summary or other remittance advice showing by the assigned General Land Office lease number the amount of royalty being paid on each lease. Any royalty not paid or affidavits and supporting documents not filed when due shall become delinquent and shall have added to the sum owing a delinquency penalty of one percent (1%) of such sum for each thirty (30) day period of delinquency or a fractional period thereof; provided, however, that each such penalty shall never be less than Five Dollars ($5). The lessee shall bear all responsibility for paying or causing royalties to be paid as prescribed by the due date provided herein. Payment of the delinquency penalty shall in no way operate to prohibit the State's right of forfeiture as provided by law nor act to postpone the date on which royalties were originally due. The above penalty provisions shall not apply in cases of title dispute as to the State's portion of the royalty or to that portion of the royalty in dispute as to fair market value.

5. (A) RESERVES, CONTRACTS AND OTHER RECORDS: Lessee shall annually furnish the Commissioner of the General Land Office with its best possible estimate of oil and gas reserves underlying this lease or allocable to this lease and shall furnish said Commissioner with copies of all contracts under which gas is sold or processed and all subsequent agreements and amendments to such contracts within thirty (30) days after entering into or making such contracts, agreements or amendments. Such contracts and agreements when received by the General Land Office shall be held in confidence by the General Land Office unless otherwise authorized by Lessee. All other contracts and records pertaining to the production, transportation, sale and marketing of the oil and gas produced on said premises, including the books and accounts, receipts and discharges of all wells, tanks, pools, meters, and pipelines shall at all times be subject to inspection and examination by the Commissioner of the General Land Office, the Attorney General, the Governor, or the representative of any of them. The State shall have a first lien upon all oil and gas produced from the area covered by this lease, to secure payment of all unpaid royalty and other sums of money that may become due under this lease.

(B) DRILLING RECORDS: Written notice of all operations on a State of Texas lease shall be submitted to the Commissioner of the General Land Office by Lessee or operator within five (5) days of spud date, workover, re-entry, temporary abandonment or plug and abandonment of any well or wells. Such written notice to the General Land Office shall include copies of Railroad Commission forms for application to drill, well tests, completion reports and plugging records. Lessee shall supply the General Land Office with any records, memoranda, accounts, reports, cuttings and cores, or other information relative to the operation of the above described premises, which may be requested by the General Land Office, in addition to those herein expressly provided for. Lessee shall have an electrical and/or radioactivity survey made on the bore-hole section, from the base of the surface casing to the total depth of well, of all wells drilled on the above described premises and shall transmit a true copy of the log of each survey on each well to the General Land Office within fifteen (15) days after the making of said survey.

Figure 2.1 – *Continued*

6. DEVELOPMENT: Notwithstanding any provision of this lease to the contrary, after a well producing or capable of producing oil or gas has been completed on the leased premises, Lessee shall exercise the diligence of a reasonably prudent operator in drilling such additional well or wells as may be reasonably necessary for the proper development of the leased premises and in marketing the production thereon.

7. OFFSET WELLS: If oil and/or gas should be produced in commercial quantities in a well on land privately owned or on State land leased at a lesser royalty, which well is within one thousand (1,000) feet of the area included herein, the Lessee shall, within sixty (60) days after such initial production on such land, begin in good faith and prosecute diligently the drilling of an offset well on this area, and such offset well shall be drilled to such depth as may be necessary to prevent the undue drainage of this area, and the Lessee, manager or driller shall use all means necessary in a good faith effort to make such offset well produce oil and/or gas in commercial quantities.

8. DRY HOLE CLAUSE: If, during the primary term hereof and prior to discovery and production of oil or gas on said land, Lessee should drill a dry hole or holes thereon, or if after discovery and production of oil or gas the production thereof should cease from any cause, this lease shall not terminate if on or before the rental paying date next ensuing after the expiration of sixty (60) days from date of completion of said dry hole or cessation of production Lessee commences additional drilling or reworking operations thereon, or commences or resumes the payment of annual delay rental in the same manner as provided in Paragraph Number 2 of this lease. If a dry hole be completed and abandoned during the last year of the primary term, Lessee's rights shall remain in full force and effect without further operations until the expiration of the primary term. Should the first well or any subsequent well drilled on the above described land be completed as a shut-in oil or gas well within the primary term hereof, Lessee shall resume payment of annual rental in the same manner as provided in Paragraph Number 2 in this lease on or before the rental paying date next ensuing after sixty (60) days from the date of completion of such shut-in oil or gas well and the failure to make such annual rental payment shall subject the lease to forfeiture under the provisions of Paragraph Number 17 hereof. If at the expiration of the primary term or at any time thereafter a shut-in oil or gas well is located on the leased premises payments shall be made in accordance with the provisions of Paragraph Number 10 hereof.

9. CESSATION, DRILLING, AND REWORKING: In the event production of oil or gas on the leased premises after once obtained shall cease from any cause at the expiration of the primary term hereof or at any time or times thereafter, this lease shall not terminate if Lessee commences additional drilling or reworking operations within sixty (60) days thereafter, and the lease shall remain in full force and effect so long as such operations continue in good faith and in workmanlike manner without interruptions totaling more than sixty (60) days during any one such operation; and if such drilling or reworking operations result in the production of oil or gas, the lease shall remain in full force and effect so long as oil or gas is produced therefrom in paying quantities or payment of shut-in oil or gas well royalties or compensatory royalties is made as hereinafter provided or as provided elsewhere in the statutes of the State of Texas. Lessee shall give written notice to the General Land Office within five (5) days of any cessation of production.

10. SHUT-IN ROYALTIES: If at the expiration of the primary term or at any time after the expiration of the primary term a well or wells capable of producing oil or gas in paying quantities are located on the leased premises but oil or gas is not being produced for lack of suitable production facilities or a suitable market and the lease is not being maintained in force and effect, before the expiration of the primary term or if the primary term has expired, within sixty (60) days after Lessee ceases to produce oil or gas from the well, Lessee may pay as a shut-in oil or gas royalty an amount equal to double the annual rental provided in the lease but not less than $1,200 a year for each well capable of producing oil or gas in paying quantities; if the shut-in oil or gas royalty is paid, the lease shall be considered to be a producing lease and the payment shall extend the term of the lease for a period of one year from the end of the primary term or from the first day of the month next succeeding the month in which production ceased and after that if no suitable production facilities or suitable market for the oil or gas exists, Lessee may extend the lease for four additional and successive periods of one year by paying the same amount each year on or before the expiration of the extended term; if, during the period the lease is kept in effect by payment of the shut-in oil or gas royalty, oil or gas is sold and delivered in paying quantities from a well located within 1,000 feet of the leased premises and completed in the same producing reservoir or in any case in which drainage is occurring, the right to continue to extend the lease by paying the shut-in oil or gas royalty shall cease, but the lease shall remain effective for the remainder of the year for which the royalty has been paid and for an additional period of not more than five years from the expiration of the primary term by Lessee paying compensatory royalty at the royalty rate provided in the lease of the value at the well of production from the well which is causing the drainage or which is completed in the same producing reservoir and within 1,000 feet of the leased premises; the compensatory royalty is to be paid monthly to the commissioner beginning on or before the last day of the month next succeeding the month in which the oil or gas is sold and delivered from the well located within 1,000 feet of or draining the leased premises and completed in the same reservoir; if the compensatory royalty paid in any 12-month period is in an amount less than the annual shut-in oil or gas royalty, Lessee shall pay an amount equal to the difference within 30 days from the end of the 12-month period; and none of these provisions will relieve Lessee of the obligation of reasonable development nor the obligation to drill offset wells as provided in Section 52.034 of the N.R.C.

11. EXTENSIONS: If, at the expiration of the primary term of this lease, production of oil or gas has not been obtained on the leased premises but drilling operations are being conducted thereon in good faith and in a good and workmanlike manner, Lessee may, on or before the expiration of the primary term, file in the General Land Office written application to the Commissioner of the General Land Office for a thirty (30) day extension of this lease, accompanied by payment of Three Thousand Dollars ($3,000.00) if this lease covers six hundred forty (640) acres or less and Six Thousand Dollars ($6,000.00) if this lease covers more than six hundred forty (640) acres and the Commissioner shall, in writing, extend this lease for a thirty (30) day period from and after the expiration of the primary term and so long thereafter as oil or gas is produced in paying quantities; provided further, that Lessee may, so long as such drilling operations are being conducted make like application and payment during any thirty (30) day extended period for an additional extension of thirty (30) days and, upon receipt of such application and payment, the Commissioner shall, in writing, again extend this lease so that same shall remain in force for such additional (30) day period and so long thereafter as oil or gas is produced in paying quantities; provided, however, that this lease shall not be extended for more than a total of three hundred ninety (390) days from and after the expiration of the primary term unless production in paying quantities has been obtained.

Figure 2.1—*Continued*

12. USE OF WATER; SURFACE: Lessee shall have the right to use water produced on said land necessary for operations hereunder and solely upon the leased premises; provided, however, Lessee shall not use potable water or water suitable for livestock or irrigation purposes for water flood operations without the prior written consent of Lessor. Lessee shall have the right to use so much of the surface of the land that may be reasonably necessary for drilling and operating wells and transporting and marketing the production therefrom, such use to be conducted under conditions of least injury to the surface of the land.

13. POLLUTION: In developing this area, Lessee shall use the highest degree of care and all proper safeguards to prevent pollution. In the event of pollution, Lessee shall use all means at its disposal to recapture all escaped hydrocarbons or other pollutant and shall be responsible for all damage to public and private properties. Lessee shall build and maintain fences around its slush, sump, and drainage pits and tank batteries so as to protect livestock against loss, damage or injury; and upon completion or abandonment of any well or wells, Lessee shall fill and level off all slush pits and cellars and completely clean up the drilling site of all rubbish thereon.

14. IDENTIFICATION MARKERS: Lessee shall erect, at a distance not to exceed 25 feet from each well on the premises covered by this lease, a legible sign on which shall be stated the name of the operator, the lease designation and the well number. Where two or more wells on the same lease or where wells on two or more leases are connected to the same tank battery, whether by individual flow line connections direct to the tank or tanks or by use of a multiple header system, each line between each well and such tank or header shall be legibly identified at all times, either by a firmly attached tag or plate or an identification properly painted on such line at a distance not to exceed three (3) feet from such tank or header connection. Said signs, tags, plates or other identification markers shall be maintained in a legible condition throughout the term of this lease.

15. ASSIGNMENTS: The lease may be transferred at any time. All transfers must be recorded in the county where the area is located, and the recorded transfer or a copy certified to by the County Clerk of the county where the transfer is recorded must be filed in the General Land Office within ninety (90) days of the execution date, as provided by Section 52.026, N.R.C., accompanied by a filing fee of Ten Dollars ($10.00).

16. RELEASES: Lessee may relinquish the rights granted hereunder to the State at any time by recording the relinquishment in the county where this area is situated and filing the recorded relinquishment or certified copy of same in the General Land Office within ninety (90) days after its execution accompanied by a filing fee of Ten Dollars ($10.00). Such relinquishment will not have the effect of releasing Lessee from any liability theretofore accrued in favor of the State.

17. FORFEITURE: (A) If Lessee shall fail or refuse to make the payment of any sum within thirty days after it becomes due, or if Lessee or an authorized agent should knowingly make any false return or false report concerning production or drilling, or if Lessee shall fail or refuse to drill any offset well or wells in good faith as required by law and the rules and regulations adopted by the Commissioner of the General Land Office, or if Lessee should fail to file reports in the manner required by law or fail to comply with rules and regulations promulgated by the General Land Office or the School Land Board, or refuse the proper authority access to the records pertaining to operations, or Lessee or an authorized agent should knowingly fail or refuse to give correct information to the proper authority, or knowingly fail or refuse to furnish the General Land Office a correct log of any well, or if Lessee shall knowingly violate any of the material provisions of this lease, or if this lease is assigned and the assignment is not filed in the General Land Office as required by law, the rights acquired under this lease shall be subject to forfeiture by the Commissioner, and he shall forfeit same when sufficiently informed of the facts which authorize a forfeiture, and when forfeited the area shall again be subject to lease to the highest bidder, under the same regulations controlling the original sale of leases. However, nothing herein shall be construed as waiving the automatic termination of this lease by operation of law or by reason of any special limitation arising hereunder.

(B) Forfeitures may be set aside and this lease and all rights thereunder reinstated before the rights of another intervene upon satisfactory evidence to the Commissioner of the General Land Office of future compliance with the provisions of the law and of this lease and the rules and regulations that may be adopted relative thereto.

18. RIVERBED TRACTS: In the event this lease covers a riverbed, Lessee is hereby specifically granted the right of eminent domain and condemnation as provided for in Sections 52.092-52.093, N.R.C., as a part of the consideration moving to Lessor for the covenants herein made by Lessee.

19. DRILLING RESTRICTIONS: In the event this lease covers land leased under the provisions of Subchapter B, Chapter 52, N.R.C., no surface location on this area may be closer than six hundred sixty (660) feet from the center of any navigable ship channel, and special permission from the Commissioner of the General Land Office will be necessary to make any surface location between six hundred sixty (660) feet and two thousand one hundred sixty (2,160) feet from the center of any such navigable ship channel. Also in such event this lease shall be subject to all rules and regulations promulgated by the Commissioner of the General Land Office, and amendments thereto, governing drilling and producing operations on permanent free school lands.

20. REMOVAL OF EQUIPMENT: Upon the termination of this lease for any cause, Lessee shall not, in any event, be permitted to remove the casing or any part of the equipment from any producing, dry, or abandoned well or wells without the written consent of the Commissioner of the General Land Office or his authorized representative; nor shall Lessee, without the written consent of said Commissioner or his authorized representative remove from the leased premises the casing or any other equipment, material, machinery, appliances or property owned by Lessee and used by Lessee in the development and production of oil or gas therefrom until all dry or abandoned wells have been plugged and until all slush or refuse pits have been properly filled and all broken or discarded lumber, machinery, or debris shall have been removed from the premises to the satisfaction of the said Commissioner or his authorized representative.

Figure 2.1—*Continued*

21. FORCE MAJEURE: Should Lessee be prevented from complying with any express or implied covenant of this lease, from conducting drilling operations thereon, or from producing oil and/or gas therefrom, after effort made in good faith, by reason of war, rebellion, riots, strikes, acts of God or any order, rule or regulation of governmental authority, then while so prevented, Lessee's obligation to comply with such covenant shall be suspended upon proper and satisfactory proof presented to the Commissioner of the General Land Office in support of Lessee's contention and Lessee shall not be liable for damages for failure to comply therewith (except in the event of lease operations suspended as provided in the rules and regulations adopted by the School Land Board); and this lease shall be extended while and so long as Lessee is prevented, by any such cause, from drilling, reworking operations or producing oil and/or gas from the leased premises; provided, however, that nothing herein shall be construed to suspend the payment of rentals during the primary or extended term, nor to abridge Lessee's right to a suspension under any applicable statute of this state.

22. RAILROAD COMMISSION HEARINGS ON GAS: No natural gas or casinghead gas, including both associated and nonassociated gas, produced from the mineral estate subject to this lease may be sold or contracted for sale to any person for ultimate use outside the State of Texas unless the Railroad Commission of Texas, after notice and hearing as provided in Title 3 of the N.R.C., finds that:

(a) the person, agency, or entity that executed the lease in question does not require the natural gas or casinghead gas to meet its own existing needs for fuel;

(b) no private or public hospital, nursing home, or other similar health-care facility in this state requires the natural gas or casinghead gas to meet its existing needs for fuel;

(c) no public or private school in this state that provides elementary, secondary, or higher education requires the natural gas or casinghead gas to meet its existing needs for fuel;

(d) no facility of the state or of any county, municipality, or other political subdivision in this state requires the natural gas or casinghead gas to meet its existing needs for fuel;

(e) no producer of food and fiber requires the natural gas or casinghead gas necessary to meet the existing needs of irrigation pumps and other machinery directly related to this production; and

(f) no person who resides in this state and who relies on natural gas or casinghead gas to provide in whole or part his existing needs for fuel or raw material requires the natural gas or casinghead gas to meet those needs;
provided, however, the Railroad Commission of Texas may grant exceptions to these provisions as set forth in Section 52.296 of the N.R.C.

23. SUCCESSORS AND ASSIGNS: The covenants, conditions and agreements contained herein shall extend to and be binding upon the heirs, executors, administrators, successors or assigns of Lessee herein.

IN TESTIMONY WHEREOF, Witness the signature of the Commissioner of the General Land Office, under the seal of the General Land

Office, this _____ day of _____, 19_____.

_____
COMMISSIONER OF THE GENERAL LAND OFFICE

Approved

Audit_____
Legal_____
Engineering_____
Geology_____
Execution_____

Figure 2.2. Sample federal forms for competitive leasing
(Courtesy of U. S. Department of the Interior, Bureau of Land Management)

UNITED STATES
DEPARTMENT OF THE INTERIOR
BUREAU OF LAND MANAGEMENT

EQUAL OPPORTUNITY IN EMPLOYMENT
CERTIFICATION OF NONSEGREGATED FACILITIES

Bid, offer, or contract number or
other identification

By the submission of this bid or offer and/or by entering into this contract, the bidder, offeror, lessee, subcontractor, or applicant certifies that he does not maintain or provide for his employees any segregated facilities at any of his establishments, and that he does not permit his employees to perform their services at any location, under his control, where segregated facilities are maintained. He certifies further that he will not maintain or provide for his employees any segregated facilities at any of his establishments, and that he will not permit his employees to perform their services at any location, under his control, where segregated facilities are maintained. The bidder, offeror, applicant, or subcontractor agrees that a breach of this certification is a violation of the Equal Opportunity clause in this contract. As used in this certification, the term "segregated facilities" means, but is not limited to, any waiting rooms, work areas, rest rooms and wash rooms, restaurants and other eating areas, time clocks, locker rooms and other storage or dressing areas, parking lots, drinking fountains, recreation or entertainment areas, transportation, and housing facilities provided for employees which are segregated by explicit directive or are in fact segregated on the basis of race, color, religion, sex, or national origin, because of habit, local custom, or otherwise. He further agrees that (except where he has obtained identical certifications from proposed subcontractors for specific time periods) he will obtain identical certifications from proposed subcontractors prior to the award of subcontracts exceeding $10,000 which are not exempt from the provisions of the Equal Opportunity clause; that he will retain such certifications in his files; and that he will forward the following notice to such proposed subcontractors (except where the proposed subcontractors have submitted identical certifications for specific time periods):

NOTICE TO PROSPECTIVE SUBCONTRACTORS OF REQUIREMENT
FOR CERTIFICATIONS OF NONSEGREGATED FACILITIES

A Certification of Nonsegregated Facilities, as required by the May 9, 1967, order (32 F.R. 7439, May 19, 1967) on Elimination of Segregated Facilities, by the Secretary of Labor, must be submitted prior to the award of a subcontract exceeding $10,000 which is not exempt from the provisions of the Equal Opportunity clause. The certification may be submitted either for each subcontract or for all subcontracts during a period (i.e., quarterly, semiannually, or annually).

In accordance with 41 CFR 60, as amended May 19, 1967, and Executive Order No. 11246 of September 24, 1965, as amended, this certification is applicable to all bids, offers, contracts and subcontracts as well as agreements with applicants who are themselves performing federally assisted contracts, which may exceed $10,000 and are not exempt from the provisions of the Equal Opportunity clause of the Order.

Form 1140–3 (June 1975)

GPO 851-002

Figure 2.2—*Continued*

Form 1140-8
(November 1973)

UNITED STATES
DEPARTMENT OF THE INTERIOR
BUREAU OF LAND MANAGEMENT

EQUAL OPPORTUNITY
COMPLIANCE REPORT CERTIFICATION

Bid or invitation number or other
identification:

In accordance with 41 CFR 60-1.7(b) and Executive Order No. 11246 of September 24, 1965, as amended, the following certification will be completed by prospective contractors and subcontractors.

1. Have you participated in any contractual agreement which contained the Equal Opportunity Clause?
   ☐ Yes ☐ No *(If "yes," answer question 2)*

2. Were you required pursuant to the regulations on Equal Opportunity (41 CFR 60-1) to file a compliance report * as a result of such contractual agreements? ☐ Yes ☐ No *(If "yes," answer question 3)*

3. Did you file the compliance report as required? ☐ Yes ☐ No

In the event any work under this proposed contractual agreement is subcontracted, I will secure this same certification *(paragraphs 1 through 3 hereof)* from proposed subcontractors prior to award of any subcontract.

_____
(Name of Bidder)

_____
(Signature of Authorized Officer)

_____
(Title)

_____
(Date)

---

* All employers with 50 or more employees who are covered by Executive Order No. 11246, i.e. holders of Federal Government contracts, subcontracts, or Federally assisted construction contracts or subcontracts, amounting to more than $50,000; and holders of Federal Government bills of lading, depositories of Federal Government funds, or issuing and paying agents of U.S. Savings Bonds and Notes in any amount are required to file SF-100.

Figure 2.2 – *Continued*

UNITED STATES
DEPARTMENT OF THE INTERIOR
BUREAU OF LAND MANAGEMENT

Bid, invitation number, or other identification

INDEPENDENT PRICE DETERMINATION CERTIFICATE

Bid date

Bidder or offeror *(name)*

Address *(include zip code)*

Specify government-owned property bid on *(item)*

A. By submission of this bid or proposal, each bidder or offeror certifies, and in the case of a joint bid or proposal, each party thereto certifies as to its own organization, that in connection with this sale:

1. The prices in this bid or proposal have been arrived at independently, without consultation, communication, or agreement, for the purpose of restricting competition, as to any matter relating to such prices, with any other bidder or offeror or with any competitor;

2. Unless otherwise required by law, the prices which have been quoted in this bid or proposal have not been knowingly disclosed by the bidder or offeror and will not knowingly be disclosed by the bidder or offeror prior to opening, in the case of a bid, or prior to award, in the case of a proposal, directly or indirectly to any other bidder or offeror or to any competitor; and

3. No attempt has been made or will be made by the bidder or offeror to induce any other person or firm to submit or not to submit a bid or proposal for the purpose of restricting competition.

B. Each person signing this bid or proposal certifies that:

1. He is the person in the bidder's or offeror's organization responsible within that organization for the decision as to the prices being bid or offered herein and that he has not participated, and

will not participate, in any action contrary to A. 1 through 3 above; or

2. (i) He is not the person in the bidder's or offeror's organization responsible within that organization for the decision as to the prices being bid or offered herein but that he has been authorized in writing to act as agent for the persons responsible for such decision in certifying that such persons have not participated, and will not participate, in any action contrary to A. 1 through 3, above, and as their agent does hereby so certify; and

(ii) He has not participated, and will not participate, in any action contrary to A. 1 through 3, above.

C. This certification is not applicable to a foreign bidder or offeror submitting a bid or proposal for a contract which requires performance or delivery outside the United States, its possessions, and Puerto Rico.

D. A bid or proposal will not be considered for award where A. 1, 3, or B., above, has been deleted or modified. Where A. 2, above, has been deleted or modified, the bid or proposal will not be considered for award unless the bidder or offeror furnishes with the bid or proposal a signed statement which sets forth in detail the circumstances of the disclosure and the head of the agency, determines that such disclosure was not made for the purpose of restricting competition.

(Signature of Authorized Officer)

Name and Title *(type or print)*

INSTRUCTIONS

Submit a properly completed and signed original copy of this form, with offers or bids for sales of all government-owned property to Bureau of Land Management as follows:

A. Include with sealed bids, written quotations and written offers.
B. At auction, at close of bidding and before award of spot bid sale.

GPO 838-259

Form 1140-6 (April 1971)

Figure 2.2—*Continued*

	FORM APPROVED OMB NO. 42–R1753	
UNITED STATES DEPARTMENT OF THE INTERIOR BUREAU OF LAND MANAGEMENT	Name of oil and gas field	
COMPETITIVE OIL AND GAS AND GEOTHERMAL RESOURCES LEASE BID 30 U.S.C. 181 et. seq.; 30 U.S.C. 1001–1025	Known geothermal resources area	
	State	Date of sale

The following bid is submitted for ☐ competitive oil and gas ☐ geothermal resources lease on the land identified below.

PARCEL NUMBER OR LAND DESCRIPTION	AMOUNT OF BID	
	TOTAL BID	DEPOSIT SUBMITTED WITH BID

1. Are you a citizen of the United States? ☐ Yes ☐ No

2. If a corporation or other legal entity, specify kind

3. Are you the sole party in interest in this lease? ☐ Yes ☐ No

CHECK APPROPRIATE BOX BELOW CONSISTANT WITH PURPOSE OF THIS BID

☐ I CERTIFY That my interests, direct and indirect, in oil and gas leases, offers to lease and options in the above State do not exceed 246,080 acres, including the average covered by this bid, of which not more than 200,000 acres are under options. If this bid is submitted for lands in Alaska, I further certify, as above, that by holdings in each of the Alaska leasing districts do not exceed 300,000 acres of which not more than 200,000 acres are under option in each said districts.

☐ I CERTIFY That I am qualified to hold any lease which may issue as a result of this sale under the Geothermal Steam Act of 1970 (84 Stat. 1566) and the regulations thereunder and that my interest in geothermal leases in the above State does not exceed 20,480 acres.

_____ (Signature of Bidder)   _____ (Address of Bidder)

_____ (Type or print name of Bidder)   _____ (City, State, and zip code)

Title 18 U.S.C. Section 1001, makes it a crime for any person knowingly and willfully to make to any department or agency of the United States any false, fictitious or fraudulent statements or representations as to any matter within its jurisdiction.

(Instructions on reverse)   Form 3000–2 (October 1978)

Figure 2.2 – *Continued*

INSTRUCTIONS

1. Separate bid for each parcel is required. If no parcel number has been assigned to tract, then land description or identification should be furnished.

2. Bid *must* be accompanied by one-fifth for Oil and Gas Lease and one-half for Geothermal Resources Lease of total amount of bid. The amount should be cash or money order, certified or cashier's check, or bank draft which *must* be made payable to the Bureau of Land Management.

3. Mark envelope Bid for Oil and Gas Lease in *(name of field)* or Bid for Geothermal Resources Lease in *(name of KGRA)*. Be sure correct parcel number of tract on which bid is submitted and date of bid opening are noted plainly on envelope. No bid may be modified or withdrawn unless such modification or withdrawal is received prior to time fixed for opening of bids.

4. Mail or deliver bid to office and place indicated in *Notice of Sale or Publication.*

5. If bid is submitted by an agent, attorney-in-fact, or association *(including a partnership)*, corporation, guardian, or a trustee the showing required by 43 CFR 3102.6 and 43 CFR 3202.2 should accompany bid. If bidder is an association or a corporation, the showing required by 43 CFR 3102.4 and 43 CFR 3202.2 should accompany bid, *except* that if the required information has previously been filed, a reference by serial number to the record in which it was filed, together with a statement as to any amendments, will be sufficient. If the geothermal lease bidder is a municipality or governmental unit, the bid *must* be accompanied by evidence of qualifications as set forth in 43 CFR 3202.2–1(c).

6. If bidder is *not* the sole party in interest in the lease for which bid is submitted, full disclosure of interests of all other parties *must* be made as required by 43 CFR 3102.7 and 43 CFR 3202.2–5, accompanied by a separate showing of qualifications of such parties to hold the lease interest.

NOTICE

The Privacy Act of 1974 and the regulation in 43 CFR 2.48(d) provide that you be furnished the following information in connection with information required by this bid for a Competitive Oil and Gas or Geothermal Resources Lease.

AUTHORITY: 30 U.S.C. 181 et. seq.; 30 U.S.C. 1001–1025.

PRINCIPAL PURPOSE: The information is to be used to process your bid.

ROUTINE USES: (1) The adjudication of the Bidder's right to the resources for which this bid is made. (2) Documentation for public information. (3) Transfer to appropriate Federal agencies when concurrence is required prior to granting a right in public lands or resources. (4)(5) Information from the record and/or the record will be transferred to appropriate Federal, State, local or foreign agencies, when relevant to civil, criminal or regulatory investigations or prosecutions.

EFFECT OF NOT PROVIDING INFORMATION: Disclosure of the information is voluntary. If all the information is not provided, your Bid may be rejected.

GPO 848–002

The Transfer of Interests in Land

The owner of fee simple property may, as we have seen, transfer or convey to others all or specified portions of his legal interest in that property. The ways of achieving such a transfer vary, but three common ones are by lease, by sale, and by devise (or gift) under a will. Though the landowner may lease parts of his property for a variety of purposes, we will consider here only the oil and gas lease and the interests conveyed in such a document. It will be helpful to begin with the simplest possible case, that of a landowner leasing his unsevered oil and gas rights to a company that will develop and sell those minerals.

INTERESTS TRANSFERRED BY LEASE

An oil and gas lease has many possible definitions. However it is defined, it is always viewed as conveying an interest in real estate. Hence it must be in writing or it will violate the Statute of Frauds. It must be dated, must name the parties to the transaction, describe the land and the terms of the agreement, and (in many states) name the preparer of the instrument. Anyone drafting such an instrument would do well to make those terms as *clear* and as *specific* as possible. The courts construe (or interpret) oil and gas leases very strictly, and legal conflicts have been resolved—quite literally—by examining the placement of a comma. To make the lease binding, the lessor must sign; the lessee need not. To make the lease effective among the agreeing parties, witnesses are not necessary unless state law requires them for all binding contracts. In most states, witnesses and acknowledgments *are* needed if the lease is to be recorded. A prudent lessor will want his lease recorded if only to keep the status of his property clear for future inquirers. A prudent lessee will also find recording important; it protects him from competing oil and gas lessees and from creditors.

The Lessor's Interests

In carving from his fee simple property the subordinate interests of a lessee, a landowner by no means gives to an oil company rights equivalent to his own. A lease is limited, first of all, by time. It is granted for a *primary term,* a specified number of years, and for as long thereafter as oil or gas is found in paying quantities. (Five- or three-year leases are common.) During this primary term (and during subsequent production), the landowner may limit the lessee's rights in a variety of ways by inserting special clauses and stipulations into the lease. The most commonly reserved rights of the landowner, however, include bonus, delay rental, and royalty.

Bonus. In granting an oil and gas lease, the landowner hopes, of course, that his lessee will strike it rich and share the wealth for years to come. More immediately, he can hope for a good *lease bonus*—a sum paid to the lessor when he executes the lease. Such a lump sum is typically based on the number of acres leased, and it can vary widely from area to area. How much the landowner is likely to receive depends on how "hot" his property is. With adjacent production and good prospects, he may demand a high price for a lease. In an area without production, the landowner may feel fortunate to receive a modest bonus for his signature.

Delay rental. If the lessee does not wish to drill by the end of a specified period (almost always 1 year), he may extend his lease—"keep the lease alive"—during the rest of the primary term by paying an agreed-upon *delay rental* for the privilege. Commonly, the first rental sum will fall due on the anniversary date of the lease, that is, 1 year from its effective date. Each year that drilling is delayed will bring the landowner more rental payments; in most parts of the country, these will average from 1 to 5 dollars per acre. If the rent is paid on time, the lease continues in force for another year. Failure to pay on time or to pay correctly generally cancels the lease.

Royalty. The royalty is the landowner's agreed-upon percentage of the total mineral production of his land. It is normally cost-free and continues as long as the lease does—or for a stated period. Clearly, this percentage *may* turn out to be the landowner's most important economic interest; little wonder if he drives as hard a bargain for it as he can, especially if the prospects for production seem good. The traditional $\frac{1}{8}$, or 12.5 percent, royalty, for so many years the typical share of production reserved by the landowner, has been giving way in some parts of the country to a larger figure. It is not uncommon these days for the lease to specify a $\frac{3}{16}$ royalty; $\frac{1}{5}$, $\frac{7}{32}$, or $\frac{1}{4}$ may be received for a particularly promising tract. Royalty payments are, in most cases, paid by the purchaser of the produced oil even though the lease may provide that the lessee shall make such payments. Royalty payments for gas produced from leased property are usually paid by the lessee or the operator.

Other rights. All the rights granted in the lease revert to the landowner should rentals not be paid on time, should the lessee fail to begin operations or produce any minerals during the primary term, depending on the specific obligation in the lease, or should production in paying quantities stop during the extended term. (Shut-in wells are an exception to the last two conditions; shut-in wells will be discussed in chapter 6.) The surface of the land remains, of course, the landowner's to use as he wishes, always provided that he does not interfere with his lessee's reasonable operations. It should be noted that many conflicts (and subsequent litigation) over surface damages during drilling or production could probably have been avoided by clearer, more careful drafting of lease agreements.

It should also be pointed out that all the rights mentioned so far—to a bonus, to delay rentals and royalties, to use of the land's surface, and so on—are separate and assignable interests in real property. Each can be conveyed, in part or in total, by the landowner to someone else. He can even convey different fractional parts of all or any of these various interests by means of the same written instrument if he so desires. The complications involved in such conveyances can be formidable; we will be looking at some of the possibilities when we consider the transfer of interests in land by *sale.*

An oil and gas lease has been held by the courts to *imply* certain obligations and benefits known as *implied covenants,* in addition to those specifically set out in the agreement. Generally, these benefits accrue to the landowner, though he may also have implied obligations (to allow his lessee to enter or cross property adjacent to that under lease, for example). Among the things that the landowner may, by implication, expect are the following: that the lessee will drill an initial exploratory well; that he will reasonably develop the property if the first well produces; that he will protect the property from drainage; that he will explore further; that he will conduct with care and diligence all operations that affect the lessor's royalty interest; and that he will do his best to market the oil or gas produced. Breaches of implied convenants may bring court-awarded damages or cancellation of all or portions of the lease.

The Lessee's Interests

The most important rights granted the lessee are the rights to enter the land, to search for oil or gas, and to produce and remove any that he finds. These rights are exclusive, and they may be referred to, collectively, as the leasehold or working interest. *Working interest* is operating interest. It is that interest in oil and gas that includes responsibility for all drilling, developing, and operating costs.

Working interest. The lessee or owner of an oil and gas lease used to be able to count on a ⅞ share of all the minerals he produced. Against that share came all the costs of exploration and development, plus any payments of the kinds mentioned below. Higher royalties for landowners have reduced that once-typical figure somewhat. The working interest can still, of course, be very profitable. It shares with the landowner's interests a certain legal flexibility, too. That is, a lessee can (by state law or by specific lease provision) transfer to other people all or a fraction of his interest in all or a specified part of the property he has leased. The lessee of a large tract might, for example, find it advantageous to farm out, or grant all or a portion of his interest in some part of his leasehold, to a third person. That third person would pay the original lessee in money or an interest in production and agree to drill a well on the property. The lessee can also convey to others (or reserve to himself) payments called *overriding royalties* and *production payments.*

An *overriding royalty* is a designated percentage of the lessee's working interest; like the landowner's royalty, it is free from all production costs, except taxes. It comes "off the top," and it continues as long as the lease is in effect. Such payments sometimes compensate people who bring good prospects to the attention of an oil company; occasionally, they form part of the lease itself and thus go to the landowner. It was once quite common for landowners to ask for an overriding royalty of, say, 1⁄16 in addition to ⅛ of total production. Now that mineral owners frequently ask for 3⁄16 royalty, they less frequently bargain for an override. Clearly, 1⁄16 of a ⅞ working interest plus ⅛ of total production mean fewer dollars than does a flat 3⁄16 of total production.

A *production payment* resembles an overriding royalty in being a cost-free fraction of the working interest. It differs chiefly in its duration. While an override lasts as long as the lease, a production payment ends when a specified amount of money (or number of barrels) has been reached. For instance, a production payment might stop after $100,000—taken from a $\frac{1}{32}$ share of the working interest—has been paid.

Net working interest. The net working interest is the share remaining to the working interest owners after all royalties, overriding royalties, and production payments have been assigned or reserved to their respective owners. The full working interest owns 100 percent of the oil and gas wells it brings into production and must pay 100 percent of all exploring, drilling, and development expenses. If its leasehold is burdened with heavy royalties and other payments out of production, it may be hard pressed to turn much of a profit.

INTERESTS TRANSFERRED BY SALE

The model used in discussing leaseholds was a simple one: one landowner leasing his unsevered mineral estate to one oil company, which—perhaps with other companies or individuals—then proceeded to develop the oil and gas it had discovered. In practice, such straightforward situations are rare. The complications that arise almost invariably spring from the freedoms associated with fee simple property, especially the freedom to buy and sell and divide both future and existing interests in it. A tract of any size is as likely to have many owners as to have one. These owners may hold their interests for life, for a specified term, or in perpetuity. Checking the title to any given piece of property can be a considerable undertaking. Owners sometimes misrepresent their interests—for example, *overconveying,* or conveying a larger fraction of an interest than they in fact possess—more out of ignorance than out of greed. Ambiguities in deeds and other legal instruments are commonplace. In discussing the various kinds of interests that can be transferred by sale—surface interests, mineral interests, royalty interests, and special interests—the need for maximum clarity in any instrument (lease or deed or will) must be emphasized. Clarity is particularly important in specifying fractional interests and in naming the minerals to be transferred.

Surface Interests

When someone buys property without acquiring the mineral rights also—or sells the mineral rights of property he owns—he becomes the owner of a fee in surface and is entitled to use the surface estate as he thinks best. He may not interfere with the operations of an oil and gas lessee, and he must expect such a lessee to exercise his own surface rights, described in the lease, to enter the land, drill for minerals, dig necessary pits and drainage ditches, put up telephone lines, and take water from the lessor's tank or pond. Use of the surface for roads, pipelines, pits, storage tanks, and so forth is an *easement* (a *servitude* in Louisiana) acquired by the lessee; it remains in effect as long as the lease does. Other specific rights, of both the lessee and the surface owner, will be described in the discussion of lease negotiations and common lease provisions.

Whatever his obligations toward the surface owner, a lessee cannot be held accountable for damages unless he is demonstrably negligent. If, for example, a lessee fails to make reasonable provisions for safeguarding the surface owner's livestock — allowing contaminated water, for instance, to flow across the surface where cattle may drink it — livestock deaths or injuries may be chargeable to the lessee. Otherwise, prudent and reasonable operations exempt him from responsibility for accidents. Lessees do sometimes pay surface owners for various inconveniences, of course, simply to maintain their cooperation and good will.

Mineral Interests

Separate or severed mineral interests can be created by reservation or by sale. In the first instance, a landowner would sell his property while reserving all or a part of its mineral interest to himself. In the second, he would sell all or some part of the minerals. The legal instrument used for a sale of the mineral interest is a *mineral deed,* which may convey all the rights mentioned as belonging to a landowner: the right to enter the land and explore it for minerals; the right to produce minerals; the right to execute an oil and gas lease; and the rights to receive a bonus, rentals, and royalties.

Nonownership states view a mineral deed as conveying precisely such *rights,* not as conveying the minerals themselves. Ownership-in-place states, however, see mineral deeds as transferring fee simple titles to the actual minerals. In either case, mineral deeds can convey *all* or some *fraction* of the mineral estate, and the conveyance may be in perpetuity or for a stated number of years. A fractional interest is usually described as *undivided.* Smith sells to Jones "undivided ¼ interest" in an 80-acre tract known as Foggy Bottom. This phrase means that Jones now has a ¼ interest in the entire 90 acres, or 20 net undivided mineral acres. A *divided* ¼ interest (far less common) would give Jones a 100 per-

cent interest in 20 specific, legally describable acres of the Foggy Bottom tract. If Jones, no matter what his purchased share, were only a *term mineral* interest owner, his portion of Foggy Bottom would revert to Smith at the end of the stated term.

Finally, it is important to distinguish a *mineral deed* from a *royalty deed.* Landowners often use those terms as if they were interchangeable; they are not, and considerable legal confusion can arise from failing to indicate which type of conveyance is meant. A mineral deed creates an actual severance of the estate. A royalty deed simply transfers a share of oil or gas production from one person to another.

Royalty Interests

Royalty interests, like mineral interests, can be transferred — totally or in part — by sale, or they can be reserved — totally or in part — by a landowner who wishes to transfer only specified portions of his property. He might, for example, sell both the surface and the mineral estates while reserving for himself and his heirs ½ of the royalty interest. Assuming that the land is leased by its new owner for benefits that include a ⅛ royalty, the original owner will receive a ¹⁄₁₆ share of the estate's gross production. To take another example, a landowner might decide to keep his property and merely sell (by means of a *royalty deed*) some fraction of the royalty interest. He might even divide the royalty interest into several shares, retain one share for himself, and become a co-owner of the royalty interest along with several other owners. Depending on the laws of the state in which he lives, he can — by royalty deed — make these arrangements perpetual, for fixed terms, or for the lifetimes of the purchasers.

A royalty owner who is *also* a mineral interest owner has, of course, the right to execute oil and gas leases. A person who simply owns a severed portion of a royalty interest has no right to execute leases; he is called a *nonparticipating royalty owner* and does not participate in bonuses or rentals. Neither does his royalty interest give him rights of entry, exploration for minerals, or production. (He does have the right to information about these activities, however, and may enter the property to gain such information.)

When royalty has been completely severed from the mineral estate, the mineral fee owner may still have *executive rights,* or rights to lease for oil and gas production. He acts for himself as lessor and for others who own the royalty interest. The exercise of his power to lease — his executive right — has been the subject of a number of court opinions. Some courts have held the lessor to a high standard of fiduciary responsibility; others have simply urged him to conduct his business with "diligence and discretion." (Still others have said that such a power without an interest is a nullity. In other words, a naked executive right to execute leases is a nullity.)

Executive rights also come into operation when one person is granted the power to lease another's property (as a trustee, for example, or a guardian). These rights can be completely severed from other interests in property. When so severed, they usually terminate with the death of the grantor or upon the occurrence of other specified events.

Special Interests

Railroads, cities, churches, and other corporations or institutions often acquire land — or rights-of-way across it — for their own special purposes. These purposes are commonly written into the deed that conveys the property, sometimes with a reversionary clause stipulating that land no longer used for the purpose mentioned must revert to the heirs of the grantor. Courts frequently have to decide whether such special-purpose land can be leased for oil and gas development and who can lease it. Deeds that are ambiguous or silent on the matter may lead to such judicial decisions. Restrictive language in a deed is carefully interpreted to determine if even a fee simple owner — a railroad, for example, or a municipality — can lease for mineral exploration and production. (Without restrictive clauses in the deed, such fee simple owners can, of course, lease like any other landowner.) When mineral development is judged incompatible with the special purpose described in a deed — as it might be in the case of a cemetery or churchyard — the hopeful oil company may still have practicable alternatives. An agreement to drill directionally under the land may be acceptable to the court, as may a pooling arrangement. In the case of cemeteries in particular, nondrilling leases are often granted; the field of which a cemetery is part can then be exploited by pooling or directional drilling without disturbing the graves.

Land Measurement and Land Description

Any conveyance of land—by lease, by deed, or by will—must include a legal description of the property being transferred. An adequate description, whether it appears in the conveying instrument or in an earlier document cited by the instrument, should permit the tract to be identified *on the ground;* it should also distinguish the tract from neighboring properties. In the United States, however, this task of describing land is somewhat complicated by our national history; the fact that various parts of our territory were acquired from other countries—gradually, and by means ranging from purchase to conquest—has left us without a single, consistent method of identifying and describing land. We also lack a single, uniform set of measurements for setting out the lengths, breadths, and areas of individual pieces of property. Most landowners, it is true, know the dimensions of their tracts in *acres, feet,* and *miles,* but to arrive at those measurements, some owners—particularly in the southwestern states—must translate from very different Spanish or French units of measurement. Many landowners will identify their property by means of the U.S. government's rectangular survey system, but some must use a considerably older method known as metes and bounds, even when their land has been surveyed and recorded on an official *plat,* or surveyor's map. The discussion of units of measurement and of methods used to divide and describe property must include these variations on the standard systems.

UNITS OF MEASUREMENT

Descriptions of land originally claimed, possessed, and surveyed by English speakers will generally be set out in *feet, yards, miles,* and *acres.* Thus, property owners in Massachusetts or in Virginia will commonly find—when they investigate old documents that describe their land—these familiar English units of linear and square measurement. They may also find slightly more esoteric units of the kind employed by

TABLE 4.1
Surveyor's Measurements

1 surveyor's chain = 100 links of 7.92 inches each.

1 rod = 16½ feet.

4 rods = 1 chain.

1 pole = 1 rod.

1 mile = 80 chains or 5,280 feet.

1 acre = 10 square chains or 43,560 square feet.

1 acre in square form = 208.71 feet on each side.

The radius of a 1 degree curve is practically 5,730 feet.

To find the radius of any curve, divide this number by the number of degrees in the curve desired.

To find a true bearing from any given magnetic, if the given bearing is NE or SW, add the magnetic declination, and if NW or SE, subtract.

SOURCE: *The AAPL Guide for Landmen*, 50.

surveyors: the *links, chains, rods,* and so on that have their origins in particular pieces of surveyor's equipment. (Tables 4.1 and 4.2

TABLE 4.2
Chains and Feet

Chains	Feet	Chains	Feet
1	66	51	3366
2	132	52	3432
3	198	53	3498
4	264	54	3564
5	330	55	3630
6	396	56	3696
7	462	57	3762
8	528	58	3828
9	594	59	3894
10	660	60	3960
11	726	61	4026
12	792	62	4092
13	858	63	4158
14	924	64	4224
15	990	65	4290
16	1056	66	4356
17	1122	67	4422

TABLE 4.2 – *Continued*

Chains	Feet	Chains	Feet
18	1188	68	4488
19	1254	69	4554
20	1320	70	4620
21	1386	71	4686
22	1452	72	4752
23	1518	73	4818
24	1584	74	4884
25	1560	75	4950
26	1716	76	5016
27	1782	77	5082
28	1848	78	5148
29	1914	79	5214
30	1980	80	5280
31	2046	81	5346
32	2112	82	5412
33	2178	83	5478
34	2244	84	5544
35	2310	85	5610
36	2376	86	5676
37	2442	87	5742
38	2508	88	5808
39	2574	89	5874
40	2640	90	5940
41	2706	91	6006
42	2772	92	6072
43	2838	93	6138
44	2904	94	6204
45	2970	95	6270
46	3036	96	6336
47	3102	97	6402
48	3168	98	6468
49	3234	99	6534
50	3300	100	6600

SOURCE: *The AAPL Guide for Landmen*, 50.

convert these units into feet; tables 4.3 and 4.4 set out standard English measurements.)

Many property titles, however, do not go back to English claims. They derive instead from so-called foreign grants, or property originally granted to an individual landowner by Spain, France, or Mexico when those nations still owned parts of what later became U.S. territory. Titles are based upon such grants in parts of Florida, Louisiana, Colorado, Utah, Nevada, California, Arizona,

TABLE 4.3
Acreage

Acres	Square Feet	1 Acre Equals Rectangle	
		Length	Width
1	43,560		
2	87,120	16.5	2,640.
3	130,680	33.	1,320.
4	174,240	50.	871.2
5	217,800	66.	660.
6	261,360	75.	580.8
7	304,920	100.	435.6
8	348,480	132.	330.
9	392,040	150.	290.4
10	435,600	208.71033	208.71033

SOURCE: *The AAPL Guide for Landmen*, 51.

New Mexico, and Texas. In the last four states, anyone who goes to the county courthouse to look up the legal documents pertaining to his land may find—at the far end of the title chain—a grant set out in Spanish *varas* rather than in English units of measurement. Similarly, a person who undertakes such a search in Louisiana may find a grant using French *arpents*. Use of the arpent is especially

TABLE 4.4
Linear and Square Measurements

Linear Measure

1 inch	equals	.0833 ft.
7.92 inches	equals	1 link
12 inches	equals	1 foot
1 vara	equals	33⅓ inches
2.778 feet	equals	1 vara
3 feet	equals	1 yard
25 links	equals	16½ feet
25 links	equals	1 rod
100 links	equals	1 chain
16½ feet	equals	1 rod
5½ yards	equals	1 rod
4 rods	equals	100 links
66 feet	equals	1 chain
80 chains	equals	1 mile
320 rods	equals	1 mile
5280 feet	equals	1 mile
1760 yards	equals	1 mile

TABLE 4.4—*Continued*

Square Measure

144 sq. in.	equals	1 sq. foot
9 sq. feet	equals	1 sq. yard
30¼ sq. yds.	equals	1 sq. rod
16 sq. rods	equals	1 sq. chain
1 sq. rod	equals	272¼ sq. ft.
1 sq. ch.	equals	4356 sq. ft.
10 sq. ch.	equals	1 acre
160 sq. rods	equals	1 acre
4840 sq. yds.	equals	1 acre
43560 sq. ft.	equals	1 acre
640 acres	equals	1 sq. mile
1 section	equals	1 sq. mile
1 Twp.	equals	36 sq. miles
1 Twp.	equals	6 miles sq.

An Acre Is:

43,560 sq. ft.
165 feet × 264 feet.
198 feet × 220 feet.
5280 feet × 8.25 feet.
2640 feet × 16.50 feet.
1320 feet × 33 feet.
660 feet × 66 feet.
330 feet × 132 feet.
160 square rods.
208'8½" square or
208.71033 feet square*
  or any rectangular tract, the product of the length and width of which totals 43,560 sq. ft.
  (*(208.71033)² = 43,560.002 sq. ft.)

SOURCE: *The AAPL Guide for Landmen*, 51.

common in southeastern Louisiana; and in Texas, the Spanish vara is more likely to be applied to land in the southern and eastern portions of the state.

A problem for anyone wishing to translate French and Spanish measurements into English ones is the degree to which they vary—the vara from state to state and the arpent from one Louisiana parish to another. The equivalencies given in tables 4.5 through 4.8 are those most often used in Texas (for the vara) and in Louisiana (for the arpent).

TABLE 4.5
Spanish Measurements Used in Texas

1 league and 1 labor = 4,605.54 acres = 26,000,000 square varas (square of 5,000 varas)

1 labor   =   177.136 acres = 1,000,000 square varas (square of 1,000 varas)

1 league   = 4,428.4   acres = 25,000,000 square varas (square of 5,000 varas)

½ league   = 2,214.2   acres = 12,500,000 square varas (square of 3,535.5 varas)

⅓ league   = 1,476.13 acres = 8,333,333 square varas (square of 2,886.7 varas)

¼ league   = 1,107.1   acres = 6,250,000 square varas (square of 2,500 varas)

1 section   =   640   acres = 3,613,040.64 square varas (square of 1,900.8 varas)

½ section   =   320   acres = 1,806,520.32 square varas (square of 1,344.0 varas)

¼ section   =   160   acres = 903,260.16 square varas (square of 950.4 varas)

⅛ section   =   80   acres = 451,630.08 square varas (square of 672.0 varas)

¹⁄₁₆ section   =   40   acres = 225,815.04 square varas (square of 475.2 varas)

4,840 square yards =   1   acre = 5,645.376 square varas (square of 75.1 varas)

⅓ league — 1,476.1 acres, 2,886.7 varas square, 8,019 feet square

¼ league — 1,107.1 acres, 2,500 varas square, 6,944.444 feet square

1 caballeria — 108 acres

1 section — 640 acres, 1,900.8 varas square, 5,280 feet square

1 sitio — 1 league

1 vara — 3 geometrical feet, 33⅓ inches

100 feet — 36 varas

100 yards — 108 varas

1 minute of latitude — 1 nautical mile, 1.151 statute miles

1 degree of latitude — 60 minutes, 60 nautical miles, 69.06 statute miles

TO REDUCE

Varas to feet — divide by .36

Varas to yards — divide by 1.08

Yards to varas — multiply by 1.08

Varas to rods — divide by 5.94

Rods to varas — multiply by 5.94

Varas to chains — divide by 23.76

Chains to varas — multiply by 23.76

Square varas to acres — multiply by 177.136 and point off six places (divide by 5,645.376)

Square feet to acres — multiply by 22.9568 and point off six places (divide by 43,560)

SOURCE: *The AAPL Guide for Landmen*, 47–48.

TABLE 4.6
Feet and Varas

1 foot = .36 vara	1 vara = 33⅓ inches
2 feet = .72 vara	1 vara = 2.78 feet
3 feet = 1.08 varas	2 varas = 5.56 feet
4 feet = 1.44 varas	3 varas = 8.33 feet
5 feet = 1.80 varas	4 varas = 11.11 feet
6 feet = 2.16 varas	5 varas = 13.89 feet
7 feet = 2.52 varas	6 varas = 16.67 feet
8 feet = 2.88 varas	7 varas = 19.44 feet
9 feet = 3.24 varas	8 varas = 22.22 feet
10 feet = 3.60 varas	9 varas = 25.00 feet

SOURCE: *The AAPL Guide for Landmen*, 48.

Finally, something should be said about the metric system of measurement. Not many landowners or lessees will encounter land descriptions given in *metres* (the basic linear unit)

TABLE 4.7
General Conversion of English and Spanish Units

1 pole
1 perch   = 16½ feet or 5½ yards or 5.94
1 rod   varas

1 chain = 100 links, 66 feet, 23.76 varas

1 link = 7.92 inches

1 mile (statute) = 1,900.8 varas, 1,760 yards, 5,280 feet, 80 chains, 320 rods, 0.868 min. of latitude

1 acre = 75.136 varas square, 208.710 feet square, 5,645.376 square varas, 43,560 square feet

1 labor = 1,000 varas square, 177.136 acres, 1,000,000 square varas, 2,777.777 feet square

1 league = 5,000 varas square, 25,000,000 square varas, 25 labors, 4,428.4 acres, 13,888.888 feet square

1 league & 1 labor = 5,099.018 varas square, 25,999,982.402 square varas, 4,605.536 acres, 14,163.917 feet square

½ league = 2,214.2 acres, 3,535.533 varas square, 9,820.925 feet square

SOURCE: *The AAPL Guide for Landmen*, 47.

TABLE 4.8
French Measurements Used in Louisiana

1 arpent = 191.833 feet.
1 square arpent contains 0.84628 acres.
1.1834 square arpents = 1 acre.

Conversion Table – Arpents and Acres

½	arpent =	0.4231	of an acre
1	arpent =	0.8463	of an acre
2	arpents =	1.6926	acres
3	arpents =	2.5388	acres
4	arpents =	3.3851	acres
5	arpents =	4.2314	acres
6	arpents =	5.0777	acres
7	arpents =	5.9240	acres
8	arpents =	6.7702	acres
9	arpents =	7.6165	acres
10	arpents =	8.4628	acres
12.5	arpents =	10.5785	acres
15	arpents =	12.6942	acres
17.5	arpents =	14.8099	acres
20	arpents =	16.9256	acres
22.5	arpents =	19.0413	acres
25	arpents =	21.1570	acres
30	arpents =	25.3884	acres
35	arpents =	29.6198	acres
37.5	arpents =	31.7355	acres
40	arpents =	33.8512	acres
45	arpents =	38.0826	acres
50	arpents =	42.3140	acres
60	arpents =	50.7768	acres
70	arpents =	59.2396	acres
80	arpents =	67.7024	acres
90	arpents =	76.1652	acres
100	arpents =	84.6280	acres
120	arpents =	101.5536	acres
130	arpents =	110.0164	acres
140	arpents =	118.4792	acres
150	arpents =	126.9420	acres
160	arpents =	135.4048	acres
170	arpents =	143.8676	acres
180	arpents =	152.3304	acres
190	arpents =	160.7932	acres
200	arpents =	169.2560	acres

SOURCE: *The AAPL Guide for Landmen*, 49.

or *hectares* (the basic square unit). Only a few states have begun to "go metric" as yet. Minnesota, for example has a number of official county-format maps in metres, but even in

Minnesota, most elevations are still given in feet. According to the National Mapping Division of the United States Geologic Survey, new series of government maps will be produced in metres, but old series still in production will continue to be drawn in feet. Most government agencies, including the Bureau of Land Management and the Minerals Management Service, have not yet converted to the metric system. Occasionally, thanks to some of the new map series, a lessee of offshore land may find his leased tract described in hectares. (The most commonly used equivalencies are given in table 4.9.)

TABLE 4.9
Metric Measurements

Linear Measurement

10 millimetres	=	1 centimetre	=	0.397 inches
10 centimetres	=	1 decimetre	=	3.937 in.
10 decimetres	=	1 metre	=	39.37 in. or 3.28 ft
10 metres	=	1 decametre	=	393.7 in.
10 decametres	=	1 hectometre	=	328 ft, 1 in.
10 hectometres	=	1 kilometre	=	0.62137 mile
10 kilometres	=	1 myriametre	=	6.2137 miles

Land Measurement

1 centiare	=	1 sq. metre	=	1,550 sq. in.
1 are	=	100 centiares	=	119.6 sq. yards
1 hectare	=	100 ares	=	2.471 acres
1 sq. kilometre	=	1,000,000 sq. m	=	0.3861 sq. mile

NOTE: Where the metric system is consistently used, the basic unit for large-scale mapping and surveying is the *square kilometre*. Field measurement usually employs the *hectare,* and urban lots the *are.*

METHODS OF DESCRIPTION

The very first settlers in this country, and many later ones on the frontier, dispensed with such formalities as surveying and recording land. They simply took possession, moved in, and began clearing and farming their new property. Only later did they realize the advantages of laying out tracts according to some regular system. By that time, land ownership in much of New England and the frontier states resembled a patchwork quilt.

Even tracts inside the 6-mile-square townships that were laid out in parts of the thirteen colonies (and in Vermont, Maine, Kentucky, and Tennessee) might be of varying sizes and shapes. Surveying and recording these tracts didn't make them any neater. On the contrary, surveying land *after* it has passed into private hands merely acknowledges the patchwork pattern—or lack of pattern. Tracts of the crazy quilt variety can be described, however, by a method called *metes and bounds*.

Metes and Bounds

Mete comes from a root word meaning "to measure" and is closely related to another root meaning "stake" or "post" or "tree." *Bound* is simply a limit or boundary. A description of land by metes and bounds, then, basically gives the measured boundaries of a particular tract. Such a description—and the surveyor marking off and later mapping such a tract—must rely rather extensively on so-called natural boundaries. Riverbeds, stream courses, rocks, roads, ridges, and even fences often serve to delimit one piece of property from another.

Descriptions by metes and bounds are still used, not only in the states we have mentioned but also in parts of the South and Southwest where the French, Spanish, and Mexican governments often granted land in tracts of irregular shape and size. Such foreign grants in California have now been integrated into the U.S. government's rectangular survey system, but Texas—which kept title to its public lands when it came into the Union—was never part of the U.S. survey. Parts of Texas, therefore, have their own rectangular survey pattern, and parts still consist of small, quite irregular tracts that must be identified by county and by individual survey. Where land has been surveyed in parcels, as in many Texas counties, and where a given piece of property does not fill up an entire survey, descriptions must rely to some degree on markers like trees, streams, rocks, and so on. Thus, if Richard Roe's property is coextensive with the J. J. Puffin Railroad Company survey, describing that property is quite simple. If, on the other hand, Mr. Roe's land consists of a small wedge-shaped tract in the northeast corner of the survey, description

may require mention of two small streams, a protruding piece of granite, a mesquite tree, and the neighboring John Doe stock tank.

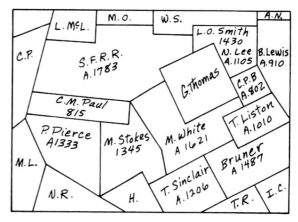

Figure 4.1. Small, oddly shaped surveys in a Texas county

(Fig. 4.1 shows small, irregularly shaped surveys in one portion of a Texas county.)

Rectangular Survey System

In 1785, the Continental Congress adopted an ordinance calling for a rectangular system of land measurement to be used in all newly acquired territories lying north of the Ohio River. Ohio was the first state to benefit from the system; later, the rectangular survey was used in Alabama, Florida, Mississippi, the states north of the Ohio River and those west of the Mississippi (with the exception of Texas).

The basic unit of the system—a square 6 miles wide and 6 miles long—is called a congressional township. (Its dimensions were clearly suggested by the colonial township mentioned earlier.) To cut a region up into townships, surveyors start from the intersection of a north-south line called a *principal meridian* and an east-west line called a *base line*. Additional parallel lines are marked off and numbered at 6-mile intervals on either side of the principal meridian and the base

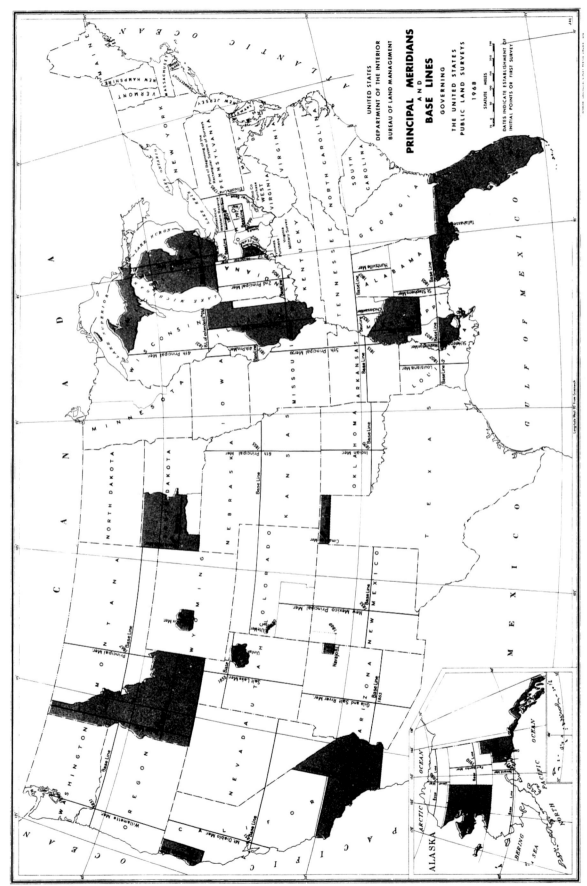

Figure 4.2. Principal meridians and base lines governing the United States public land surveys (Courtesy of U. S. Geological Survey)

line. (Figure 4.2. shows the principal meridians and base lines of the United States.) A region is thus divided into north-south tiers commonly referred to as *townships* and east-west columns called *ranges;* the intersections of these north-south township lines and east-west range lines form 6-mile squares. Figure 4.3 illustrates this pattern of township and range lines; it also shows the first step in identifying a particular tract by locating the township in which it lies.

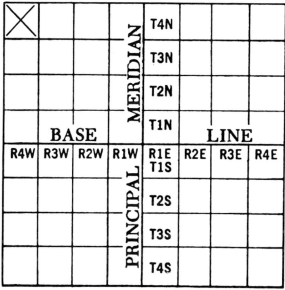

Figure 4.3. Congressional townships numbered from a base line and a principal meridian. Township numbers are vertical, and range numbers are horizontal. A tract lying within township 4 north, range 4 west is found in the 4th tier north of the base line and the 4th column west of the meridian. (Courtesy of AAPL)

Each township is further divided into 36 sections of a square mile, or 640 acres. These sections are numbered from 1 to 36, starting in the northeast corner with number 1 and going straight west to number 6, then dropping down one tier and going straight east to number 12. The pattern is repeated until the southeast corner (section 36) has been reached. Figure 4.4 shows an official plat of a

36	31	32	33	34	35	36	31
1	6	5	4	3	2	1	6
12	7	8	9	10	11	12	7
13	18	17	16	15	14	13	18
24	19	20	21	22	23	24	19
25	30	29	28	27	26	25	30
36	31	32	33	34	35	36	31
1	6	5	4	3	2	1	6

Figure 4.4. Plat of a sectioned township. A hypothetical tract lies in section 5, and its legal description can be extended to read section 5 T4N R4E. (Courtesy of AAPL)

township with the shaded sections representing the 6-mile square itself and the lighter rows representing adjoining sections of neighboring townships. (It should be noted that not all townships are precisely 6 miles square, owing to the convergence of range lines. Discrepancies are made up on the north and west boundaries.)

Finally, each section of a township is subdivided into quarters of 160 acres and smaller fractions like eighths (80 acres), sixteenths (40 acres), and so on. The trick to reading a subdivided section number is to remember that each division stands in the same relation to the quarter that the quarter stands to the section as a whole. Each subdivision, that is, will be indicated by letters and numbers that locate it within the section, the quarter section, the quarter-quarter, and so forth. Figure 4.5 locates a 20-acre tract in the southeast quarter of a divided section. It further pinpoints the location by specifying the northwest quarter of that quarter—and the

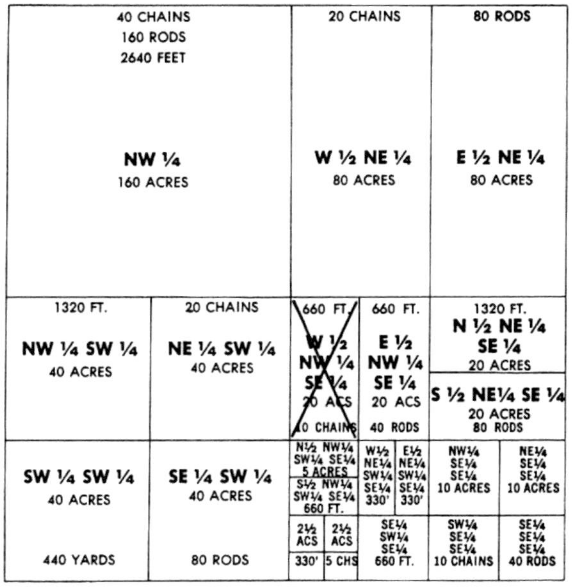
40 CHAINS
160 RODS
2640 FEET
NW ¼
160 ACRES
20 CHAINS
W ½ NE ¼
80 ACRES
80 RODS
E ½ NE ¼
80 ACRES
1320 FT.
NW ¼ SW ¼
40 ACRES
20 CHAINS
NE ¼ SW ¼
40 ACRES
660 FT.
W ½
NW ¼
SE ¼
20 ACS
10 CHAINS
660 FT.
E ½
NW ¼
SE ¼
20 ACS
40 RODS
1320 FT.
N ½ NE ¼
SE ¼
20 ACRES
S ½ NE¼ SE ¼
20 ACRES
80 RODS
SW ¼ SW ¼
40 ACRES
440 YARDS
SE ¼ SW ¼
40 ACRES
80 RODS
N½ NW¼
SW¼ SE¼
5 ACRES
S½ NW¼
SW¼ SE¼
660 FT.
W½
NE¼
SW¼
SE¼
330'
E½
NE¼
SW¼
SE¼
330'
NW¼
SE¼
SE¼
10 ACRES
NE¼
SE¼
SE¼
10 ACRES
2½
ACS
2½
ACS
330'
5 CHS
SE¼
SW¼
SE¼
660 FT.
SW¼
SE¼
SE¼
10 CHAINS
SE¼
SE¼
SE¼
40 RODS

Figure 4.5. A subdivided section. X marks the 20-acre tract that can be fully described as W ½ NW¼ SE ¼ of section 5 T4N R4E Tornado County, Kansas. (Courtesy of AAPL)

west half of that quarter-quarter. To locate a small parcel of land within a subdivided section, then, read the numbers *backward.*

One caution for reading subdivisions: Look carefully for any commas. They indicate separate tracts and can make a great difference in the number of acres under discussion. For example, a reading of S ½, NW ¼ indicates two tracts—the first amounting to 320 acres (one-half section) and the other 160 acres (one-quarter section). The total number of acres is 480. Without the comma, the description would run S ½ NW ¼, describing a single tract of 80 acres.

Urban Subdivisions

Individual lots, often small, make up the blocks of a typical town or city subdivision. These lots are usually quite easy to find on a subdivision plat; all the blocks are numbered and each lot on a block is also numbered. After a housing subdivision (generally owned by one person or company) has been surveyed, the entire tract is mapped to show the arrangement of streets, blocks, and lots. The legal description of a lot ready for sale may read: "Lot 10, Block 6, of the J. D. Hepplewhite Subdivision to the City of Dallas, per plat on file in Book..., page..., of the Map Records of Dallas County, Texas."

COMPLETENESS OF DESCRIPTION

In any transfer of land, a clear and complete description of the property is essential. Confusion as to *what* land has been conveyed can lead to bad feeling, at best, and to expensive litigation at worst. To sum up the items that should be included in a legal description: the names of the county or parish and the state in which the land lies; details of any known survey plat, with the date, surveyor's name, and recording information; the date (with book and page references to the recording of the transaction) on which the present owner acquired the land. If the land appears in the U.S. government's rectangular survey, the section, portion of the section, township, and range should be listed. If more than one meridian runs through the state, the name of the relevant meridian should be given. Property not included in the rectangular survey must be carefully described by metes and bounds with the names of the bounding owners, all bearing marks, and all information needed for unambiguous identification. For urban property, a description will need the names of the subdivision and the city, the lot and block numbers, and a reference to the surveyor's plat with name, date, and recording details.

Preparations for Leasing

PRELIMINARY EXPLORATIONS

Along with the steadily increasing costs of exploration, drilling, and production, many oil and gas operators find that they must take into account a greater degree of business "savvy" and bargaining power on the part of mineral interest owners than was once the case. Whether these owners are public agencies or private citizens, more of them are treating their mineral rights as assets to be rationally managed rather than as mysteries to be ignored until an oil company representative shows an interest in them. Private owners, for example, are organizing themselves into groups like the National Association of Royalty Owners (NARO) in order to keep up with the tax laws, plan lobbying strategies, and exchange information on everything from accounting systems to the uses of home computers. Not all owners are this concerned about their minerals, of course, and some nonresident owners are still ignorant of the fact that they *do own* mineral interests outside their home states and counties. Nevertheless, a variety of conditions—including a series of

highly publicized energy crises and a shaky national economy—has combined to make many owners better informed and warier custodians of their mineral resources. The work of geologists and geophysicists, landmen, and lease brokers in identifying and leasing oil and gas properties has become correspondingly sophisticated and challenging.

Geologists and Geophysicists

The decision to acquire leases in a given area—along with related decisions about how much to offer, what to concede in the way of special conditions and clauses, and so forth—rests upon the best geophysical or geological information that a company can procure. In a "hot" area, information about the subsurface and its possible oil- or gas-bearing formations may be relatively scarce. New areas, for example, sometimes elicit frenetic leasing activity in spite of the absence of abundant data. Speculation and hunch can be rife in such areas precisely because there has not yet been time or opportunity to gather clear information. Producing areas, on the other hand, may offer such information in quite accessible forms. Company geologists or geophysicists can often do much exploratory work from their offices—using maps, published data, and logs and production figures from existing wells. Further information can be gleaned from professional associations (like the American Association of Petroleum Geologists), from private scouting companies, from well log libraries (most of which charge their members a fee and provide them with various data services), and from state regulatory agencies. When seismic information must be obtained on the land, a petroleum company will seek the consent of the landowner. The two parties may enter into a contract known as a seismic option agreement that allows seismic exploration for a specified price per acre. The company can then set up its equipment, generate underground vibrations, and measure them to learn about subsurface formations. Once enough information has been gathered, the company can then lease the acreage that seems most promising for a price agreed upon in the seismic option contract.

The larger the company, the more time and money it can generally afford to spend on exploration. Large companies can also invest in the latest technological refinements to improve their information, though even small companies can now take advantage of automated systems for data storage and retrieval, computerized mapping, and computerized risk estimates. No matter how large the operation, however, or how ample and sophisticated the information obtained for it, an element of guesswork always remains. Inspired (or uninspired) hunch often plays its part, especially in areas where production is not yet under way. The questions persists: how much

information is enough to justify leasing? Or, as one operator put it, "Do we lease as much as we can and *then* finish our homework? Or do we gather data until we're just about certain and then try to lease what's left?" Most companies try to strike a balance between timely acquisition of leases and reasonable completeness of information. There is always the risk, on the one hand, of losing prospects to rival operators; on the other hand, no one wants to commit precious capital to a venture that, with a little more exploration, would have revealed itself as unpromising.

Landmen

Once the geologists have identified a likely looking area of interest, they outline it on a plat or map that goes to the company land department. A landman must then find out whether the tracts lying within the area of interest are available for leasing and, if they are, who owns the relevant mineral rights. During his preliminary check of the records (to be described later in this chapter), the landman may discover that all of the desired tracts are already under lease. If, however, some promising land is still available, the landman will receive a lease purchase authority and go on to the next stage of his work—contacting landowners and offering to lease their property. After the leases have been acquired and before actual drilling begins, a more intensive examination of records and titles will be necessary. A part of this work may also be undertaken by the landman. Finally, an oil company's land department must monitor the continuous development of its leased properties, oversee royalty and other payments, and make day-to-day decisions on matters of major and minor concern. For example, a landman may need to arrange complicated joint ventures with other oil companies before drilling can proceed; or, he may need to pacify an angry surface owner who claims that his most valuable cow died from drinking errant crude oil.

To accomplish their various tasks, landmen should have a good working knowledge of the law — especially real estate, inheritance, oil and gas, and tax law. They should be familiar with the drafting, executing, and recording of certain kinds of legal instruments; and they should be able to do certain kinds of legal research. Some landmen are, in fact, attorneys. More hold degrees in business or petroleum land management, degrees that may be supplemented by a real estate license. A landman needs, in addition, a thorough familiarity with the state and federal regulations that affect his work. State agencies such as the Texas Railroad Commission or the Oklahoma Corporation Commission or the Louisiana Department of Conservation formulate the rules that govern well spacing, well density, pooling procedures, and other crucial details. To be ignorant of any such rules — or of conditions that might warrant an *exception* being granted to one or more of them — is to risk losing opportunities to lease.

Finally, a successful landman must be persuasive. He must be socially adept and adaptable, well informed and comfortable in meeting, talking, and negotiating with a wide variety of people. Unless he can convince landowners to sign leases (assuming that the prices his company will pay are reasonable), he will fail at his primary task. If he does convince them to sign and earns a merited trust in the process, he has served the landowner, his company, and the industry well.

Lease Brokers

A lease broker is, essentially, an independent landman. He often works with several operators or companies in a given area; a company landman may coordinate the efforts of one or more independent brokers, relying on them to do much of the legwork of preliminary record checks and the "people work" of preliminary or even concluding negotiation. Brokers quite commonly live in the areas where they work. Their intimate knowledge of the local situation — its land, its people, its resources — can be very valuable to representatives of large companies. This local knowledge, when accompanied by the proper experience, can make the broker more effective in the field than a company landman; the landman can then become more nearly an administrator and a negotiator with other companies. Multilist brokers have also begun to represent mineral owners to oil companies interested in acquiring leases. This development makes it easier for a landowner who wishes to lease to give notice of that fact. He need not simply wait until an oil company gets in touch with him.

PRELIMINARY TITLE CHECKS

Purpose

A preliminary check of the records or title check done by a landman or lease broker *before* a lease is signed should not be confused with the much more detailed examination of title done by a lawyer *after* a lease is signed. In the first instance, the landman wants to know the names and addresses of the current mineral interest owners so that he can talk with them — and get their signatures on a lease. He also wants to learn who owns the surface of the land that interests him, whether the property (both surface and subsurface) is already leased or otherwise encumbered, and whether any of the owners he plans to deal with are legally unable to execute a lease. His job at this point is to clear the way for a new lease.

The more information that the landman can collect in his preliminary search, the better. He will save himself steps later on. He may also uncover problems that, had they come to light only after a lease was agreed upon, could have caused his employers considerable difficulty. He does not usually aim, however, at establishing which owners have good title to land. A good title can be sold or successfully defended in court, and a lawyer who specializes in title work will establish who holds good title—along with the full legal status of the land in question—once a lessee has decided to drill a well. The landman will, in his preliminary work, learn the owners of record, try to look at all the documents in the land's history of ownership, and briefly describe these documents in a *run sheet,* which he can later hand over to an attorney who plans to make a full examination of title.

Sources of Information

The Statute of Frauds stipulates that real estate transactions, to be binding, must be in writing. Anyone who wishes to learn the history of a tract's ownership, then, may do so. The instruments relating to that history (or copies of them) are nearly always recorded and filed in public county offices. Portable copies of such tract ownership records are called *abstracts of title.* The landman in search of information about a given tract may investigate one or more of the following sources: the relevant public records (federal, state, or county), the records of the local abstract company, and the records of the landowner himself.

State and federal records. Information about state-owned lands can be obtained from the state boards and commissions listed in chapter 2 (see table 2.1). Records relating to lands owned by the U. S. government are on file in Washington, D. C., in the Bureau of Land Management and in the state land offices of the BLM. A landman is well advised to check the records in these state offices, even if his company employs a Washington attorney to look over the records in the national BLM office. The Washington files may not contain all the information needed to proceed with plans to lease.

Abstract companies. Where the landman begins his search for the owners of privately held property depends upon his experience and resources. Some years ago, he would very probably have begun with a visit to a friendly abstract company. Such companies, also known as abstract plants, were primarily in the business of preparing and selling abstracts of title. They kept indexes and records, which they sometimes allowed landmen to examine free of charge (hence the adjective *friendly).* These indexes were a very helpful place to begin a check of the records; from them, the landman could learn the book and page numbers required to find the relevant instruments in the county records. In many areas, though, this working rapport has slowly deteriorated. These days, the local abstract plant may be more hostile than hospitable to landmen. There are a number of reasons for the change.

First, many abstract companies, especially in larger cities and towns, have been replaced by or transformed into title companies. Their business has shifted from the selling of abstracts to the insuring of property titles. In most states, these insured titles do not involve oil and gas properties. California is the exception. (See Appendix C for information on leasing in California.) They are sought by lenders, builders, and private sellers of residential and commercial real estate. While the title companies still keep active abstract departments—staffed by researchers, examiners, and abstractors—they are mindful of increased costs. Even plants that still specialize in oil and gas work resist the idea of giving away information. One abstractor added that "our files are hard to use without special instructions. We don't want people misplacing or misfiling our materials." A veteran landman agreed that carelessness in the use of abstractors' files has damaged the old rapport. He also pointed out that privileges like the free examination of indexes have been overworked and, in some cases, abused. "If friendly abstract plants are rare these days, landmen have brought the situation on themselves."

Friendly or hostile, most abstract companies will, of course, do work for a fee. A complete abstract that includes all the documents related to a tract's ownership since the original land grant or patent can be extremely expensive to prepare. Prices run from about $4 to $7 per page, and some abstracts cost thousands of dollars. The preparation can also be time-consuming. Since a landman may need information in a hurry, and has no wish to pay more for it than is necessary, he often dispenses with a complete abstract in the early stages of his inquiry. Instead, he may order a *takeoff,* or list of the instruments pertaining to a given tract. The takeoff costs far less than a complete, or *base abstract,* and often includes a brief summary or description of the listed documents. Alternatively, the landman might pay a fee to look at the indexes of a plant that allows, but charges for, such examinations. With luck, he might even find a friendly plant that will make its files available without a charge. Abstract plants vary, of course, and their records are not always complete, reliable, or easy of

access. A truly reliable abstract plant can be a real boon—and the preferred starting place—for a landman. An unknown or less reliable one may seem a less attractive place to begin than the county courthouse.

County records. Each state has its own system for recording legal instruments—systems that depend, in part, on how the land in that state was measured and patented. Recorded instruments are kept in county courthouses; the county clerk (or, in Louisana, the clerk of court for the parish) can help an inquirer use the courthouse indexes to find the legal documents he requires. These indexes may be arranged by the names of grantors and grantees, by tract (with the instruments relevant to each tract listed chronologically), or by some combination method. In some counties, computers are used to facilitate searches. After locating the instruments pertinent to a title chain in the county indexes, the landman must look at the pages in the books that record the information he needs. This information will include the record owners, any prior mineral reservations or mineral deeds, any existing leases or liens on the surface or mineral estates, and any court proceedings—probates, foreclosures, judgments, and so forth—that might affect title. Records of such proceedings can usually be found in the court clerk's office. Records of tax payments will be filed in the county assessor's office; a check of these records will yield the names and current addresses of people who pay taxes on the tracts in question.

Landowners. A final and often very helpful source of information is the landowner himself, particularly if he lives on his land. Some oil companies, in fact, routinely ask their landmen to give landowners printed ownership questionnaires early in their discussions of possible leases and to obtain as much detail about the land's legal history as possible. Since mineral interests can be very complicated, involving the business (and sometimes the marital) transactions of dozens of owners, detailed knowledge is essential. A landowner who can produce deeds, wills, mortgages, leases, tax records, and so on can be a great help in determining who—if anyone—shares in the ownership of his mineral interests and must therefore be con-

tacted before a lease is signed. Resident owners are also more likely to produce partial or even complete abstracts of title when queried about their land's history. Base abstracts are often lent to landmen on the understanding that any supplements ordered to bring the abstract up to date will be given to the landowner when the company has finished with them.

PRELIMINARY NEGOTIATIONS

Landman and landowner do not always negotiate a lease while leaning comfortably on a gate or drinking a cup of coffee. Many leases are acquired by telephone or letter, and even those that are negotiated in face-to-face encounters are often sold or traded by the acquiring company; the landowner, and in some cases the landman, may not be acquainted with the final lessee. However a lease is acquired, it is always *bargained* for. Each party wants to make the best deal he can, and each negotiates with certain questions and constraints uppermost in his mind. The landman will be mindful of his company's resources and policies; he will also be sensitive to the local situation and the going price in his area. The landowner, for his part, will be concerned with making an informed evaluation of the landman's offer. The landowner will wonder about additional matters like tract size and spacing—and just how becoming a lessor will affect his tax returns.

Concerns of the Landman

Company size, policy, and financial resources. A landman's instructions, when he is authorized to buy leases, will include the maximum bonus, rental, and royalty that can be paid landowners, the minimum primary term for the lease, and any permissible varia-

tions on the company's standard lease form. (Such variations will be discussed in chapters 6 and 7.) Clearly, the size and leasing policies of the buying company will help to set these maximum prices as well as the lower limit on the primary lease term offered. The smaller the company, the more limited are its financial resources—and the more cautious its buying policy is likely to be. There are high-risk, high-return companies, of course, even among the independents; small companies of this sort are usually working with promotional money from investors. But in general a small company will look for low-risk buys, aiming at steady development and a reliable cash flow. Larger companies, especially those with diversified interests, can afford to take more and bigger risks. The large company will also find that its land costs—the bonuses, rentals, and royalties it pays landowners—make up a smaller part of its total outlay than is true of a small, independent operator. When the large company can comfortably afford to meet a canny landowner's demand for, say, ⅕ royalty instead of ⅛, the small operator may be financially unable to buy a lease on such terms unless the bonus consideration is reduced accordingly.

The length of the lease's primary term may also be more critical to the small company. If the money to drill must be raised through joint ventures that take several years to arrange, a longer primary term is clearly desirable. On the other hand, if a long primary term means a reduction in the bonus payment, a short-term lease may have its attractions—especially since a small company's ability to move quickly can give it a competitive edge over larger companies. Large companies commonly bargain for, and can pay larger bonuses to acquire, primary terms of considerable length. From the company's point of view, ample time in which to finish exploration, make drilling decisions, and raise the capital for test wells and possible completions is a decided advantage. From the landowner's point of view, it may not be.

No matter what the size and resources of the company are, its exploration and leasing policies for a particular area will rarely be spelled out anywhere in detail. Silence is protective, and companies naturally wish to withhold from rivals the details of their plans and procedures. It may be prudent for company personnel to know as much as they need for doing their jobs, and no more. What they don't know about their company's commitments, drilling objectives, and well locations, they cannot inadvertently reveal. Nor need they pretend to be ignorant.

Area considerations. Bonus, rental, and royalty figures vary widely from state to state. Within a given state, too, variations may be considerable; a specific area or even a specific tract may earn offers near the top of the scale while a neighboring tract or area is leased for a much lower figure. Bonuses, for example, have been as high as $5,000–$10,000 per acre in really productive parts of states like Oklahoma, California, and Louisiana. (Some tracts in these states and in South Texas have also commanded delay rentals as high as their bonuses.) However, in a state with limited production, like Tennessee, a bonus of $5–$10 per acre has been common; a rental of $1 per acre per year and a primary term of 5 or 10 years will satisfy most landowners.

Between these extremes, dependable producing areas in Kansas and Illinois earn bonuses of $100 or more per acre; rentals run at $1 or $2 per year, and 3-year primary terms tend to be the rule. When royalties are concerned, Tennessee owners still commonly receive ⅛ of total production, but ³⁄₁₆ is becoming the new standard in several states. A ⅙ royalty would be moderately low these days for a promising tract, and, moving up the scale, ⅕ to ¼ is frequently asked by some (Louisiana) landowners. Needless to say, a landman will not make an initial offer that tops the scale of permissible prices or royalties. He will try to save his company money, and to that end he may suggest a 5-year lease at the rate of ⅛ royalty and $1 per year in rent. The landowner then has the problem of deciding whether these figures are acceptable or whether he can extract better ones by careful bargaining.

Concerns of the Landowner

Evaluation of offers. To evaluate the terms first offered, a landowner will often ask for time to think it over. Thinking it over generally means making telephone calls to neighboring owners, bankers, attorneys, accountants, or local lease brokers (if the landowner happens to know any) in order to clarify the vague idea that "I may be able to do better." If the landowner has leased before, or is simply a shrewd manager of his property, he may already have a good idea of the going rate in his area. He will have followed newspaper accounts of any drilling or exploration in the neighborhood, will have investigated state and federal lease sale prices, and may have joined local associations or even subscribed to information services that keep him well supplied with facts and figures.

In addition to checking on prices, the landowner will have formed a notion of what constitutes an acceptable primary lease term. If the prospects for production look uncertain or risky, it may be in his best interests to grant the lessee a primary term as long as the company proposes. This concession would be especially tempting if it meant a larger bonus. On the other hand, many landowners hold out for short primary terms. A short term can mean prompt development of the property *or* the opportunity to lease again in a year or two — and to garner fresh bonuses and rentals.

Tract size and spacing. The *spacing* of oil and gas wells (how far apart in feet wells must be and how far from property or lease lines) together with their *density* (how many acres must be assigned to each well) are determined by the oil and gas regulatory agencies of the various states. These agencies decide how a given pool or reservoir can best be developed, with waste avoided, efficient production ensured, and owners' correlative rights protected. A landowner preparing to lease his property should obtain a copy of the spacing and density regulations that apply to his area, keeping in mind the possibility that exceptions may be warranted in his case. If an exception to the rule will minimize waste or prevent confiscation of property (from drainage across property lines, for example), he has a good argument for an exception. He should know, too, that a given oil or gas field may be subject to special rules; the state agency will be glad to provide information on specific areas and fields. (Regulatory agencies for the ten top producing states, with their addresses, can be found in table 5.1).

Once a landowner knows the well density permitted in a given field, he may wish to lease in tracts of that size. For example, if a regulatory agency requires 80 acres per well, an owner may decide not to grant a 160-acre lease but instead to lease in 80-acre tracts. If

he can persuade a lessee to accept these terms, the landowner has protected himself from the possibility that his lessee might tie up all 160 acres by drilling and producing only one well on the tract. Leasing in smaller units can leave more land free to be leased later or to be re-leased when a lease expires. A well drilled on one 80-acre tract cannot hold the land in the adjacent 80 acres. The size limits that might benefit an owner vary, of course, from field to field and state to state. Deep wells require far more acreage than do shallow wells. In Louisiana, for example, deep gas wells are sometimes drilled on tracts of 1,500 acres or more. Owners of such tracts would need to agree to have their land developed on these terms. In other states, landowners may be advised by their attorneys to lease in units no larger than a quarter-quarter section (40 acres).

From the oil company's point of view, such attempts on the part of the landowner to limit lease size or control spacing are undesirable. Some hard bargaining may be necessary before these matters are agreed upon. Some companies have even declared their unwillingness to negotiate with an owner who limits lease size. While a shrewd landowner is rarely so inflexible in his demands as to lose a good opportunity to lease, he may indeed prefer to hold out until he finds a company or operator willing to meet all or some of his requirements.

Tax benefits and problems. A knowledgeable landowner does not wait until he is about to sign on the dotted line before considering his tax situation. Just as an oil company usually has its own legal staff and accountants, so the landowner who manages his estate with any care will have an attorney to advise him. (He may also have an accountant, investment counselor, insurance agent, or trust officer.) Mineral and royalty owners are subject — like anyone else whose income isn't

TABLE 5.1
State Regulatory Agencies for the Top Ten Oil-Producing States*

1. Texas
   Texas Railroad Commission
   Drawer 12967
   Austin, TX 78111
   512/445-1100

2. Alaska
   Alaska Oil and Gas Conservation
     Commission
   3001 Porcupine Drive
   Anchorage, AK 99501
   907/279-1433

3. Louisiana
   Department of Natural Resources
   Office of Conservation
   Box 44275
   Baton Rouge, LA 70804
   504/342-5540

4. California
   Department of Conservation
   Division of Oil and Gas
   1416 Ninth Street, Room 1310
   Sacramento, CA 95814
   916/445-9686

5. Oklahoma
   Corporation Commission
   Division of Oil and Gas
   Jim Thorpe Building
   Oklahoma City, OK 73105
   405/521-2267

6. Wyoming
   Oil and Gas Conservation Commission
   Box 2640
   Casper, WY 82602
   303/234-7147

7. New Mexico
   Oil Conservation Division
   Energy and Minerals Department
   Box 2088
   Santa Fe, NM 87501
   505/827-2434

8. Kansas
   Corporation Commission
   430 State Office Building
   Topeka, KS 66612
   913/296-3355

9. North Dakota
   Industrial Commission
   Oil and Gas Division
   900 East Boulevard
   Bismarck, ND 58505

10. Michigan
    Department of Natural Resources
    Box 30028
    Lansing, MI 48909
    517/373-1256

*Ranking as of November 1983 (API statistics)

neatly covered by a W-2 form—to a bewildering array of special taxes, exemptions, credits, and deductions. In addition to coping with the IRS, the landowner must ascertain and pay any state taxes that apply to him. Since the tax laws change from year to year, merely keeping abreast of what he *must* do can be a confusing process. To learn and take advantage of what he *may* do requires help from professional tax consultants and estate planners. More and more landowners are seeking such help before they lease their property.

In view of the increasing complexity of the tax laws and the accounting procedures required to comply with them, there is little point in supplying many details about the landowner's tax problems. It may be helpful, however, to mention how the payments discussed earlier—bonuses, royalties, and delay rentals—are viewed by the IRS. In assessing any income from mineral production, the landowner should know that a *depletion* deduction may be allowed by the IRS and/or the state. Such a deduction is granted to compensate for the loss of an irreplaceable and depleting capital asset. Depletion deductions can be computed in two ways; the method that generally applies to a mineral owner's income uses a *percentage* of taxable production. For example, royalties (both ordinary and overriding) are taxed as regular income; royalties are also subject to state, county, and federal taxes that are generally withheld by the first purchaser of the minerals. A landowner will find state and, sometimes, county taxes withheld from his royalty checks as a matter of course; federal windfall profit tax (WPT) will also be withheld. On what remains, he must pay federal income tax, *but* he may deduct a given percentage of his gross royalty income. In 1983, the allowed deduction was 16 percent; in 1984 and thereafter, it is 15 percent.

Delay rentals, on the other hand, are not subject to depletion or to WPT. They are taxed as ordinary income. At present, the IRS does not permit landowners to take a percentage depletion on lease bonuses, either. The issue of lease bonuses is a vexed one, however, and still being tested in the courts. Landowners have been heartened by a ruling from the U.S. Court of Appeals for the Seventh Circuit which said that lease bonuses—viewed in law as advance royalty payments—*are* eligible for percentage depletion. Eligibility would not be altered by the absence of produced oil or gas in the tax year in which payments are received. In view of the possibility that a landowner might have to *pay back* a depletion allowance should production not occur before the lease terminates, though, landowners are proceeding cautiously in the matter. Some file *protective claims* with their tax returns. These help to ensure a refund for the person who does not take a percentage depletion on a lease bonus—should the courts firmly and finally decide in favor of depletion. Some states still permit a depletion allowance on lease bonuses when the landowner pays state taxes.

Finally, it was at one time a fairly common practice for landowners to spread out a lease bonus over several years to minimize the amount of federal taxes to be paid. In 1968, however, the IRS said (in Revenue Ruling 68-606) that a taxpayer who uses the cash receipts and disbursements method of accounting must pay taxes on the fair market value of a bonus contract in the year in which the lease is executed. This ruling applies where a cash-basis taxpayer receives an unconditional bonus on a lease that is freely transferable and readily saleable. If the contract is *not* transferable or there is no market for its resale, a cash-basis taxpayer need pay taxes only on the income actually realized during the tax year. (Ready saleability of the lease does not affect the need for an accrual-method taxpayer to pay tax on the total bonus in the year that the lease is executed.)

However he manages his mineral interests, a landowner or royalty owner needs—like every taxpayer—to keep copies of all relevant documents. Especially important are copies of deeds, leases, and the check skirts from all production checks. These last will have needed information on the gross volumes of oil and gas sold, gross values, gross taxes, and the interest and net amounts received by the payee.

6

Elements of the Lease

LEASE FORMS

In the course of negotiations, a landowner will almost certainly find himself pondering a printed form that is the usual or the standard lease form used by the landman or the company he represents. This instrument, often several pages long and full of closely printed clauses, is likely to seem daunting to the inexperienced lessor. (The truly experienced lessor may whip out a lease form of his own, to the landman's dismay.) The days of short, simple, handwritten leases are more than 100 years in the past. Such early oil leases were modeled on instruments that permitted exploration and drilling for salt water; simple as they were, they contained several basic elements still found in oil and gas leases. These include a description of the land, a conveyance of specified rights, an obligation to drill and to pay a percentage of the production to the landowner, and a forfeiture clause. The development of the petroleum industry has brought with it more, and more complicated, lease clauses. The courts have often construed (interpreted) leases when the parties fell into disagreement over terms or compensation.

Much history and considerable litigation have produced lease forms that any prudent landowner will wish to have examined by his attorney; the sheer complexity of such instruments often requires this step. Many attorneys who specialize in oil and gas work do not attempt to decide for their clients what prices should be asked or settled for. They have enough to do. in explaining and amending lease clauses so that landowners thoroughly understand the terms they are confronted with.

State and Federal Forms

The forms used by state and federal governments for the lease of their lands are clearly standardized in the sense of being printed up in uniform batches for the various agencies. While such forms may vary with the *kinds* of property to be leased, a prospective lessee has only to query the proper office to get samples and instructions on how to proceed. (See figures 2.1 and 2.2 at the end of chapter 2 for sample state and federal forms). In contrast, the lease forms used by private companies vary far more widely. There are literally hundreds of different forms in use, and more are being drawn up all the time.

Forms Printed by Private Companies

The "Producers 88." Many of the lease forms used by the industry are titled "Producers 88" or "Standard Form 88, Producers Special." The "88" title is often joined with a term like "Revised" or "Pooling" or some other designation. When an operator, landman, or royalty owner refers to a "standard lease," it is usually some form of the "Producers 88" (fig. 6.1 at the end of this chapter) that he has in mind. Oddly enough, the standard title now runs across the top of hundreds of very different forms, all of them considerably changed from the original "Producers Special." That original form was run off by an Oklahoma printing company, which simply indicated the number of the form it was currently printing at the top of the document. Historically, the number *88* has, so far as anyone can tell, no more significance than that. The oil and gas lease being printed up was called a "producers" form because the printer wanted to create a form acceptable to a number of oil producers in his own state of Oklahoma and nearby states. Since the printing company had the reputation of not changing its forms without changing titles as well, Oklahoma landowners felt that they could rely on the "Producers 88." The form quickly became so popular that many landowners refused to sign leases that did not bear the familiar title. (In Louisiana, the closest thing to a standard lease form is probably one of the Bath forms printed by the M. L. Bath Company of Shreveport. For details, see Appendix D. Lease forms most commonly used in the top ten oil-producing states in the United States are discussed in Appendix E; examples of many are given.)

Revised versions of the "88." The original 88 form was, of course, drawn up to meet the needs of those who would be obtaining leases. Today many oil and gas companies have their own 88 forms, and careful attention is given to drafting the clauses in these updated versions of the "Producers Special." A number of printing companies also produce 88 forms and revise them regularly to keep them consistent with court decisions on leasing. Indications of such revisions generally appear on the form, often in the upper left-hand corner. For example, a form might be titled "Producers 88 (12, 82) Revised."

The so-called standard form, then, appears in so many variations that it is no standard at all. The courts have long recognized this fact, though some landowners and even some attorneys have not. In *Fagg v. Texas Co.,* 57 S. W. 2d 87 (Tex. Civ. App. 1933), an option to lease that called for the use of "an 88 form lease" was held by the court to be invalid. The description of the form was judged too vague to be useful, given the number of different 88 forms on the market. "As we see it, the reference to an 88 Form lease is as incapable of definite application as if the term 'oil and gas lease form' had been used instead." (Robert E. Sullivan, *Handbook of Oil and Gas Law,* New York: Prentice-Hall, 1955, p. 70, note 1.) In areas with intensive drilling and exploration, 88 forms can usually be bought in local office supply stores, drug stores, and variety stores. They are frequently sold in several different versions, and the buyer must exercise some care to be sure of getting the precise form that he wants.

Forms Prepared for Individuals and Associations

Landowners' forms. A number of local and regional associations, formed to advance the interests of surface and mineral owners, print lease forms which they recommend that their members use (fig. 6.2 at the end of the chapter). These forms vary a great deal, and a lease suitable for one region may be regarded with horror by landmen and oil companies in another area. In general, forms printed for landowners or even specifically requested by them will be very carefully scrutinized by potential lessees. In some cases, a landowner will have no great objection to using the oil company's form but will have additions and alterations in mind. When these are extensive—or when the landowner asks for a typed rather than a printed lease—the landman will often suggest that the drafting be done by attorneys.

Attorneys' forms. Many oil and gas attorneys who regularly represent landowners not only draft leases but also have their own printed lease forms. And quite a number of these printed forms are titled "Producers Special 88"—out of deference to convention, since the forms are not likely to favor the producer. They are often modeled on state lease forms that, quite naturally, favor the lessor. In Texas, for example, the forms that can be obtained from the General Land Office for the leasing of minerally classified lands are sometimes used as examples by attorneys drawing up their own forms for the printer.

(Note the state lease form given in chapter 1.)

The urge to produce a neatly printed form seems almost universal in the industry. The proliferation of paper owes something, no doubt, to the tendency most people have to accept printed information more readily than that conveyed by less "official" means. Typed or handwritten emendations to leases may be objected to, while the same provisions, in a printed lease form, arouse no objections. Best of all, from the clerical and administrative points of view, are standard, familiar forms that present none of the unusual features of a hand-drawn or special lease. The landowner, of course, may take a different view of the matter, reading the fine print with care and holding out for his cherished emendations.

A lease negotiation is rather commonly a battle of wits, with the lease form serving as the field of the contest. Capable attorneys on both sides, however, know the value of lease clauses that are fair to all the parties. Unfair or unreasonable terms, even if accepted, can lead to dissatisfaction and to litigation later on. A good oil and gas attorney will do his best to look after his client's interest *and* draft an instrument that all the parties can live with. If he does his job well, his client should not need—or want—to contest the lease once the wells begin to flow.

LEASE PROVISIONS

The most common lease provisions include title; date; parties; consideration; granting clause; description; Mother Hubbard clause; habendum clause; royalty clause; shut-in royalty clause; drilling and delay rental clause; dry hole, cessation of production, and continuous drilling clauses; pooling and unitization clause; surrender clause; damage clause; assignment clause; warranty and pro-portionate reduction clauses; force majeure clause; and legal effect clause and lessor's signature. Some of these clauses, though commonplace, apply only to gas wells. Virtually all the clauses are negotiable, as more and more landowners are discovering. Certainly all need care and thought in the drafting. While it might not seem that matters as apparently simple as the title of the lease or the names of the parties could give rise to dispute, even these elements should be as clear and unambiguous as possible. Otherwise, a judge may someday be forced to consider and rule on the intended meaning of a doubtful sentence, phrase, or bit of punctuation.

Title

The sample lease in figure 6.1 is titled "Oil, Gas and Mineral Lease." Like some other forms it includes the word *mineral* in its title and refers to "other minerals" in the body of the lease. Since some older leases have been used to justify the mining of coal, iron, uranium, clays, and other substances (though the lessor intended only the removal of oil or natural gas), the courts have tended to rule very carefully on what can be called a mineral. Lessor and lessee should avoid ambiguities by naming the specific substances which the lease is to cover.

In addition to limiting the lease title to "Oil and Gas," some attorneys add a provision which specifies that the oil and gas in question are those "derived from petroleum substances only" or "derived from petroleum or associated hydrocarbons." If by-products like sulfur or helium are expected in any quantity, such products are usually named in the lease; separate royalties may be arranged for one or more of them. In any case, unintended substances like lignite or uranium should not slip into a lease via a vague catchall phrase like "other minerals."

Date

An undated lease is not void but generally takes effect when it is executed and delivered. Any lease *should* be dated, however, and its dating may prove important if there should be any dispute later about which of two documents is the earlier. The controlling date, for any lease, is the one written in the instrument — not the date on which it was executed (signed), notarized, or recorded.

Parties

A lease must name all the parties involved in the agreement. The *grantor,* who grants the lease, is referred to in the body of the lease as the *lessor* even if more than one person executes the instrument as a lessor. The *grantee,* or person receiving the right to search for and produce oil or gas, is subsequently referred to as the *lessee.* In some states, lessors' addresses, as well as their names, must appear on the lease. Some states (Louisiana, for example) also require indication of the parties' marital status.

Where possible, cotenants (co-owners) are usually named as lessors in one lease. The awkward alternative is to have each owner execute a separate lease that covers only his undivided interest. Lessees also try to provide for the possible failure of one or more of the named lessors to execute the lease. In such a case, the lease is generally enforceable between the lessee and any lessors who do sign.

Consideration

Consideration is the benefit required to make a contract valid. Even in states that do not view oil and gas leases as contracts but as, for example, conveyances of interests in land, consideration is still required. This benefit to the lessor can be broken down into payments in cash and payments in kind. Royalties are usually described as payments in kind, that is, as the landowner's share of the oil or gas actually produced. Delay rentals and lease bonuses are paid in cash. All three payments appear in the oil and gas lease; royalties and rentals have their own separate clauses, and the lease bonus is mentioned in the *granting clause*. In government leases, the amount of the bonus commonly appears in full. In private leases, the bonus consideration is often set out as a nominal amount—$10.00 or so—while the real bonus is paid by draft or check. In Louisiana, a "serious consideration" is necessary to complete the transfer; elsewhere, nominal amounts will generally suffice to support all the terms and provisions spelled out in a lease.

Granting Clause

The important granting clause specifies the rights and interests granted by the lessor to the lessee. The words used to establish a leasehold are words like *grant, devise, lease,* and *let.* In return for consideration (the bonus), a lessee usually obtains the *exclusive* rights to search and drill for, then to produce oil and gas. While such rights could, in theory, be nonexclusive, it is doubtful that several lessees would consent to a competitive cotenant arrangement.

The kinds of operations that can be carried out in the course of exploration, drilling, and production should be clearly described. Many leases, however, use rather broad terms for listing these operations. As a result of such vagueness, the courts have defined a number of activities as *implied* by an oil and gas lease, whether these are spelled out in the granting clause or not. In Texas, for example, these implied rights include permission to enter and exit from the property, to set up equipment, to drill, to use improved recovery techniques and saltwater injection. Use of the land's surface, though, has given rise to so much disagreement and litigation that both lessor and lessee will be prudent not to rely on implication. The extent of surface use—for roads, pipelines, tanks, power stations, employee housing, and so on—should be specified.

The granting clause is also the place for being very clear about which minerals are covered by the lease. In addition to oil and natural gas, other related substances found in the oil and gas stream (distillate, condensate, casinghead gas, helium, sulfur, etc.) need to be mentioned. If the lessor is concerned about having his land restored after production has ceased, he may add a stipulation requiring the lessee to leave the property as he found it, or as nearly so as possible. Finally, the granting clause is usually the section of the lease that *describes* the land.

Description

A legal description following one of the methods discussed in chapter 4 is a necessary element in an oil and gas lease. If the lessor owns the entire undivided interest in the land being leased, a description should be perfectly straightforward. If the lessor owns only a part interest in the mineral estate, certain points need to be considered. If, for example, the description makes use of an earlier instrument, like a deed, it may include the fractional interest conveyed in that earlier instrument. But the landowner may *now* own or intend to lease a different fractional interest. Reliance on instruments like deeds should be discriminating. The purely descriptive parts of earlier documents should be used, and the question of whether to specify the fractional interest owned by the lessor should be decided separately.

Since many leases are taken as quickly as possible after a check of the county records, a lessee is often in the position of not knowing whether a lessor does in fact own all or only a portion of his mineral rights. This uncertainty (left unclarified until the title examination) has led to the use of "lesser interest" or "proportionate reduction" clauses that allow lessees to reduce rents and royalties proportionately *if* it turns out that the owner owns less than all of the minerals. From the lessee's point of view, it is desirable that no confusion arise to limit this right to reduce rents and royalties. When a lease does contain a lesser interest clause, the landman will usually urge that the land description omit any reference to a fractional undivided interest. Leases that contain *both* a lesser interest clause and a description specifying a partial interest have led to litigation, and in some cases to decisions in favor of the lessor. From the landowner's point of view, a lesser interest clause (though fair in and by itself) seems inconsistent with another commonly included clause that warrants title. Attorneys who represent landowners will very frequently argue for the removal of warranty clauses. This done, there is little to object to in a lesser interest clause that allows an oil company to pay in proportion to actual ownership. Finally, landowners may wish to follow the land description with a *depth limitation,* thereby leasing their minerals to specified depths from the drill pad. Strata below these depths are not covered by the terms of the lease. It is generally desirable to measure depth limits in feet, yards, or metres rather than by reference to named producing strata, though either method can have unusual or unwanted results when drilling reveals more about the geology underlying the land. Measurement in standard units is, in some cases, so difficult that the safer, less ambiguous reference would be to the "base of a known formation."

Mother Hubbard Clause

The Mother Hubbard clause, also referred to as a coverall clause, sometimes follows the land description. Its intention is to perfect that description by including in the lease any small or oddly shaped bits of land owned by the lessor and "contiguous with," "adjoining,"

or "adjacent to" the described tract. Such bits and pieces, it is reasoned, can be left out of surveys and boundary descriptions. A Mother Hubbard clause scoops up "lands adjoining the herein described land up to the boundaries of the abutting landowners" and includes them in the lease. The difficulty arises when such a clause seems to make the lease apply to lands that the landowner himself did not intend to lease. A broadly worded clause could be broadly interpreted by the courts, and in fact litigation has put various Mother Hubbard clauses to the test. To avoid such problems, many attorneys suggest omitting the clause or at least carefully limiting its applicability—for example, to 5 or 10 percent of the amount of land in the legal description.

Habendum Clause

The habendum clause is sometimes called the *term* clause and fixes the duration of the lessee's interest, just as the granting clause fixes the nature of that interest. The primary term—generally used as an exploration period—is given in days or years; during this term, the lessee is obliged to begin or complete a well (as specified in the lease) *or* pay delay rentals that usually begin on the next anniversary date of the instrument. The secondary term is conditional and depends upon the production of oil or gas (or other minerals.) Even when it is not so stated in the lease, courts have generally held that production in "paying quantities" or in "commercial quantities" is required to hold the lease in effect during this secondary term. The courts have variously interpreted *paying* production to mean "profitable" or such as would encourage a reasonable and prudent operator to continue even in the absence of cash profit. In view of these interpretations, lessors may want to establish a standard for paying production and list the operational costs to be considered, how temporary low production is to be viewed, and so on.

Royalty Clause

Royalty is the percentage of production paid to the landowner. Oil royalties may be paid in kind; the lessor may, if he chooses, receive his oil from the lessee and market it himself. In fact, most lessors prefer to receive the posted market price of the oil in money.

Gas royalties are normally paid in money. Establishing the value of the gas, however, has led to much confusion, disagreement, and litigation. Landowners who want the "market value at the mouth of the well" have been urging their interpretation of this phrase on some producers hard-pressed by the rapid rise in gas prices. Such producers may be caught by long-term contracts with pipeline companies; yet, according to this interpretation, they might be required to pay royalties calculated on current market values while receiving payment from gas purchasers at older, and much lower, prices.

One possible way out of this dilemma, for the producer or the landowner, is for the landowner to take gas royalties in kind and arrange to market the gas himself. Some Louisiana owners, for example, do their own marketing if the producer is unable or unwilling to. If the owner prefers not to market his gas, he may specify in the royalty clause that he will join the lessee in any marketing contract undertaken as an "arm's length" transaction. (Such a transaction assumes willing, uncompelled sellers and buyers.) A variation on this kind of agreement would include the possibility that the lessee purchase the lessor's gas at arm's length prices. In any case, the landowner should not receive a royalty based on a lower price than that received by the lessee. (Such is the intended meaning of "market value at the mouth of the well" in producers' leases that use the phrase.)

The royalty clause is the place to specify any separate royalties for substances produced as by-products of the oil and gas stream—sulfur, for instance. It is also the place to mention "free use of gas" by the landowner. Many landowners wish to include this moneysaving provision, but they should certainly consider the risks involved and be willing to stipulate that their use of gas from the producer's wells is at their own risk and expense. Finally, landowners concerned about prompt receipt of royalties sometimes place a royalty due date in the lease. Failure to make timely payment may involve the addition of interest charges and/or the termination of the lease after a month's written notice.

Shut-In Royalty Clause

Shut-in payments—substitutes for production on gas wells shut in by the producer—must be paid to royalty owners, including the lessor *if* he owns a royalty interest. The purpose of this provision is to allow a lessee to hold the lease on a nonproducing well until he can find a market or until a transmitting pipeline becomes available. (Producing wells are sometimes shut in for workover or because of a cutback in production by the pipeline company.) Today, landowners are likely to limit shut-in privileges to definite terms of 2, 3, or 5 years and to negotiate for higher shut-in royalties. They believe that higher royalties will spur producers to find markets or give up their leases. Shut-in royalties, of whatever size, are intended to apply to wells that can produce in commercial amounts; the lease should probably mention this condition.

Drilling and Delay Rental Clause

Also known as the "unless" clause, the drilling and delay rental provision has replaced the old drill-or-pay notion. Drill or pay was a means of forestalling conflict over the question of how quickly leased land should be developed. In the early days of the industry, landowners' only consideration came from royalties; they wanted their property made productive as rapidly as possible. On the other hand, oil companies had begun to acquire leases in order to have petroleum reserves and had their own timetables for development of these reserves. Eventually, this source of conflict was partially settled by lease provisions that gave the lessee three choices: he could drill or pay rental to defer drilling or terminate the lease. These days, a lease usually expires 1 year from the date on the instrument *unless* the operator begins operations for drilling or makes timely payment of delay rental. To defer drilling past the primary term of the lease generally voids the instrument.

A number of states, Texas among them, are severe about nonpayment or untimely payment of delay rentals. A check or draft posted in good time but lost in the mail may be viewed with leniency, but other excuses may do nothing to save the lease. Lessors sometimes wonder, when they do not receive a rental check, just what constitutes the "commencement" of drilling. To avoid dispute about this issue, the required operations are frequently specified in the lease. Finally, one kind of lease, called a *paid-up lease,* settles the whole matter of future rentals by providing for their payment along with the cash bonus. No further action is required during the primary term.

Dry Hole, Cessation of Production, and Continuous Drilling Clauses

The dry hole clause allows an operator to keep his lease in the event that he drills a dry hole. He has a specified period of time—which can range from 60 days to a year—

within which to begin drilling a second well *or* resume payment of delay rentals. Similarly, if production stops for some reason, the cessation of production clause allows the lessee a specified length of time during which to begin new operations. These might include workover on a sluggish well to make it produce in paying quantities. Usually, the clause calls for restored production, commencement of a new well, or a return to delay rentals.

A continuous development clause aims to keep drilling operations going steadily after the primary term has expired. Designated intervals (of 180 days, for example) between completion and new drilling require the operator to develop leased land up to its allowable density. Some landowners leave the *rate* of development up to the lessee. Others are particular about the designated time limits; failure to comply with these intervals commonly releases the undeveloped portions of the leased land.

Pooling and Unitization Clause

The terms *pooling* and *unitization* are often used interchangeably, but they refer to different undertakings. When a lessee pools leased land, he is usually combining small or irregular tracts into a unit big enough to meet state spacing regulations for drilling. The unit size required will vary from one state to another and sometimes from one field to another. As an example, a lessee may need units of 40 acres to drill oilwells and units of 640 acres to drill deep gas wells. A clause in his lease that permits him, at his discretion, to merge separately acquired tracts and treat them as a single unit is advantageous in several ways. He can develop the tracts more efficiently and more economically, since he needn't worry about drilling offset wells. Nor need the lessee pay as many delay rentals; a producing well anywhere on the pooled acreage will mean the beginning of royalty payments to all the landowners and the end of rentals to all. Unless the landowners have specified otherwise, a well anywhere on the unit will also hold the leases on each pooled tract through the primary and secondary terms. Royalty is almost invariably shared on the basis of percentage of surface acres in the pool.

Unitization involves combining tracts, too, but generally on a larger scale. Whole reservoirs, or large sections of them, are often unitized to make secondary and tertiary recovery operations possible. The principle is the same, and the advantages to the operator very similar. Landowners may also benefit from these arrangements. They will want to negotiate the relevant clauses with care, though, because the legal effects are quite complex. For example, royalty owners must share production with other parties in the unit. This sharing is often calculated on the percentage of reservoir each owner has contributed to the unit. If engineering and geological studies show the reservoir to be unequally distributed underneath the tracts of land, one owner may have a lower or a higher percentage of royalty than others with tracts of the same size. (A unitization requires ratification by a substantial majority of the owners involved precisely because sharing may not be proportionate to the acreage contributed. Pooling, however, generally requires no consent from the landowners but does require the consent of the nonparticipating royalty owners.)

A pool or unitization can also affect the habendum clause in each owner's lease. To keep a well anywhere on the unit from holding all the leased land, owners sometimes require the insertion of a Pugh clause (discussed in the next chapter). Such a clause provides for the release of nonproducing acreage and

strata at a specified date or in the absence of specified development.

Surrender Clause

A surrender clause spells out the procedure for lessee's voluntary surrender of all or part of his leased interests. He can also terminate the lease by failing to comply with its conditions, but such failure is presumably involuntary. It is always prudent to require from the lessee a written notice of surrender; this notice can be recorded and will provide the landowner with a clear title if he wishes to lease his property again.

Damage Clause

Many operators voluntarily pay for damage to the surface. However, most leases do include a clause which specifies that the lessee will be liable to the surface owner for damage to all growing crops and other items listed. Some damage clauses omit the reference to growing crops. Some add improvements to the site, along with any special considerations like timber or pasture that need protection. The damage clause should be particularly tailored to the requirements of the individual landowner.

Assignment Clause

Leases can be freely assigned by lessor or lessee. Ordinarily, neither must have the other's permission to sell, trade, gamble away, or otherwise transfer a lease to someone else. From the lessee's point of view especially, this assignable character of a lease can be quite an asset; leases frequently change hands a number of times before and sometimes after production begins. It is a good idea, therefore, to require that both parties give notice of such transfers. The landowner will need to know the names and addresses of all the assignees that the original lessee has dealt with, if only to be sure about who has a right to be on the property. Should delay rental payments ever stop (suggesting that the lessee has simply dropped the lease), the landowner will also want to know whom to contact to get a release. Lessees who assign only a part of their interest are, of course, obliged to arrange for the timely payment of delay rentals (dividing these, perhaps, between themselves and their assignees) to keep the lease in force.

On the other hand, the lessee should be promptly informed of any assignments by the landowner so that rentals and royalties will be paid to the proper persons. The lessee must also change the lease records to reflect changes in ownership. An assignment clause usually specifies that such changes are not binding on a lessee *until* he has received some formal notice. In general, assignments that change and/or divide leased interests must not increase the obligations or decrease the rights of the lessee.

Warranty and Proportionate Reduction Clauses

As the discussion of land description pointed out, many landowners and their attorneys believe that the warranty and the proportionate reduction clauses contradict each other. The first seems to guarantee clear title, while the second provides for the possibility that an owner owns less than his land description claims. Although few owners dispute the justice of a proportionate reduction in rentals and royalties if their interests turn out to be smaller than at first thought, a number of owners refuse to provide title guarantees at all and insist that warranty clauses be removed. Whether or not a lessee will strike the warranty clause—or agree to

something less than a general warranty of title—will depend in part on how badly he wants the property. Other portions of this clause are less likely to arouse objections. These generally include the lessee's rights in the event that the lessor defaults on obligations like taxes and mortgages.

Force Majeure Clause

The force majeure clause usually contains a reminder that the lease is subject to state and federal laws. It also excuses the lessee from the timely performance of his obligations *if* certain kinds of events (beyond the lessee's power to control) should occur. Such events tend to be catastrophic or at least highly unpleasant. Examples are acts of war or rebellion, fire, flood, and other disasters known as "acts of God." Forms of government interference that cannot be blamed on the lessee may also be taken into consideration.

Legal Effect Clause and Lessor's Signature

The legal effect clause binds the parties and declares the lease effective for the lessor when he signs the instrument. Lessors' signatures are dated and, depending upon the state in which the lease is executed, must follow certain conventions. More will be said about the execution of leases in the next chapter. Here it can be pointed out that a lessor needs to sign in the same form he or she used in acquiring the land. If maiden names, nicknames, initials, and so forth appear on earlier instruments like deeds, then these forms should be duplicated—with any additions or alternatives—on the lease. Representatives of other persons should clearly specify the legal capacity in which they are signing, along with their own names and the names of those they represent.

Figure 6.1. Example of a Producers 88 lease form
(Courtesy of Pound Printing)

Producers 88 (12 79) Revised
With 320 Acres Pooling Provision

POUND PRINTING & STATIONERY COMPANY
2325 Fannin. Houston. Texas 77002 (713) 659-3159

OIL, GAS AND MINERAL LEASE

THIS AGREEMENT made this_____ day of_____, 19___, between
_____

Lessor (whether one or more), whose address is:_____
_____ Zip Code_____,

and_____
_____,

Lessee, (whether one or more), whose address is: _____
_____ Zip Code_____,

WITNESSETH:

1. Lessor in consideration of_____
Dollars ($_____), in hand paid, of the royalties herein provided, and of the agreements of Lessee herein contained, hereby grants, leases and lets exclusively unto Lessee for the purpose of investigating, exploring, prospecting, drilling and mining for and producing oil, gas and all other minerals, conducting exploration, geologic and geophysical surveys by seismograph, core test, gravity and magnetic methods, injecting gas, water and other fluids, and air into subsurface strata, laying pipe lines, building roads, tanks, power stations, telephone lines and other structures thereon and on, over and across lands owned or claimed by Lessor adjacent and contiguous thereto, to produce, save, take care of, treat, transport and

own said products, and housing its employees, the following described land in _____County, Texas, to-wit:

This lease also covers and includes all land owned or claimed by Lessor adjacent or contiguous to the land particularly described above, whether the same be in said survey or surveys or in adjacent surveys, although not included within the boundaries of the land particularly described above. For all purposes of this lease, said land is estimated to comprise _____ acres, whether it actually comprises more or less.

2. Subject to the other provisions herein contained, this lease shall be for a term of _____ ( ) years from this date (called "primary term") and as long thereafter as oil, gas or other mineral is produced from said land or land with which said land is pooled hereunder.

3. The royalties to be paid by Lessee are:
(a) On oil, one-eighth of that produced and saved from said land, the same to be delivered at the well. If Lessor elects not to take delivery of the royalty oil, Lessee may from time to time sell the royalty oil in its possession, paying to Lessor therefor the net proceeds derived by Lessee from the sale of such royalty oil. Lessor's royalty interest in oil shall bear its proportionate part of the cost of treating the oil to render it marketable oil and, if there is no available pipeline, its proportionate part of the cost of all trucking charges.
(b) On gas, including all gases, liquid hydrocarbons and their respective constituent elements, casinghead gas or other gaseous substance, produced from said land and sold or used off the premises or for the extraction of gasoline or other product therefrom, the market value at the well on one-eighth of the gas so sold or used, provided that on gas sold at the well the royalty shall be one-eighth of the net proceeds derived from such sale. Lessor's royalty interest in gas, including all gases, liquid hydrocarbons and their respective constituent elements, casinghead gas or other gaseous substance, shall bear its proportionate part of the cost of all compressing, treating, dehydrating and transporting incurred in marketing the gas so sold at the wells.
(c) On all other minerals mined and marketed, one-tenth either in kind or value at the well or mine, at Lessee's election, except that on sulphur mined and marketed the royalty shall be fifty cents ($.50) per long ton.
(d) While there is a gas well on said land or on lands pooled therewith and if gas is not being sold or used off the premises for a period in excess of three full consecutive calendar months, and this lease is not then being maintained in force and effect under the other provisions hereof, Lessee shall tender or pay to Lessor annually at any time during the lease anniversary month of each year immediately succeeding any lease year in which a shut-in period occurred one-twelfth (1/12) of the sum of $1.00 per acre for the acreage then covered by this lease as shut-in royalty for each full calendar month in the preceding lease year that this lease was continued in force solely and exclusively by reason of the provisions of this paragraph. If such payment of shut-in royalty is so made or tendered by Lessee to Lessor, it shall be considered that this lease is producing gas in paying quantities and this lease shall not terminate, but remain in force and effect. The term "lease anniversary month" means that calendar month in which this lease is dated. The term "Lease year" means the calendar month in which the lease is dated, plus the eleven succeeding calendar months.
(e) If the price of any oil, gas, or other minerals produced hereunder is regulated by any governmental authority, the value of same for the purpose of computing the royalties hereunder shall not be in excess of the price permitted by such regulation. Should it ever be determined by any governmental authority, or any court of final jurisdiction, or otherwise, that the Lessee is required to make any refund on oil, gas, or other

Figure 6.1–*Continued*

minerals produced or sold by Lessee hereunder, then the Lessor shall bear his proportionate part of the cost of any such refund to the extent that royalties paid to Lessor have exceeded the permitted price, plus any interest thereon ordered by the regulatory authority or court, or agreed to by Lessee. If Lessee advances funds to satisfy Lessor's proportionate part of such refund, Lessee shall be subrogated to the refund order or refund claim, with the right to enforce same for Lessor's proportionate contribution, and with the right to apply rentals and royalties accruing hereunder toward satisfying Lessor's refund obligations.

(f) Lessee shall have free use of oil, gas, coal, water from said land, except water from Lessor's wells, for all operations hereunder, and the royalty on oil, gas and coal shall be computed after deducting any so used.

4. Notwithstanding anything herein to the contrary, it is a condition of this lease that it shall not terminate upon any failure of the Lessee, for whatever reason, to make payments of any required shut-in royalty or rentals, either or both, herein provided for on or before the due dates thereof unless and until: (1) Lessor notifies Lessee in writing by registered mail or certified mail, return receipt requested, of non-payment of the shut-in royalty or rentals; and (2) Thereafter Lessee fails to make payment of the shut-in royalty or rentals to Lessor within fifteen (15) days following Lessee's actual receipt of such written notice. Payment of shut-in royalty or rentals by Lessee to Lessor within fifteen (15) days following Lessee's actual receipt of said written notice from Lessor shall be deemed timely and sufficient to maintain this lease in force and effect. The provisions of this paragraph are a part of the consideration for this lease, are contractual, and constitute a warranty from Lessor to Lessee. It is the desire and agreement of Lessor and Lessee to avoid forfeiture of this lease should Lessee fail to make payment of any required shut-in royalty or rentals on or before the scheduled due dates thereof, and to afford Lessee an opportunity to make such payments within fifteen (15) days following actual receipt of written notice of non-payment from Lessor, thereby maintaining this lease in force. Such written notice from Lessor to Lessee shall state the full particulars concerning non-payment of shut-in royalty or rentals, identify the lease and land involved, the due date and amount claimed by Lessor, and Lessor's full name, current address and telephone number.

5. (a) Lessee, at its option, is hereby given the right and power to pool, unitize or combine the acreage covered by this lease or any portion thereof as to oil and gas, or either of them, with any other land covered by this lease, and/or with any other land, lease or leases in the immediate vicinity thereof to the extent hereinafter stipulated, when in Lessee's judgment it is necessary or advisable to do so in order properly to explore, or to develop and operate said leased premises in compliance with the spacing rules of the Railroad Commission of Texas, or other lawful authority, or when to do so would, in the judgment of Lessee, promote the conservation of oil and gas in and under and that may be produced from said premises. Units pooled for oil hereunder shall not substantially exceed 40 acres each in area, plus a tolerance of ten percent (10%) thereof, and units pooled for gas hereunder shall not substantially exceed in area 320 acres each plus a tolerance of ten percent (10%) thereof, provided that should governmental authority having jurisdiction prescribe or permit the creation of units larger than those specified, for the drilling or operation of a well at a regular location or for obtaining maximum allowable from any well to be drilled, drilling or already drilled, units thereafter created may conform substantially in size with those prescribed or permitted by government regulations.

(b) Lessee under the provisions hereof may pool or combine acreage covered by this lease or any portion thereof as above provided as to oil in any one or more strata and as to gas in any one or more strata. The units formed by pooling as to any stratum or strata need not conform in size or area with the unit or units into which the lease is pooled or combined as to any other stratum or strata, and oil units need not conform as to area with gas units. The pooling in one or more instances shall not exhaust the rights of the Lessee hereunder to pool this lease or portions thereof into other units. Upon execution by Lessee of an instrument describing and designating the pooled acreage as a pooled unit, said unit shall be effective as to all parties hereto, their heirs, successors, and assigns, irrespective of whether or not the unit is likewise effective as to all other owners of surface, mineral, royalty, or other rights in land included in such unit. Within a reasonable time following the execution of said instrument so designating the pooled unit, Lessee shall file said instrument for record in the appropriate records of the county in which the leased premises are situated. Any unit so formed may be re-formed, increased, decreased, or changed in configuration, at the election of Lessee, at any time and from time to time after the original forming thereof, and Lessee may vacate any unit formed by it hereunder by instrument in writing filed for record in said county at any time when there is no unitized substance being produced from such unit.

(c) Lessee may at its election exercise its pooling option before or after commencing operations for or completing an oil or gas well on the leased premises, and the pooled unit may include, but it is not required to include, land or leases upon which a well capable of producing oil or gas in paying quantities has theretofore been completed or upon which operations for the drilling of a well for oil or gas have theretofore been commenced. In the event of operations for drilling on or production of oil or gas from any part of a pooled unit which includes all or a portion of the land covered by this lease, regardless of whether such operations for drilling were commenced or such production was secured before or after the execution of this instrument or the instrument designating the pooled unit such operations shall be considered as operations for drilling on or production of oil and gas from land covered by this lease whether or not the well or wells be located on the premises covered by this lease and in such event operations for drilling shall be deemed to have been commenced on said land within the meaning of paragraph 6 of this lease; and the entire acreage constituting such unit or units, as to oil and gas, or either of them, as herein provided, shall be treated for all purposes, except the payment of royalties on production from the pooled unit, as if the same were included in this lease.

(d) For the purpose of computing the royalties to which owners of royalties and payments out of production and each of them shall be entitled on production of oil and gas, or either of them, from the pooled unit, there shall be allocated to the land covered by this lease and included in said unit (or to each separate tract within the unit if this lease covers separate tracts within the unit) a pro rata portion of the oil and gas, or either of them, produced from the pooled unit after deducting that used for operations on the pooled unit. Such allocation shall be on an acreage basis - that is to say, there shall be allocated to the acreage covered by this lease and included in the pooled unit (or to each separate tract within the unit if this lease covers separate tracts within the unit) that pro rata portion of the oil and gas, or either of them, produced from the pooled unit which the number of surface acres covered by this lease (or in each such separate tract) and included in the pooled unit bears to the total number of surface acres included in the pooled unit. Royalties hereunder shall be computed on the portion of such production, whether it be oil and gas, or either of them, so allocated to the land covered by this lease and included in the unit just as though such production were from such land. The production from an oil well will be considered as production from the lease or oil pooled unit which it is producing and not as production from a gas pooled unit; and production from a gas well will be considered as production from the lease or gas pooled unit from which it is producing and not from an oil pooled unit.

(e) The formation of any unit hereunder shall not have the effect of changing the ownership of any delay rental or shut-in production royalty which may become payable under this lease. If this lease now or hereafter covers separate tracts, no pooling or unitization of royalty interest as between any such separate tracts is intended or shall be implied or result merely from the inclusion of such separate tracts within this lease but Lessee shall nevertheless have the right to pool as provided above with consequent allocation of production as above provided. As used in this paragraph 5, the words "separate tract" mean any tract with royalty ownership differing, now or hereafter, either as to parties or amounts, from that as to any other part of the leased premises.

6. (a) If operations for drilling are not commenced on said land or on acreage pooled therewith as above provided on or before one year from this date, the lease shall then terminate as to both parties, unless on or before such anniversary date Lessee shall pay or tender (or shall make a bona fide attempt to pay or tender, as hereinafter stated) to Lessor or to the credit of Lessor in_____ Bank at _____, Texas, (which bank and its successors are Lessor's agent and shall continue as the depository for all rentals payable hereunder regardless of change in ownership of said land or the rentals) the sum of_____
_____ Dollars
($_____), (herein called rentals), which shall cover the privilege of deferring commencement of drilling operations for a period of twelve (12) months. In like manner and upon like payments or tenders annually, the commencement of drilling operations may be further deferred for successive periods of twelve (12) months each during the primary term. The payment or tender of rental under this paragraph and of royalty under paragraph 3 on any gas well from which gas is not being sold or used may be made by the check or draft of Lessee mailed or delivered to the parties entitled thereto or to said bank on or before the date of payment. If such bank (or any successor bank) should fail, liquidate or be succeeded by another bank, or for any reason fail or refuse to accept rental, Lessee shall not be held in default for failure to make such payment or tender of rental until thirty (30) days after Lessor shall deliver to Lessee a proper recordable instrument naming another bank as agent to receive such payments or tenders. If

Figure 6.1—*Continued*

Lessee shall, on or before any anniversary date, make a bona fide attempt to pay or deposit rental to a Lessor entitled thereto according to Lessee's records or to a Lessor, who, prior to such attempted payment or deposit, has given Lessee notice, in accordance with subsequent provisions of this lease, of his right to receive rental, and if such payment or deposit shall be ineffective or erroneous in any regard, Lessee shall be unconditionally obligated to pay to such Lessor the rental properly payable for the rental period involved, and this lease shall not terminate but shall be maintained in the same manner as if such erroneous or ineffective rental payment or deposit had been properly made, provided that the erroneous or ineffective rental payment or deposit be corrected within 30 days after receipt by Lessee of written notice from such Lessor of such error accompanied by such instruments as are necessary to enable Lessee to make proper payment. The down cash payment is consideration for this lease according to its terms and shall not be allocated as a mere rental for a period. Lessee may at any time or times execute and deliver to Lessor or to the depository above named or place of record a release or releases of this lease as to all or any part of the above-described premises, or of any mineral or horizon under all or any part thereof, and thereby be relieved of all obligations as to the released land or interest. If this lease is released as to all minerals and horizon under a portion of the land covered by this lease, the rentals and other payments computed in accordance therewith shall thereupon be reduced in the proportion that the number of surface acres within such released portion bears to the total number of surface acres which was covered by this lease immediately prior to such release.

(b) Lessor hereby designates _____ Bank at _____, Texas, and its successors as Lessor's agent to serve as the depository for any payment due with respect to any shut-in gas well. Payment of shut-in gas royalty may be made in the manner provided in paragraph 6(a) hereof for the payment or tender of rentals, including all terms with respect to the deposit of same in the designated depository bank, notwithstanding paragraph 6(a) being otherwise stricken or inoperative due to this lease having a primary term not exceeding one year, if such be the case.

7. If prior to discovery and production of oil, gas or other mineral on said land or on acreage pooled therewith, Lessee should drill a dry hole or holes thereon, or if after discovery and production of oil, gas or other mineral, the production thereof should cease from any cause, this lease shall not terminate if Lessee commences operations for drilling or reworking within ninety (90) days thereafter or if it be within the primary term, commences or resumes the payment or tender of rentals or commences operations for drilling or reworking on or before the rental paying date next ensuing after the expiration of ninety (90) days from date of completion of dry hole or cessation of production. If at any time subsequent to ninety (90) days prior to the beginning of the last year of the primary term and prior to the discovery of oil, gas or other mineral on said land, or on acreage pooled therewith, Lessee should drill a dry hole thereon, no rental payment or operations are necessary in order to keep the lease in force during the remainder of the primary term. If at the expiration of the primary term, oil, gas or other mineral is not being produced on said land, or on acreage pooled therewith, but Lessee is then engaged in drilling or reworking operations thereon or shall have completed a dry hole thereon within ninety (90) days prior to the end of the primary term, the lease shall remain in force so long as operation on said well or for drilling or reworking of any additional well are prosecuted with no cessation of more than ninety (90) consecutive days, and if they result in the production of oil, gas or other mineral, so long thereafter as oil, gas or other mineral is produced from said land or acreage pooled therewith. In the event a well or wells producing oil or gas in paying quantities should be brought in on adjacent land and within three hundred thirty (330) feet of and draining the leased premises, or acreage pooled therewith, Lessee agrees to drill such offset wells as a reasonably prudent operator would drill under the same or similar circumstances.

8. Lessee shall have the right at any time during or after the expiration of this lease to remove all property and fixtures placed by Lessee on said land, including the right to draw and remove all casing. When required by Lessor, Lessee will bury all pipe lines below ordinary plow depth, and no well shall be drilled within two hundred (200) feet of any residence or barn now on said land without Lessor's consent.

9. The rights of either party hereunder may be assigned in whole or in part, and the provisions hereof shall extend to their heirs, successors and assigns; but no change or division in ownership of the land, rentals or royalties, however accomplished, shall operate to enlarge the obligations or diminish the rights of Lessee; and no change or division in such ownership shall be binding on Lessee until thirty (30) days after Lessee shall have been furnished by registered U.S. mail at Lessee's principal place of business with a certified copy of recorded instrument or instruments evidencing same. In the event of assignment hereof in whole or in part, liability for breach of any obligation hereunder shall rest exclusively upon the owner of this lease or of a portion thereof who commits such breach. In the event of the death of any person entitled to rentals, shut-in royalty or royalty hereunder, Lessee may pay or tender such rentals, shut-in royalty or royalty to the credit of the deceased or the estate of the deceased until such time as Lessee is furnished with proper evidence of the appointment and qualification of an executor or administrator of the estate, or if there be none, then until Lessee is furnished with evidence satisfactory to it as to the heirs or devisees of the deceased and that all debts of the estate have been paid. If at any time two or more persons be entitled to participate in the rental payable hereunder, Lessee may pay or tender said rental jointly to such persons or to their joint credit in the depository named herein, or, at Lessee's election, the proportionate part of said rentals to which each participant is entitled may be paid or tendered to him separately or to his separate credit in said depository; and payment or tender to any participant of his portion of the rentals hereunder shall maintain this lease as to such participant. In event of assignment of this lease as to a segregated portion of said land, the rentals payable hereunder shall be apportionable as between the several leasehold owners ratably according to the surface area of each, and default in rental payment by one shall not affect the rights of other leasehold owners hereunder. If six or more parties become entitled to royalty hereunder, Lessee may withhold payment thereof unless and until furnished with a recordable instrument executed by all such parties designating an agent to receive payments for all.

10. (a) The breach by Lessee of any obligation arising hereunder shall not work a forfeiture or termination of this lease nor cause a termination or reversion of the estate created hereby nor be grounds for cancellation hereof in whole or in part. In the event Lessor considers that operations are not at any time being conducted in compliance with this lease, Lessor shall notify Lessee in writing of the facts relied upon as constituting a breach hereof, and Lessee, if in default, shall have sixty days after receipt of such notice in which to commence the compliance with the obligations imposed by virtue of this instrument. The provisions of this paragraph 10(a) shall be applicable to the payment by Lessee of shut-in gas royalty and rentals except that the time for the Lessee to cure any non-payment thereof is otherwise stated in paragraph 4 hereof.

(b) After the discovery of oil, gas or other mineral in paying quantities on said premises, Lessee shall develop the acreage retained hereunder as a reasonably prudent operator, but in discharging this obligation it shall in no event be required to drill more than one well per forty (40) acres, plus an acreage tolerance not to exceed 10% of 40 acres, of the area retained hereunder and capable of producing oil in paying quantities and one well per 320 acres plus an acreage tolerance not to exceed 10% of 320 acres of the area retained hereunder and capable of producing gas or other mineral in paying quantities.

11. Lessor hereby warrants and agrees to defend the title to said land and agrees that Lessee at its option may discharge any tax, mortgage or other lien upon said land, either in whole or in part, and in event Lessee does so, it shall be subrogated to such lien with right to enforce same and apply rentals and royalties accruing hereunder toward satisfying same. Should Lessee become involved in any dispute or litigation arising out of any claim adverse to the title of Lessor to said land, Lessee may recover from Lessor its reasonable and necessary expenses and attorneys fees incurred in such dispute or litigation, with the right to apply royalties accruing hereunder toward satisfying said expenses and attorneys fees. Without impairment of Lessee's rights under the warranty in event of failure of title, it is agreed that if this lease covers a less interest in the oil, gas, sulphur, or other minerals in all or any part of said land than the entire and undivided fee simple estate (whether Lessor's interest is herein specified or not), or no interest therein, then the royalties, delay rental, and other monies accruing from any part as to which this lease covers less than such full interest, shall be paid only in the proportion which the interest therein, if any, covered by this lease, bears to the whole and undivided fee simple estate therein. All royalty interest covered by this lease (whether or not owned by Lessor) shall be paid out of the royalty herein provided. Should any one or more of the parties named above as Lessors fail to execute this lease, it shall nevertheless be binding upon the party or parties executing the same. Failure of Lessee to reduce rental paid hereunder shall not impair the right of Lessee to reduce royalties.

12. When drilling, production or other operations on said land or land pooled with such land, or any part thereof are prevented, delayed or interrupted by lack of water, labor or materials, or by fire, storm, flood, war, rebellion, insurrection, sabotage, riot, strike, difference with workers, or failure of carriers to transport or furnish facilities for transportation, or as a result of some law, order, rule, regulation or necessity of governmental authority, either State or Federal, or as a result of the filing of a suit in which Lessee's title may be affected, or as a result of any cause whatsoever

Figure 6.1 – *Continued*

beyond the reasonable control of Lessee, the lease shall nevertheless continue in full force and effect. If any such prevention, delay or interruption should commence during the primary term hereof, the time of such prevention, delay or interruption shall not be counted against Lessee and the running of the primary term shall be suspended during such time; if any such prevention, delay or interruption should commence after the primary term hereof Lessee shall have a period of ninety (90) days after the termination of such period of prevention, delay or interruption within which to commence or resume drilling, production or other operations hereunder, and this lease shall remain in force during such ninety (90) day period and thereafter in accordance with the other provisions of this lease. Lessee shall not be liable for breach of any express or implied covenants of this lease when drilling, production or other operations are so prevented, delayed or interrupted.

13. This lease states the entire contract between the parties, and no representation or promise, verbal or written, on behalf of either party shall be binding unless contained herein; and this lease shall be binding upon each party executing the same, regardless of whether or not executed by all owners of the above described land or by all persons above named as "Lessor", and, notwithstanding the inclusion above of other names as "Lessor", this term as used in this lease shall mean and refer only to such parties as execute this lease and their successors in interest.

IN WITNESS WHEREOF, this instrument is executed on the date first above written.

_____ Lessor	_____ Lessor
S.S. or Tax I.D. No._____	S.S. or Tax I.D. No._____
_____ Lessor	_____ Lessor
S.S. or Tax I.D. No._____	S.S. or Tax I.D. No._____
_____ Lessor	_____ Lessor
S.S. or Tax I.D. No._____	S.S. or Tax I.D. No._____

SINGLE ACKNOWLEDGMENT

THE STATE OF TEXAS,
COUNTY OF

BEFORE ME, the undersigned, a Notary Public in and for said County and State, on this day personally appeared

known to me to be the person whose name   subscribed to the foregoing instrument, and acknowledged to me that   he   executed the same for the purposes and consideration therein expressed.

GIVEN UNDER MY HAND AND SEAL OF OFFICE,

this the   day of   A.D. 19

(L.S.)

My commission expires:

_____
Notary Public in and for the State of Texas

Notary's Printed Name: _____

SINGLE ACKNOWLEDGMENT

THE STATE OF TEXAS,
COUNTY OF

BEFORE ME, the undersigned, a Notary Public in and for said County and State, on this day personally appeared

known to me to be the person whose name   subscribed to the foregoing instrument, and acknowledged to me that   he   executed the same for the purposes and consideration therein expressed.

GIVEN UNDER MY HAND AND SEAL Of office,

this the   day of   A.D. 19

(L.S.)

My commission expires:

_____
Notary Public in and for the State of Texas

Notary's Printed Name: _____

Figure 6.1 – *Continued*

SINGLE ACKNOWLEDGMENT

THE STATE OF TEXAS,
COUNTY OF

BEFORE ME, the undersigned, a Notary Public in and for said County and State, on this day personally appeared

known to me to be the person whose name   subscribed to the foregoing instrument, and acknowledged to me that   he   executed the same for the purposes and consideration therein expressed.

GIVEN UNDER MY HAND AND SEAL OF OFFICE,

this the   day of   A.D. 19

(L.S.)

My commission expires: Notary Public in and for the State of Texas

Notary's Printed Name: _____

Producers 88 (12/79) Revised
With 320 Acres Pooling Provision

No. _____

Oil, Gas and Mineral Lease

FROM

TO

Dated _____, 19

No. Acres _____

_____ County, Texas

Term _____

This instrument was filed for record on the _____ day of _____, 19 _____, at _____ o'clock _____ M., and duly recorded in Volume _____, Page _____ of the _____ Records of this office.

_____ County Clerk

By _____, Deputy

When recorded return to

POUND PRINTING & STATIONERY COMPANY
2325 FANNIN STREET HOUSTON, TEXAS 77002
PHONE 659-3159

CORPORATION ACKNOWLEDGMENT

THE STATE OF TEXAS,
COUNTY OF

BEFORE ME, the undersigned, a Notary Public in and for said County and State, on this day personally appeared

                    , known to me to be the person and officer whose name is subscribed to the foregoing instrument, and acknowledged to me that the same was the act of the said

a corporation, and that he executed the same as the act of such corporation for the purposes and consideration therein expressed, and in the capacity therein stated.

GIVEN UNDER MY HAND AND SEAL OF OFFICE, this the   day of   A.D. 19

(L.S.)

My commission expires: Notary Public in and for the State of Texas

Notary's Printed Name: _____

**Figure 6.2. Example of a landowners' lease form
(Courtesy of Stephens County Mineral Owners Association in Oklahoma))**

OIL AND GAS LEASE

1. AGREEMENT, Made and entered into this _____ day of _____, 19_____, by and between _____,

2. party of the first part, hereinafter called lessor (whether one or more), and _____ party of the second part, hereinafter called lessee.
WITNESSETH, That the said lessor, for and in consideration of _____

3. _____ DOLLARS, cash in hand paid, receipt of which is hereby acknowledged and of the covenants and agreements hereinafter contained on the part of lessee to be paid, kept and performed, has granted, demised, leased and let and by these presents does grant, demise, lease and let unto the said lessee, for the sole and only

4. purpose of exploring by geophysical and other methods, mining and operating for oil (including but not limited to distillate and condensate), gas (including casinghead gas and helium and all other constituents), and for laying pipe lines, and building tanks, power stations and structures thereon, to produce, save and take care of said products, all that certain tract of land, together with any reversionary rights therein, situated in the County of _____ State of Oklahoma, described as follows, to-wit: _____

_____

of section _____Township, Range _____, and containing _____ acres more or less.

5.   It is agreed that this lease shall remain in force for a term of _____ years from date (herein called primary term) and as long thereafter as oil or gas, or either of them is produced from said land by the lessee.
   In consideration of the premises the said lessee covenants and agrees:

6.   1st. To deliver to the credit of lessor free of cost, in the pipe line to which it may connect its wells, the three-sixteenths ($\frac{3}{16}$) part of all oil (including but not limited to condensate and distillate) produced and saved from the leased premises.
   2nd. To pay lessor for gas of whatever nature or kind (with all of its constituents) produced and sold or used off the premises or used in the manufacture of products therefrom, three sixteenths ($\frac{3}{16}$) at the prevailing market price at the well for the gas sold, used off the premises or in the manufacture of products therefrom, said payment to be made monthly. Lessor shall have the privilege at his risk and expense of using gas from any well producing gas only, on the leased premises for stoves and inside lights in the principal dwelling thereon, out of any surplus gas not needed for operation thereunder. Provided that if a gas well is completed and shut in for lack of market, lessee shall pay annually on or before the anniversary date next ensuing, an amount equal to one dollar per mineral acre owned by lessor, but in no event shall a shut-in gas well extend this lease more than one year beyond the primary term.
   3rd. To pay lessor for gas produced from any oil well and used off the premises, or for the manufacture of casinghead gasoline or dry commercial gas, three-sixteenths ($\frac{3}{16}$) of the proceeds, at the mouth of the well, at the prevailing market rate for the gas during which time gas shall be used, said payments to be made monthly.

Figure 6.2 — *Continued*

7. If drilling operations or mining operations are not commenced on the leased premises on or before one year from this date, this lease shall then terminate as to both parties unless lessee on or before the expiration of said period shall pay or tender to lessor, or to the credit of lessor in _____ bank at _____ or any successor bank, the sum of _____ DOLLARS, ($_____), hereinafter called 'rental,' which shall extend for twelve months the time within which drilling operations or mining operations may be commenced.

Thereafter, annually, in like manner and upon like payments or tenders the commencement of drilling operations or mining operations may be further deferred for periods of twelve months each during the primary term. Payment or tender of rental may be made by check or draft of lessee delivered or mailed to the authorized depository bank or lessor (at address last known to lessee) on or before such date for payment, and the payment or tender will be deemed made when the check or draft is so delivered or mailed. If said named or successor bank (or any other bank which may, as hereinafter provided have been designated as depository) should fail or liquidate or for any reason refuse or fail to accept rental, lessee shall not be held in default for failure to make such payment or tender of rental until thirty days after lessor shall deliver to lessee a proper recordable instrument naming another bank to receive such payments or tenders. The above named or successor bank or any other bank which may be designated as depository shall be lessor's agent. Drilling operations or mining operations shall be deemed to be commenced when the first material is placed on the leased premises or when the first work, other than surveying or staking the location, is done thereon which is necessary for such operations.

8. Should the first well drilled on the above described land, or on acreage pooled therewith, be a dry hole, then, land in that event, if a second well is not commenced on said land, or on acreage pooled therewith, within twelve months from the expiration of the last rental period for which rental has been paid, this lease shall terminate as to both parties, unless the lessee on or before the expiration of said twelve months shall resume the payments of rentals, in the same amount and in the same manner as hereinbefore provided. And it is agreed that upon the resumption of the payment of rentals as above provided, that the provisions, hereof governing the payment of rentals and the effect thereof, shall continue in force just as though there had been no interruption in the rental payments.

If the lessee shall commence to drill a well or commence reworking operations on an existing well within the term of this lease or any extension thereof, or on acreage pooled therewith, the lessee shall have the right to drill such well to completion or complete reworking operations with reasonable diligence and dispatch, and if oil or gas, or either of them, be found in paying quantities, this lease shall continue and be in force with like effect as if such well had been completed within the term of years first mentioned.

9. Lessee is hereby granted the right at any time and from time to time to unitize the leased premises or any portion or portions thereof, as to all strata or any stratum or strata, for the production primarily of oil or primarily of gas with or without distillate. However, no unit for

Figure 6.2—*Continued*

the production primarily of oil shall embrace more than 160 acres, or for the production primarily of gas with or without distillate more than 640 acres; provided that if any governmental regulation shall prescribe a spacing pattern for the development of the field or allocate a producing allowable based on acreage per well, then any such unit may embrace as much additional acreage as may be so prescribed or as may be sued in such allocation of allowable. Lessee shall file written unit designations in the county in which the leased premises are located. Operations upon and production from the unit shall be treated as if such operations were upon or such production were from the leased premises whether or not the well or wells are located thereon. The entire acreage within a unit shall be treated for all purposes as if it were covered by and included in this lease except that the royalty on production from the unit shall be as below provided, and except that in calculating the amount of any shut-in gas royalties, only that part of the acreage originally leased and then actually embraced by this lease shall be counted. In respect to production from the unit, lessee shall pay lessor, in lieu of other royalties thereon, only such proportion of the royalties stipulated herein as the amount of his acreage placed in the unit, or as his royalty interest therein on an acreage basis bears to the total acreage in the unit. It is expressly agreed that notwithstanding anything to the contrary in this lease, all acreage not included in a unit and not producing or upon which drilling operations have not commenced, shall be released at the expiration of the primary term of this lease and it is further agreed that this lease shall terminate as to all nonproducing formations at the expiration of the primary term of this lease.

If said lessor owns a less interest in the above described land than the entire and undivided fee simple estate therein, then the royalties herein provided shall be paid to the lessor only in the proportion which his interest bears to the whole and undivided fee.

Lessee shall have the right to use, free of cost, gas and oil produced on said land for its operations thereon, but shall compensate surface owner for water used from surface or underground.

When requested by the lessor, lessee shall bury his pipelines below plow depth, normally thirty-six inches (36") depth and maintained at that depth, unless otherwise specified.

No well shall be drilled nearer than 200 feet to the house or barn now on said premises, without the written consent of the lessor.

11.   The lessee shall be liable to the surface owner and/or surface lessee of the surface owner for any and all damages or loss accruing to the surface interests in said land and to all growing crops and improvements thereupon and appurtenances and hereditaments thereunto belonging, by reason of the oil and gas mining operations hereunder.

Lessee shall have the right at any time within one year after drilling or production has ceased to remove all machinery and fixtures placed on said premises, including the right to draw and remove casing.

12.   If the estate of either party hereto is assigned, and the privilege of assigning in whole or in part is expressly allowed, the covenants hereof shall extend to their heirs, executors, administrators, successors or assigns. However, no change or division in ownership of the land or

Figure 6.2—*Continued*

royalties shall enlarge the obligations or diminish the rights of lessee. No change in the ownership of the land or royalties shall be binding on the lessee until after the lessee has been furnished with a written transfer or assignment or a true copy thereof. In case lessee assigns this lease, in whole or in part, the assignment of the lease shall not be binding on the lessor until after the lessee has furnished the lessor with a written transfer or assignment or true copy thereof, after which the lessee shall be relieved of all obligations with respect to the assigned portion or portions arising subsequent to the date of assignment.

13. All express or implied covenants of this lease shall be subject to all Federal and State Laws, Executive Orders, Rules and Regulations, and this lease shall not be terminated, in whole or in part, nor lessee held liable in damages, for failure to comply therewith, if compliance is prevented by, or such failure is the result of any such Law, Order, Rule or Regulation.

   This lease shall be effective as to each lessor on execution hereof as to his or her interest and shall be binding on those signing, notwithstanding some of the lessors above named may not join in the execution hereof. The word "lessor" as used in this lease means the party or parties who execute this lease as lessor, although not named above.

10. Lessee may at any time and from time to time surrender this lease as to any part or parts of the leased premises by delivering or mailing a release thereof to lessor, or by placing a release of record in the proper County.

14. Lessor hereby warrants and agrees to defend the title to the lands herein described, and agrees that the lessee shall have the right at any time to redeem for lessor by payment any mortgages, taxes or other liens on the above described lands, in the event of default of payment by lessor, and be subrogated to the right of the holder thereof.

15. _____

   IN TESTIMONY WHEREOF, we sign this the _____ day of _____, 19____.

   _____   _____

   _____   _____

   _____   _____

   _____   _____

                                              Lessor

Execution of the Lease

FINAL NEGOTIATIONS

Many lease forms are filled in and signed without additions or amendments. Often, though, the lessor or his attorney will bargain to include some changes; these commonly make the lease provisions more detailed and specific. For example, the pipelines and flow lines needed for oil or gas production are ordinarily buried in the ground rather than put up above the surface. Many leases describe the depth at which such lines will be buried (upon the lessor's request for their burial) as "below plow depth." Landowners sometimes wish to amend such phrases to make them more specific. They will ask that the depth be specified as 36 inches or some other measurement that suits their particular circumstances. They may also request that the topsoil be replaced after the lines are buried.

Whether such changes are acceptable to the lessee will depend, in part, on his bargaining position. If he wants to lease a highly promising piece of property, he may be willing to make a number of concessions in the form of amendments and special clauses. If he is wildcatting in unproved country, he may refuse such requests. The desirability of the property is not the only factor, of course, in any final bargaining that may occur before a lease is signed. Company policy and resources have their effect, as does the eagerness of the landowner to lease. Assuming that the landowner is not too eager, here are some, though by no means all, of the special provisions he might ask for.

Special Terms and Provisions

Plat map approval and equipment placement. Landowners concerned about protecting valuable surface features like pastures and springs may ask for the right to approve or at least be consulted on the placement of equipment, storage facilities, pipelines, and roads. They may also wish to specify a maximum width for access roads. A plat map or aerial photographs can show precisely which parts of the property are to be protected. Even leases that do not include such protective clauses for special features of the land often do stipulate that wells may not be drilled within a given distance—usually 200 feet—of buildings like houses and barns. In other cases, ongoing surface activities like irrigation may need special mention so that drilling and production equipment, storage tanks, and so forth do not interfere with the landowner's use of his property. Finally, some landowners—concerned that oil or gas production will turn their premises into a disaster area—ask for limited beautification efforts like the painting of tanks and the filling in of slush pits.

Free gas and gas purchase. In some parts of the country, like Kansas and Oklahoma, owners frequently bargain for free gas from gas-producing wells. (Free gas is generally used in the owner's home.) Owners may also want the right to buy gas at the wellhead price to use in their farming operations. Such arrangements may, however, be uncommon in other parts of the country—in Louisiana, for example, or parts of Appalachia.

Shallow wells and Pugh clauses. The point of a Pugh clause, or Freestone rider, is to release nonproducing acreage (horizontal release) or zones (vertical release) at the end of the primary term or some other specified period. The concern behind such a clause is the landowner's fear that his tract, possibly quite a large one, could be held for years by marginal production from a shallow well. Lest that happen, the landowner may ask for a Pugh clause. The clause itself can be drafted in a variety of ways, but it generally aims to release unproductive or untested zones—and lease acreage outside a producing pooled unit—if drilling or exploration does not take place by the end of the specified time.

Offset wells. Some leases leave the circumstances under which an offset well should be drilled rather vague, if they mention offset wells at all. Here again, a landowner may request greater specificity. For example, to ensure that his property is protected from drainage, he may ask that an offset well be drilled if a producing well is located within 660 feet of the lease line.

Market value clause. A market value clause is another stipulation that may be refused

outright in particular parts of the country yet sometimes be granted in others. Essentially, it guarantees that the landowner is paid the current market value for oil or gas produced—not the price received by the operator.

Use of water and other resources. It is fairly common for property owners to specify which sources of water they wish left alone and which may be used for drilling and production needs. Water wells, for instance, are often reserved for the lessor, while water tanks may be made available to the lessee. The use of water may also be restricted, say, to "drilling operations only" or to some other designated activities. If the leased property has game animals or stocked ponds and streams, the owner may forbid hunting and fishing without his express consent. Domestic animals may be protected by provisions requiring that cattle guards be installed, gates kept closed and locked, and similar precautions observed.

Site reclamation and well plugging. When exploration or production comes to an end, the well site must be restored, as far as possible, to its original condition—if the lessor has insisted on a clause to that effect. He may also have required that wells be plugged according to state regulations. This last provision aims to protect the landowner from the expense of plugging wells himself, an expense occasionally incurred when an operator simply abandons an unproductive well.

The Amendment Process

Whatever additions, deletions, and substitutions may be judged necessary for a given lease should be formulated with care and added to the printed lease form with all possible neatness and clarity. Messy lease forms will be rejected by most lessees for at least two excellent reasons. First, leases must be easily assignable. Blacked-out lines, handwritten insertions, and carelessly attached riders may lower a lease's acceptability in the eyes of potential buyers and traders. Second, any legal instrument must be unambiguous in its provisions if it is not to risk becoming a subject for litigation. When changes are made, they should be made correctly and clearly. Striking through an unacceptable line or set of lines—should be done neatly and in such a way as to leave the lines legible. Very short changes, of a word or phrase, can be typed above the strike-out. Anything longer should probably be typed on a separate sheet and identified as taking the place of "Article...." Such separately listed provisions of a lease are called *riders* or *exhibits*. They, and all other changes, should be initialed or

signed by all the parties. In this way, changes can be identified and recognized as having been made before the lease was executed. Separate sheets must be attached to the lease form, and an extra precaution would add "See rider attached" to each amended clause of that form. Some printed forms have their own printed sheets for emendations and additions.

It may go without saying that all changes made by a lessor will be very carefully examined by the lessee. Even if the lessee agrees, in principle, with a proposed change, he will want to make sure that the amendment is not poorly worded or in conflict with other provisions of the lease. Only when he and the lessor are both satisfied will the lease be ready for signing.

EXECUTION AND ACKNOWLEDGMENT

Variations in Proper Execution

A properly executed oil and gas lease is a written instrument signed by the granting party or parties. The various states differ somewhat in their special requirements for leases executed by married persons, the blind, the illiterate, corporate officers, and so on. Table 7.1 lists a number of these variations in state law, but uncertainties about the execution of a particular lease should be resolved by consulting an attorney licensed to practice law in the relevant state. The signature of the grantor should conform to that used on any earlier document, like a deed, by which the land was acquired. Nicknames, initials, and name changes can usually be handled by signing with both names. For example, a man might sign a lease "Robert E. Lee, also known as R. E. Lee," or "Robert E. Lee, also known as Bobby Lee." A woman whose name has changed since she acquired her property might sign as "Nancy Todd Cooper, a married

woman, formerly known as Nancy Todd, a single woman."

People who sign as representatives must include a *caption* that indicates the capacity in which they sign and (in most cases) the party for whom they sign. Normally, these names will appear twice, in the caption and with the signature itself. For example, an attorney signing for his client would use a form like the following:

> Robert E. Lee, appearing herein
> through Avery Smith, his Agent and
> Attorney-in-Fact, under Power of
> Attorney dated . . . , and recorded
> in book . . . Page . . . of the
> records of . . . County . . .
>
> ROBERT E. LEE
>
> By _____
> Avery Smith, Agent and
> Attorney-in-Fact

When the person signing acts as the representative of someone in a special category, that fact is usually indicated:

TABLE 7.1
Executing Instruments: Variations in the Rules

State	Community Property	Homestead Laws	Must Wife Sign	Must Husband Sign	Are Witnesses Necessary	SPECIAL RULES — Blind	SPECIAL RULES — Illiterate	N.C.M.	CORPORATE EXECUTIONS — Seal	CORPORATE EXECUTIONS — Attest	CORPORATE EXECUTIONS — Witnesses
Alabama	No	Yes (1)	No (2)	No	No		2 Witnesses	Court Order	No (5)		No
Alaska	No	Yes	No (2)	No (2)	No			Court Order	No		No
Arizona	Yes	Yes	Yes (9)	Yes (9)	No			Court Order	Yes		No
Arkansas*	No	Yes (1)	No (2)	No	2 Witnesses (7)	2 Witnesses	2 Witnesses	Court Order	Yes	Yes	2 Witnesses
California	Yes	Yes	Yes (9)	Yes (9)	No	1 Witness	2 Witnesses	Court Order	No (5)	Yes	No
Colorado	No	Yes	No (2)	No	No			Court Order	Yes	Yes	No
Florida	No	Yes	No (2)	No (2)	2 Witnesses			Court Order	Yes		Yes (8)
Idaho	Yes	Yes	Yes (9)	Yes (9)	No			Court Order	Yes		No
Illinois	No	Yes	No (2)	No (2)	No	2 Witnesses	2 Witnesses	Court Order	No	Yes	No
Indiana	No	Yes	No	No	No			Court Order	No	Yes	No
Kansas	No	Yes	No (2)	No (2)	No	1 Witness	1 Witness	Court Order	No	Yes	No
Kentucky*	No	Yes (1)	No (2)	No (2)	No			Court Order	No	No	2 Witnesses
Louisiana	Yes	Yes	Yes (9)	Yes (9)	2 Witnesses	3 Witnesses	3 Witnesses	Court Order	No		2 Witnesses
Michigan*	No	Yes	No (8)	No	2 Witnesses	None	2 Witnesses	Court Order	No		2 Witnesses
Mississippi	No	Yes	No (2)	No (2)	No		Make Mark	Court Order	Yes		No
Montana	No	Yes	No (2)	No (2)	No	None (4)	Special Acknowledgment	Court Order	Yes		No
Nebraska	No	Yes	No (2)	No (2)	No			Court Order	No		No
Nevada	Yes	Yes	Yes (9)	Yes (9)	No			Court Order	Yes		No
New Mexico	Yes	Yes	Yes (9)	Yes (9)	No	None	2 Witnesses	Court Order	No		No
New York	No	Yes	No (2)	No (2)	No			Court Order	Yes	Yes	No
North Dakota	No	Yes	No (2)	No (2)	No	None	2 Witnesses	Court Order	Yes		No
Ohio*	No	Yes (1)	No (6)	No (6)	2 Witnesses	None	None	Court Order	Yes		2 Witnesses
Oklahoma	No	Yes	No (2)	No (2)	No	Spec. Statute	2 Witnesses	Court Order	Yes	Yes	No
Pennsylvania	No	No (1)	Yes (1)	Yes (1)	2 Witnesses (3)	2 Witnesses (3)	2 Witnesses	Court Order	Yes (3)		2 Witnesses (3)
South Dakota	No	Yes	No (2)	No (2)	No	None	None	Court Order	Yes		No
Texas	Yes	Yes	Yes	Yes	No	2 Witnesses		Court Order	No		No
Utah	No	Yes	Yes (1)	No	No	At Least 1 Witness	At Least 1 Witness	Court Order	No		No
W. Virginia*,**	No	Yes	No (1)	No	2 Witnesses		1 Witness	Court Order	Yes		2 Witnesses
Wyoming	No	Yes	No (2)	No (2)	No	2 Witnesses and Special Acknowledgment	Court Order	Court Order	Yes		No

* Person who prepares instrument must sign & give address.
** An attorney must prepare lease.

(1) Special Dower Law (or curtesy) spouse must sign.
(2) Homestead property spouse must sign.
(3) Not required but safe to have it done.
(4) Use thumbprint & special acknowledgment or 2 witnesses.
(5) Not required but is prima facie evidence of authority.
(6) Wife has 1/3 dower in fee in all realty must sign.
(7) Must have 2 witnesses if no acknowledgment.
(8) If no seal.
(9) Community property spouse must sign.

SOURCE: *The AAPL Guide for Landmen*, 81–82.

Wilfred Smith, Guardian of the
Estate of Susan Cooper, a minor

Wilfred Smith, Guardian
of the Estate of Susan Cooper,
a minor.

Or

Henry Tudor, Executor of the Estate
of Catherine Howard, Deceased

Henry Tudor, Executor
of the Estate of
Catherine Howard, Deceased

The Importance of Proper Acknowledgment

Execution of an instrument refers chiefly to its signing. Acknowledgment serves to prove proper execution. An officer who provides an acknowledgment is, in effect, pledging — with a written certificate and an official signature — that the grantor signed his or her lease freely, uncoerced. The pledge also assures the identity of the signing party. Anyone who examines an executed and acknowledged lease can feel a reasonable confidence that the instrument was not obtained under duress or signed with a false name. The grantor is who he says he is. The officer frequently sought for acknowledgments is the nearest notary public, but some states allow justices of the peace, mayors, clerks of court, and other officers to serve in this capacity. While not all states require acknowledgment for an oil and gas lease to be valid *between the parties,* prudence suggests that leases be recorded — and to record an instrument in the county records, one needs to have it acknowledged.

Variations in State Requirements

Once again, variations in the statutes of the states make it highly advisable to consult those statutes — or an attorney familiar with them — when a lease is executed. Table 7.2 shows some of the varying requirements, but changes in the law are always a possible problem. The notary public or other officer who acknowledges a lease may *not* have any financial interest in that lease nor be a party to it.

TABLE 7.2
Acknowledging Instruments:
Variations in the Rules

	Statutory Form	Notary Seal Necessary	Can Witness Acknowledge	Reciprocity (1)
Alabama	Yes	Yes	Yes	Yes
Alaska	No	No	Yes	Yes
Arizona	Yes	Yes	No	Yes
Arkansas	Yes	Yes	Yes	Yes
California	Yes	Yes	Yes	Yes
Colorado	Yes	Yes	Yes	Yes
Florida	Yes	Yes	Yes	Yes
Idaho	Yes	Yes	Yes	Yes
Illinois	Yes	Yes	Yes	Yes
Indiana	Yes	Yes	Yes	Yes (2)
Kansas	No	Yes	Yes	Yes (2)
Kentucky	No	No (3)	Yes	Yes
Louisiana	No	Yes	Yes	Yes
Michigan	No	No	Yes	Yes
Mississippi	No	Yes	Yes	Yes
Montana	Yes	Yes	Yes	Yes
Nebraska	No	Yes	Yes	Yes
Nevada	Yes	Stamp	Yes	Yes
New Mexico	Yes	Yes	No	Yes
New York	Yes	No	Yes	Yes
North Dakota	Yes	Yes	Yes	Yes
Ohio	No	Yes (3)	No	Yes
Oklahoma	Yes	Yes	No	Yes
Pennsylvania	Yes	Yes	No	Yes
South Dakota	Yes	Yes	Yes	Yes
Texas	Yes	Yes	Yes	Yes
Utah	Yes	Yes	Yes	Yes
West Virginia	Yes	Yes (3)	Yes	Yes
Wyoming	Yes	Yes	No	Yes

Footnote references:
(1) Does state recognize legality of form valid in state where executed?
(2) Notary Seal must be affixed to out-of-state acknowledgment.
(3) While seal is not required, it has been deemed safe practice to require its being affixed.

SOURCE: *The AAPL Guide for Landmen,* 89.

RECORDING OF THE EXECUTED LEASE

Both lessor and lessee have a strong interest in seeing their lease recorded or officially entered into the relevant county records. All inquirers — whether competitors of the leasing parties, creditors, or the merely curious — may then see that a valid lease exists for that particular tract of land. Title cannot be challenged and defeated by, for example, a creditor of the lessee or a mortgage holder of the lessor on the grounds of an unrecorded transaction. Recording should always be carried out as promptly as seems practicable. Not only should the oil and gas lease itself be recorded, but so also should attendant instruments — assignments, releases, deeds, ratifications, judgments, and so on. Ordinarily, recording of the lease is handled by the lessee or his representative. Quite commonly, too, the recording procedure follows the issuing and honoring of a draft for payment of the lease bonus, as described below. For a discussion of the process of filing legal instruments for record, see Appendix F.

Drafts

At the time of signing, the landman may give or mail to the lessor a *draft*, or written order on a bank authorizing payment. When the landowner presents this draft and the signed lease at his bank, both lease and draft will be sent on to the lessee's bank. How promptly the landowner gets his payment depends on the nature of the draft. A *sight draft* must be picked up at the lessee's bank on the day that it arrives. A 5-day draft allows the lessee to wait for 5 days after its receipt, a 10-day draft allows a 10-day delay, and so forth. Delay times vary, then, but 10 to 15 days is a fairly common interval.

The person who picks up the draft at the lessee's bank will check it for proper execution and acknowledgment. If the landman has also sent a copy of the executed lease to the lessee's office, this copy can be compared to the original. If not, the original will need to be approved before the draft is picked up and the payment sent to the lessor's bank. If the landowner prefers not to name a bank on his lease, the lease bonus and any subsequent rental or royalty payments may be sent directly to the landowner.

Recording Procedures

The various states handle the recording of legal instruments in slightly different ways. Usually, when a lease is sent from the lessee's office to the appropriate county recorder or clerk of the court, the original instrument is returned with recording information noted on it. Louisiana keeps the original and returns a certified copy only on request. When recording in Louisiana, many lessees prefer, as a matter of common procedure, to send the original and a machine copy; the original can then be recorded and the copy certified and returned.

Generally, a lease is sent for recording as quickly as possible after it is executed and consideration paid. Once it has arrived in the lessee's office, been numbered and given a file, it goes to the recorder. (See Appendix G for information on lease filing procedures.) There may be exceptions to this rule of thumb, however. If, for example, the lessee's leasing activity in a given area is being kept secret from his competitors until all the desired leases have been obtained, some delay in recording may be prudent to prevent information leaks.

RATIFICATION

A ratification is an agreement that confirms a lease executed by someone else. Such an agreement can be formalized in a written instrument or simply inferred from the ratifying person's behavior. It can be made at almost any point after the original lessor has signed his lease. Co-owners of interest in the property are, of course, the people with the choice to ratify or not.

When ratification is primarily a matter of convenience—as when numerous co-owners ratify after one of them has signed a base lease—it amounts to a decision to join in the original lease. But co-owner Smith might decide to ratify the instrument months after co-owner Jones had signed a lease. Smith will in that case have decided that ratification serves his best interests. He may, for example, have better reason to suppose that the venture will be profitable. Ratification will entitle him to cost-free royalties, whereas failure to ratify, though it will not lose him a share in

the profits, will allow the operator to subtract from Smith's share a certain proportion of the ongoing costs of drilling and production, if the well is productive. (A dry hole will cost Smith nothing.)

If ratification takes the form of a separate written instrument, it will be acknowledged and recorded after it is signed. If it takes the form of a clause in a division order, signing such a division order may amount to ratifying the lease. (Division orders will be discussed in the next chapter.) When ratification is left implicit, behavior by a co-owner that can be taken to confirm the lease includes the accepting of payments, cooperation in the continuing of operations, and so forth. A co-owner who behaves for a period of time *as if* he found the lease acceptable and then changes to a different (and negative) behavior may be legally *estopped*—that is, prevented from denying the lease.

SUBSEQUENT INTERPRETATIONS OF THE LEASE

Legal Definitions of the Oil and Gas Lease

Oil and gas law varies as it does from state to state—creating different legal relationships and giving rise to different legal interpretations—partly because the conceptions of the *interest* created by an oil and gas lease vary. In one jurisdiction or another, this interest has been described as "a profit a prender, a corporeal hereditament, an incorporeal hereditament, an estate in land, not an estate in land, an estate in oil and gas, not an estate in oil and gas, a servitude, a chattel real, real estate..." and a good many other things besides. (See

Earl A. Brown, Jr., "Elemental Principles of the Modern Oil and Gas Lease," *Montana Law Journal,* 17 (Fall 1955), 39.) Of all the varying legal definitions, however, two emerge as particularly important: the *incorporeal hereditament* and the *determinable fee.* Stripped of its rather intimidating jargon, the first (incorporeal hereditament) can be recognized as the nonabsolute ownership theory discussed in chapter 1. Where this theory holds, oil and gas cannot be owned apart from the land. A lessee receives no more than the exclusive right to search for and remove whatever oil and gas can be reduced to possession. The determinable fee is linked to the ownership-in-place theory that allows a lesse to *own* the oil and gas under the land (and to develop it) so long as the fee continues.

What an oil and gas lease does *not* create is an ordinary tenant-landlord relationship. The novice, whether lessor or attorney, can stumble over the very word *lease,* assuming that an ordinary commercial lease provides a model of the relationships, obligations, and possible judicial constructions arising from an oil and gas lease. Earlier chapters have pointed out a number of the obligations that can be established between a petroleum lessor and a lessee. The next section takes a look at how the courts are likely to construe oil and gas leases, working on very different assumptions from those which underlie the settlement of landlord-tenant disputes.

Legal Construction of the Oil and Gas Lease

Whereas ordinary commercial leases are often construed against the lessor, oil and gas leases are construed quite strictly against the lessee. The reasoning behind such rules of interpretation is clear: doubtful cases should be decided in favor of those least able to help themselves. If, for example, Ms. Brown has a dispute with Mcgapolitan Apartments, from whom she rents a unit, she argues from a decidedly vulnerable position. Her lease has been written by Megapolitan and its lawyers. She has had little, if anything, to say about the terms and may be, in relation to her landlord, quite helpless. (She may be evicted, for example, before she can assert herself effectively.) It seems, therefore, only equitable to give Ms. Brown the benefit of any legal doubts that arise in regard to her lease.

On the other hand, an oil and gas lessor seems very unlike Megapolitan Apartments,

Inc. This time, the image that hovers in the judicial mind appears to be that of a farmer or rancher of plain speech and unsophisticated outlook who is obviously the salt of the earth. His lease has been written by a petroleum company's expert team of attorneys and consultants. He needs protecting. Since equity seems to require that a great disparity in power be remedied, the lessor will receive the benefit of the doubt when his lease is construed by the court.

Another canon (rule) of construction for oil and gas leases, a rule that favors development and frowns on delay, would probably have been more freely invoked on behalf of the lessor's father and grandfather. At present, development is not the dominant policy it once was. Conservation of resources and avoidance of waste have, over the past half century, become at least as important, as an examination of many states' conservation laws will testify. Canons concerned with discovering and implementing the *intent of the parties* are, of course, less likely to change with shifts in public concern and policy. Examples of such rules would be the insistence on determining intent from the whole instrument rather than from an isolated part or provision, the force given to specific rather than general clauses when these conflict and cannot be reconciled, and the rule which says that written—that is, special, added—clauses govern when they conflict with printed clauses.

Disputes over leases may result in a suit to *resolve* an ambiguity or in a suit to *reform* a lease. In the first instance, the problem arises from a lack of clarity in the instrument. In the second, a perceived mistake or inequity prompts one of the parties to sue in hope of relief. Courts differ on the lengths to which they will go in order to remedy situations that they agree are inequitable. Texas courts, for example, have sometimes been quite vigorous in protecting the rights of the lessor. They have also adhered avowedly to the so-called four corner rule, which requires that questions be answered from the lease itself, not from verbal or other extrinsic evidence. (One must stay within the four corners of the instrument.) Only when an ambiguity remains stubbornly unresolvable, or an inequity clearly unremedied, will the court consider *parol* (verbal) evidence or found its opinion on a theory—estoppel, for instance, or waiver—that comes from outside the lease.

Because the laws and, to a lesser degree, the canons of construction vary from state to state, anyone planning a suit to resolve or reform a troublesome lease should look for counsel expert in oil and gas law. A suit should also be the *last* means resorted to. No responsible lessor or lessee throws a phrase like "I'll sue!" around carelessly.

Preparations for Drilling, Producing, and Selling

Once he has signed a lease and received his bonus, the landowner can often go about his normal business in the happy knowledge that his share of the oil and gas paperwork is, for the moment, complete. He may monitor the situation, update his files, or negotiate leases on other properties, but unless he has access to venture capital (and the desire to use it), there isn't much that he can contribute to the drilling of a well. Not so the landman. His work has often just begun. Depending on his experience and the needs of his company or client, he may be called upon to arrange, precisely, the financing of exploration and drilling. The trades, joint ventures, and operating agreements that may be required to drill and then develop property are a complex subject in their own right; they will be considered together in a later chapter. This chapter will assume that the money to drill has been found. It will look at the other preliminary steps the landman may take part in, particularly the examining and curing of titles to leased properties.

EXAMINING TITLES

Though a preliminary check of the records is one of the landman's responsibilities, the examination of title is a job he will turn over to his company's legal department or his client's attorney. He must, however, often work with the title examiner. He knows the importance of *good title* (that is, legally defensible title) to the oil company or operator making plans to drill. In a few cases, the landman may himself be an attorney with the specialized knowledge needed to examine titles. More often, he must turn for assistance to a qualified specialist.

Title Examiners

Attorneys who examine titles to oil and gas properties may be employed by petroleum companies or may be in private practice. Their responsibilities call for methodical, painstaking work, and on their decisions rest further important decisions—to proceed with drilling, for example, or to begin royalty payments. A title examiner hopes for a perfect, unclouded title; he nearly always finds an imperfect one. What would constitute a perfect title to land? Presumably, a set of recorded instruments that showed an unbroken *chain of title* stretching all the way from the original land patent or land grant to the present owner's deed. Conveyances, leases, severances, *all* transactions involving the ownership of the land—particularly the oil and gas rights—would be on record and dazzlingly clear. There would be no gaps and no ambiguities. The present owner's claim to the property would be unassailable by missing heirs, hungry creditors, and other troublesome people. In such a case, the examiner could admire the chain of title and then write an opinion that would send his company or client out fearlessly to drill and develop.

Title Opinions

In the absence of such perfect chains of title, legal opinions about a title may be written at almost every stage of an oil or gas operation. Some companies order opinions before paying bonuses, before paying delay rentals, before drilling, and before executing division orders. In a particular situation, a number of supplementary opinions may be necessary and prudent—say, where a number of owners are involved and the various interests are complicated. The speed with which a company wishes to act can affect the number of opinions it orders, as can its general policy. Some companies are more conservative than others, and what seems necessary to one may be judged hypercautious by another. Quite commonly, though, title opinions are needed at two different stages in

an operation. The first document is called a *drill site opinion;* it is ordered for a selected drill site, and it can sometimes eliminate the need for later, different opinions. When it does, the second document—the *division order opinion*—can be simply a copy of the first. However, when more information is required in order to pay all owners their proper shares of production, an examiner will draw up a separate division order opinion to clarify the question of who gets what. (Drill site opinions often do not show *all* owners, for example.)

Companies differ on the forms they use for title opinions. Figure 8.1 at the end of the chapter shows a composite form that serves as an example. The sources of information available to a title examiner also vary. Depending on which sources are used, a title opinion is referred to as *abstract-based* or *stand-up.*

Abstract-based opinions. Title opinions often depend upon abstracts, and if a landman has not ordered an abstract at the time of his preliminary checking, he may need to do so when a drill site is selected. An experienced landman, accustomed to working with title examiners, can sometimes judge how complete the required abstract needs to be. He can give detailed instructions to the abstractor, noting what may safely be omitted and what should be included. He will also have collected other things the examiner may ask for—maps, rental and tax receipts, releases, affidavits, and so on. Again, thoroughness in the preliminary checking can save time and money later on. The landman, for example, who has acquired a landowner's base abstract (or a copy of it) and ordered supplements to bring it up to date can turn these papers over to the examiner with minimal delay. In some situations, a *takeoff* (a list and brief description of the documents relevant to the title of a particular piece of property), ordered from an abstract office at a cost much below that of a complete abstract, may be adequate for the examiner's purposes.

Stand-up opinions. Before a lease is signed, the landman usually prepares a *run sheet* that briefly describes all the relevant documents in a tract's history of ownership. (Clearly, a landman's run sheet is much like an abstractor's takeoff.) In the absence of an abstract, such a list can be a valuable starting point for the title examiner. If the examiner takes a run sheet to the county courthouse, carefully looks over all the documents that the list mentions, decides whether or not he needs additional facts, and then writes an opinion, he has produced what is known as a *stand-up title opinion.*

Stand-up opinions save the time and expense of abstract preparation. They may also seem preferable to dealing with unknown abstract plants. Here again, particular situations create particular needs. Some companies and some examiners depend heavily on run sheets prepared by experienced, reliable lease brokers or landmen. Others find abstracts well worth the investment of money and time. Whatever the examiner's sources and procedures, he is unlikely to find a perfect title—and very likely to conclude that he needs additional information to cure a defective one.

CURING TITLES

When there are gaps in the chain of title, or other defects that leave a cloud on the present owner's claim, the examiner often asks the landman to secure additional facts. The landman takes the examiner's requirements and goes in search of the requested information. These additional facts, properly attested to, are needed to *cure the title*—that is, to remedy defects and omissions that could make the present owner's claim to the property questionable. By satisfying the examiner, the landman hopes to rule out or at least minimize the risk of adverse claimants to the property and make the lease title marketable. His company or client can then drill and develop the land. To meet the requirements, he must often look for disinterested witnesses who are familiar with the facts and willing to affirm them before a notary public. (Affirmations made by the owner or occupant of the land are often vulnerable to charges of being self-serving.) Witnesses who swear to the written, notarized affirmations of fact known as *affidavits* may also be needed to testify in court.

With that possibility in mind, the landman will, for obvious reasons, prefer a younger, more robust witness to an older one in precarious health. Finally, the forms for affidavits and acknowledgments differ somewhat from state to state; the landman must take care to see that the appropriate forms are followed.

Affidavits

The person who makes an affidavit is called the affiant. Some of the more commonly used kinds of affidavits cover death and heirship; identity; nonproduction; use, occupancy, and possession; and adverse possession.

Death and heirship. A death and heirship instrument serves, in the absence of probate proceedings, to affirm that owner X has indeed died and that Y is legal heir to the property. Here is a situation in which a disinterested witness with no financial or even emotional stake in the facts is very helpful. Y, the heir, cannot be viewed as a disinterested person.

Identity. An affidavit of identity simply establishes the fact that, in a given instance, a difference in name does not mean a difference in person. For example, witnesses may swear that the "Beulah Smith" whose name appears on a property deed dated 1960 is in truth the same woman as the "Bunny Jones" who signed a lease on that property last week. (She married Mr. Jones in 1970 and hasn't used her Christian name, which her husband dislikes, since the wedding. Any number of disinterested people know these facts.)

Nonproduction. In a case of nonproduction, the facts to be established concern nonproduction under an old lease. Ordinarily, the landman should obtain a release for the property, but a number of circumstances might make it difficult or even impossible to acquire a release from the lessee. The lessee may have died or closed down his business and moved away. The lease may be quite old, virtually forgotten until the possibility of a new lease is presented to the landowner. In such a case, an affidavit executed by the lessor and/or his depository bank can testify to the facts required to terminate the lease. If the land is not under production and delay rentals are not being paid, then the land can be leased again. When old leases are concerned, the lessor may be the only person in command of all the relevant facts. He may serve as the affiant without much likelihood of challenge.

Use, occupancy, and possession. An affidavit regarding use, occupancy, and possession can be very important to the cure of an old defect in title. (An example of such a defect might be a gap in the chain of title caused by a courthouse fire that destroyed certain recorded instruments.) The affidavit itself does not cure the defect; no affidavit does that. But it can point to the existence of appropriate facts that support the present occupant's claim. For maximum effectiveness, the affidavit should be signed by at least two disinterested persons. (Separate instruments called corroborating affidavits are sometimes more convenient for the affiants in these cases.) The affiants must provide evidence for, not merely opinions or conclusions about, the present owner's possession of his property. Their evidence should cover as many years as they can accurately remember. For example, an affiant's simple conclusion that John Jones has been in possession of his 160 acres for the last 25 years would be insufficient to support Mr. Jones's claim. If the affiant can swear that Mr. Jones has lived on the property since 1955 and has kept the land fenced since 1957, he is helping to establish relevant facts. Other helpful affirmations would specify the uses to which Mr. Jones put the land. Did he raise crops on it? Graze cattle? Plant orchards or cut timber? Build and live in a house? Build barns for his livestock? Pay taxes regularly? Details like these can do much to confirm Mr. Jones's claim that he does own the land—despite the gap in the chain of title.

Adverse possession. With an affidavit of adverse possession, the occupant of land asserts a claim to it *against* someone who holds title. The possessor says, in effect, that his occupancy and use of the land—carried out openly, continuously, and visibly—gives him a better claim than the record owner can assert. The state statutes regulating claims made by adverse possession vary, particularly in regard to the time required to make possession effective. A possession of 5 years may carry certain requirements, one of 10 years certain other requirements, and one of 15 or 25 years a third set of requirements. A landman preparing or having an attorney prepare this kind of affidavit must be thoroughly familiar with the statutes in his state. He must plan to supply the facts of possession in even greater detail than would be needed for an affidavit of use, occupancy, and possession.

Proof of tax payments will often be particularly important.

The statutory language describing adverse possession can be rather ferocious, suggesting that occupant and record owner are at daggers drawn. (Terms used in the statutes include *actual, notorious, hostile,* and so on.) An affidavit of adverse possession may, of course, reflect real antagonisms in the sense of personal animosities—or it may not. It may reflect only a muddle in the history of an area or a family. Claims in virtue of adverse possession are fairly common in parts of central and east Texas where early Spanish land grants were made. Succeeding governments and jurisdictions have left any number of titles in disarray. Occupants given the chance to lease their property and profit from its development may need to clarify their situation by means of affidavits, even though no individual rival claimant is glaring at them across the fence.

Other Kinds of Documents

The other kinds of documents and legal instruments that may be needed to cure defects in title are quite various. In a claim by virtue of adverse possession, for example, proof of tax payments by the occupant can be very important. *Tax receipts* or a *tax certificate* bearing the occupant's name should be turned over to the examiner along with the necessary affidavits. *Rental receipts* may be useful in certain instances—if, say, a landowner is establishing proof of untimely or terminated rental payments in order to free his land from an old lease. *Releases* can, of course, be perfectly straightforward when the lessee is available to answer requests. The landman who finds an old lease on record and suspects that it has expired can simply as the lessee for a release. Most lessees honor such requests as a matter of course. When the lease has changed hands, the approval of the assigning party is sometimes needed to obtain a release.

The landman or examiner may also discover the existence of an old *mortgage* or *deed of trust* to the property. If the mortgage is no longer in effect, it can be released and the release recorded. If a deed of trust is still in effect, the holder of such an instrument (the creditor) has rights superior to any subsequent interest in the property. Neither the landowner nor this lessee can develop the land without the creditor's consent without taking undue risk. To avoid litigation, the landman needs to get a subordination agreement from the mortgage or lien holder. A *subordination* resolves the priority of rights and subordinates the earlier instrument to the oil and gas lease. (A foreclosure would not affect the validity of the lease.) Mortgages or liens obtained *after* an oil and gas lease are already subordinate; they do not need supplementing with special instruments to protect the lessee.

When people waive rather than assert their claims to land, they may do so by a *quitclaim deed* or a *disclaimer.* A quitclaim deed relinquishes to someone else any rights or interests a person may have in property, however those rights were acquired. Disclaimers, often signed by surface tenants, say, in effect, that the tenant *has* no interest in the title or the mineral estate. He merely uses the surface—as a tenant rather than as an owner.

Finally, *ratifications* may be judged necessary or prudent supplements to a lease when a title is being cured. If, for instance, the title examination has turned up an unexpected mineral owner, the newcomer may be willing to ratify the existing lease. Ratification can often be a more convenient step than the securing of a new lease.

PERMITTING AND DRILLING

When the examiner agrees that the title to a chosen drill site has been cured and that no outstanding claims or encumbrances impair it, the company or operator is almost ready to drill. In many states, the next step is to obtain a *well permit* from the agency that enforces the state conservation laws. The permit serves to ensure that the well site conforms to spacing regulations and other state requirements—or that the site merits the granting of an exception to such rules. The permit form generally shows information like the proposed depth of the well, the name of the operator, and so on. When an experienced landman remarks that agency approval for a well site is ordinarily a routine matter, he is assuming that the applicant has done his homework. An applicant who is unfamiliar with the rules or is trying to wrench them to fit his situation can be in for difficulties.

The necessary permit acquired, the title cured, and the landowner and/or occupant notified, drilling can at last begin. With luck and hard work, the operator may have a working well in a matter of weeks. At that point, it will be time for the division order title opinion mentioned earlier to be drawn up. This opinion will make it possible to draft and execute accurate division orders—thereby assuring payment to the various interest owners.

EXECUTING DIVISION ORDERS

A division order is a contract of sale to the *purchaser* of the oil produced by the lessee. It names all the parties who have interests in the well—and the production from it—mineral owners, royalty owners, working interest owners, and so on—and resolves their fractional shares into decimal figures. Payments for the oil or gas sold are then calculated on the basis of each owner's interest. (See Appendix H.) Division orders commonly do more, though. They often warrant title, guaranteeing that the listed percentages are correct, and they may also give the purchaser certain rights in regard to how the oil or gas is handled, what accounting procedures are used, and how market values are reckoned.

Who issues division orders and sees to the disbursing of sale proceeds? Originally, the purchaser did these things. Division orders were developed in the early days of the oil industry to accomplish two chief aims: to distribute proceeds from the sale of oil to the various owners and to protect the purchaser from claims (by these same owners) that their payments were incorrect. For oil production, the purchaser may still handle division orders and payments. He may conduct his own investigation to be sure that the sellers have unclouded, merchantable title to the product being sold. (In this case, he often asks the operator to furnish abstracts for his own attorney to examine.) He will then have division orders prepared and sent out for execution by the operator, the royalty owners, and anyone else shown to have an interest in the production. The purchaser takes responsibility for paying the owners. This purchaser may be a pipeline company, an agency affiliated with such a company, or someone else who has access to a pipeline. Whoever the purchaser is, he will usually include protective language in his division orders to guard against claims made by owners *not* listed in those orders. If the listed owners warrant (or guarantee) their interests, they have little ground for later complaints that their percentages are incorrect. (Division orders are revocable, however, and mistakes can be rectified to increase an owner's share of future production. Past production is usually protected from such claims.)

For gas production, the title to all gas goes to the lessee when the gas is produced. When the gas is sold, the lessee or his representative has the responsibility of accounting to the royalty owners and handling the division orders. Since division orders have been the subject of much litigation over the years, whoever sends a division order out for execution may find an experienced royalty owner striking through language that does not pertain to the division of interest. Ratification language may be struck out, for example, or any sentences that seem to extend or alter provisions of the lease. Owners are increasingly wary of court decisions like *Exxon Corp. v. Middleton* in Texas, a decision which found that the signing of division orders established a binding agreement to accept each payment as a final settlement of the royalty due. This, despite the fact that larger payments were owing under the terms of the lease. Since no law *requires* a royalty owner to sign a division order to get paid, some owners simply refuse to sign. Signing is an accepted industry practice, however, and one that has been honored by the courts in Texas and Louisiana. Failure to sign can result in delaying the disbursement of an owner's share of the proceeds. Consequently, most owners will be satisfied by the inclusion of a *revocation* provision that allows the division order to be cancelled by either party upon 30 days' written notice.

Figure 8.1. Sample form for a title opinion

Description of Land:

Abstracts and Other Instruments Examined:

Record Title:

    Surface Ownership:

    Mineral Ownership:

    Royalty Ownership:

    Mineral Interests under Lease:

    Mineral Interests Unleased:

    Outstanding Liens:

Basic Lease:

    Date of Lease:

    Date Recorded:

    Lessor:

    Lessee:

    Description of Land:

    Interest Conveyed:

    Primary Term:

    Royalties:

    Delay Rentals (amount and to whom payable):

    Extended Term:

    Depository Bank:

    Drilling Obligations:

    Pooling Clause:

    Shut-in Clause:

    Unusual Clauses and Provisions:

Lease Assignments:

Status of Taxes:

Severance from Sovereignty:

Comments, Objections, Requirements:

Agreements to Explore and Develop Leased Properties

Having acquired oil and gas leases from landowners, petroleum companies very commonly enter into agreements (that is, contracts) with other petroleum companies to explore and develop leased properties. At first glance, the frequency of such joint undertakings seems puzzling. Why would a company that has gone to considerable effort and expense to obtain leases invite a competitor in to share the information and the profits that drilling may produce? The short answer is: because it pays the company to do so. The longer answer points out that this has not always been the case. In the early days of the industry, when drilling was unrestricted, each company preferred to explore and develop its own leases. Fierce competition led to the rapid development of many oil fields, but it also resulted in too many wells and much wasted oil, money, and labor. The adoption of conservation laws changed the industry and made a measure of cooperation necessary if companies were to comply with governmental regulations. Increased drilling costs also encouraged (and still encourage) cooperation. Competition certainly remains, and no one would wish to eliminate it. But today most

companies arrange to share with other companies some of the risks involved in exploration and development. The people who handle these agreements between companies are usually landmen, and the agreements themselves vary a great deal in length and complexity.

Whether simple or complicated, agreements are generally discussed and offered as trades. Basically, one company agrees to drill a well on its own or another company's lease in return for support money or an assigned interest in the property. Such trades (known as *support agreements* when money is provided and as *farmouts* or *farm-ins* when an interest in the property is to be earned) can benefit all the parties concerned. The supporting company can gain valuable information at little risk. The party who drills incurs risk but also stands to profit if the well is a producer. A successful first well may prompt the companies involved to continue working together. If they do, they will almost certainly need a more detailed agreement — known as a *joint operating agreement* — to cover new obligations and contingencies.

SUPPORT AGREEMENTS

A company that offers to support the drilling of a test well offers money or acreage or both. A company that solicits support will not, of course, expect someone else to pay all the costs of the well. On the contrary, the risk and expense will be borne in large part by the company that drills. But it can often get considerable help. The terms on which that help is offered vary; no two agreements are exactly alike. Still, typical arrangements can be described, always with the understanding that conditions in a given area help to shape the kinds of trades arrived at. For example, raising money to drill a wildcat well can be very different from soliciting support to drill in the neighborhood of a steady producer.

Money Contributions

A company seeking support money is usually planning to drill on one of its own leases. If it wants to drill a test well on someone else's lease, it will suggest other types of agreement—a farmout, for example, or a joint operating agreement. Sometimes companies that are asked for acreage contributions will offer money support instead. In any case, financial help and the conditions that must be met to receive it are usually set out in a *support letter*. When signed by the parties, such a letter serves as a binding contract.

Dry hole letters. What a supporting company receives for its money is information. Testing and drilling can yield valuable data about formations that underlie the contributor's property as well as that of the drilling company. For this information, the contributor agrees to pay so much per foot drilled (often between $1 and $3 per foot, not to exceed a stipulated sum) *if the well is a dry hole*. The letter of agreement spells out details like well location and depth, tests to be run, additional tests that may be conducted by the supporting company, and so on (fig. 9.1 at the end of the chapter). Most support letters, it should be pointed out, do not create an obligation to drill. They simply describe the conditions that must be met if a contribution is claimed from the supporting company. The company planning to drill can change its mind. It can drill but decide to go "tight hole"—that is, keep all information and test results strictly to itself. And it might, of course, drill a producing well. In none of these three situations can it claim support money.

Bottomhole letters. A contributing company may feel that having a well drilled to a specified depth is worth helping to pay for—even if the well produces for the company that drills. In that case, it will make a bottomhole contribution. It will pay so much per foot whether the well proves dry or productive (bottomhole money). Or the contributor may agree to buy a portion of the acreage under lease as soon as the well reaches an agreed-upon depth (bottomhole purchase). Both these forms of support are, however, less commonly offered than is dry hole money. Dry hole letters remain the most popular form of money support agreement.

Acreage Contributions (Farmouts/Farm-ins)

A lessee may decide to farm out some of his leased acreage to a third party who wants to drill a well on it. An agreement that trades drilling obligations for an assigned interest in property is known as a *farmout*. The granting party is the *farmor* and the recipient is the *farmee*. (The agreement is a *farm-in* to the receiving party.) A farmor may let someone else drill on his lease for any of a variety of reasons. The farmor may not have the money to do his own drilling, or he may doubt that the acreage will repay the effort. He may have more good prospects in hand than he can afford to drill. Or he may have drilled a dry hole and decided to farm out the acreage rather than sell or abandon the lease. If a farmor holds leases with early expiration dates, he may want to extend them beyond the primary terms by means of production. If a farmor is in a hurry for production or simply for information that will help him decide whether to invest in lease renewals, farming out may be the most economical way to achieve his objectives.

In any event, a farmee agrees to fulfill certain drilling, and possibly other, obligations in return for an assigned interest in the land. Such a trade can be fairly simple—for example, the exchange of a leasehold and its rights for a well drilled by a specified date. Or it can be very complicated—involving money contributions as well as acreage, elaborate plans for exploration, and an agreement to begin joint operations at some particular point in the undertaking. Again it should be emphasized that no two agreements are quite the same. The details will depend on the parties' goals in a given situation.

Form types and letter types. Some farmouts are drawn up as formal contracts or filled in on preprinted commercial forms (fig. 9.2 at the end of the chapter). Large companies may have their own highly detailed forms, though many still prefer to use the letter agreements (fig. 9.3 at the end of the chapter) that have been customary in the industry for a number of years. Letter agreements tend to be shorter and less complicated than formal contracts; their relative simplicity makes them attractive

to business people in a hurry. Attorneys seem to be divided between those who deplore the persistence of informal letter agreements and those who see them as adequate for many if not most farmouts. Whether a formal or an informal agreement is used, the farmor normally (though not invariably) prepares the farmout.

Some typical provisions and appendages. In most farmouts, the farmor does not warrant title to the leased acreage but does give the farmee any abstracts or other title information that have been collected to that point. The farmee agrees to drill a test well according to the conditions specified and usually serves as the *operator* (the party who oversees and takes responsibility for operations like drilling). Conditions commonly include a date for the beginning of operations, a location and projected depth for the well, and often a time limit within which the well must be completed. The operator agrees to assume all the costs and risks of drilling, thereby freeing the farmor from liability for third-party claims. (If the operator didn't assume these costs and risks, the parties might unintentionally create a kind of partnership that leaves *both* liable.) Finally, the operator agrees to supply the farmor with specified kinds of information.

Many farmouts, like money support agreements, do not contractually oblige the operator to drill. If the described conditions are not met, the operator forfeits any rights still to be earned, and the agreement comes to an end. Upon meeting the conditions, however, the farmee earns certain rights set out in the contract. These rights can take a variety of forms. One of the simplest would be the assignment of a 100 percent working interest in the drill site. The farmor might also assign a designated undivided interest in other land included in the farmout acreage. (For the tax consequences of this kind of arrangement, see below.) Very often, the farmor assigns a

100 percent working interest in the drill site and retains an overriding royalty, while also assigning an interest in acreage outside the drill site. For example, when the farmee can earn additional 100 percent working interests in the four drilling units that corner on the drill site, he has what is known as a *checkerboard* farmout.

An overriding royalty is only one of the possible kinds of reservations that a farmor might make. He might retain rights to certain depths, for instance, or to certain specified substances. He might make his override permanent or make it convertible to an agreed-upon working interest. An overriding royalty that can be converted to a working interest creates what is known as a *back-in* farmout. The farmor can come back in as a working interest owner (typically, of 25–50 percent) once the well has paid for itself. The point at which the farmor decides whether or not to come back in can also vary. Often the choice will be made at *payout*. A well reaches the payout point when the operator has recouped his costs. What the well earns and what it has cost to drill, test, equip, and complete come into balance, and the well begins to show a profit. A farmor might arrange to exercise his back-in option at final completion or at *casing point*. An election at casing point is a decision made when the operator notifies all interested parties of his recommendation to run casing and complete the well. (One of a farmee's obligations is to keep the farmor informed about the status of his choice point.)

Other common provisions of farmouts are reassignment obligations and AMIs, or areas of mutual interest. An *area of mutual interest* is usually outlined on a plat in order to give the parties first right of refusal on leases acquired by either party after the farmout is executed. Similarly, a farmee who earns an interest in acreage that he later decides to

drop must, if his farmout includes a *reassignment obligation,* offer the acreage back to the farmor before allowing the lease to expire. Farmout agreements generally conclude with provisions for insurance and a deadline for acceptance.

A number of exhibits or appendages may be attached to a farmout. These may include an exhibit describing the leases to be earned, along with a plat of the acreage, especially if more than one lease is involved. A plat showing the AMI may also be attached. Some farmouts have an exhibit that sets out precisely all the drilling and testing requirements, together with the notices and information that must be supplied by the farmee. With an eye to the future, many farmors attach a joint operating agreement, which comes into effect if the first well produces and the farmor decides to come back in. A final exhibit will be an unexecuted copy of the assignment that will be earned.

Tax consequences of farmouts. Before 1977, a typical farmout often earned the farmee a 40–50 percent working interest in acreage outside the drill site. The amount and location of this acreage varied from one agreement to another. In 1977, however, the Internal Revenue Service issued Revenue Ruling 77-176, which had a drastic adverse effect on this kind of farmout. The IRS held that the farmee acquired and the farmor retained two distinct properties—two parcels of acreage in the case of the farmee and, in the case of the farmor, an overriding royalty interest in the drill site and (usually) a 50 percent working interest in the outside acreage. The farmee was required to report as ordinary income the full fair market value of the interest in non-drill-site land. The farmor was viewed as having sold that interest; any gain realized from the sale has to be added to his tax basis in the retained overriding royalty.

The burden of treating paper profit as realized income was considerable. Various suggestions were offered on how to soften the impact of the ruling, but only one gained widespread acceptance. That is the formation of a tax partnership between the parties. Such an arrangement means extra paperwork, especially at tax return filing, but the benefits can be substantial. (For the differences between a formal partnership and a tax partnership, as well as a discussion of the issues involved in Revenue Ruling 77-176, see Timothy M. Larason, "How to Structure the Farmout and Avoid Its Pitfalls," in *Basics of Structuring Exploration Deals,* ed. Lewis G. Mosburg, Jr., Oklahoma City; IED Exploration, 1980, 395–402.)

Encumbrances on Oil and Gas Leases. In acquiring an existing oil and gas lease by assignment from the current lessee, the assignee should become fully aware of any encumbrances placed on the lease by the actions of the assignee or previous lessees. For example, a previous lessee may have dedicated all or part of the gas to be produced from the lease to the performance of a gas sales contract, and the assignee may be legally bound to honor that commitment if a release has not been obtained.

OTHER AGREEMENTS FOR ACQUISITION OF ACREAGE

Lease Purchase Agreements

Another kind of transaction commonly set out in a letter agreement is the lease purchase. Lease purchase is probably the simplest way to acquire acreage. One company buys a block of leases from another company that has already set up files for them and outlined them on its plat of the area. Whether or not the seller keeps an interest in the acreage, whether or not he serves as the operator when the land is explored and developed are details that vary with the sale. The exhibits and additions to the basic letter of agreement can be much like those attached to a farmout, depending on the number of leases involved and any special provisions required.

Options to Explore with Acreage Selection Privileges

An agreement concerning options to explore with acreage selection privileges is basically the seismic option discussed in chapter 5. There, a company is described as securing large blocks of acreage from a land-owner by offering a price (say, $10 per acre) for all the acreage it is interested in. After exploration, which usually includes the gathering of seismic data, the company can—by the terms of the agreement—lease selected acreage that it judges to be the most promising. (The price for the selected acreage might be an additional $100 per acre.) This kind of agreement can be negotiated between petroleum companies as well as between companies and landowners. One company may wish to explore, with acreage selection privileges, leaseholds belonging to another company. If the lessee is not interested in developing the leases immediately, it may be responsive to such an offer.

JOINT OPERATING AGREEMENTS

When two or more co-owners of the operating rights in a tract of land join together to share the costs of exploration and possible development, they often do so by means of a joint operating agreement. The agreement names one of the owners as the operator and specifies how drilling is to be managed and how the costs of the undertaking are to be shared. A joint operating agreement is a complex contract for which there are model forms available. Since no form covers all possible arrangements, however, individually drafted agreements are sometimes still necessary.

As noted earlier, joint operating agreements often follow farmouts. When a test well produces in paying quantities, farmor and farmee — having become co-owners of the rights to drill for and produce minerals — may join together to continue operations. Joint operating agreements also make possible expensive explorations that no single party could attempt alone. The drilling of a deep wildcat well, for instance, can be undertaken by a group of investors or lease-owning operators who sign a joint operating agreement. In addition to exploratory operations, pooling may — and field-wide unitization almost certainly will — require operating agreements. (Pooling and unitization agreements will be discussed in the next chapter.)

Joint Operations and Joint Ventures

The chief reason to distinguish between a joint operating agreement and a joint venture is to clarify the kinds of liability that nonoperators may be subject to. A key characteristic of the *joint venture* is joint (called *solidary* in Louisiana) as well as several (separate) liability for third-party claims.

Joint venturers may all be held accountable for what any one of them does. Since joint operating agreements are built on delegated management, with a number of key decisions and responsibilities given to the operator, nonoperators naturally wish to avoid joint liability. For example, if someone sues the operator for damages owing to an injury sustained through the operator's negligence, the nonoperators don't want to be liable for the operator's carelessness. Clauses disclaiming joint liability are usually written into the agreements, but do these clauses hold up in court? If a judge decided that a third-party claim had merit, could he hold that nonoperators were joint venturers? Or could he decide that operator and nonoperators had unintentionally created a partnership that implied joint liability?

The answers to these questions vary from state to state and from one agreement to another. In general, Texas courts have not held that nonoperators are jointly liable and have supported the disclaimers written into operating agreements. Outside Texas, the law may be more ambiguous. Courts in other states have sometimes held that operating agreements amounted to a kind of joint venture called a mining partnership. (A *mining partnership* differs from a general partnership in several ways. For present purposes, it may be noted that the three requirements of a mining partnership are: joint ownership, joint operations, and a sharing of profits and losses. The similarity to a joint operating agreement is clear.)

Crucial to court decisions seems to be the amount of control, and even the right to control, enjoyed by nonoperators. If the parties to a joint operating agreement expect to play any active role — giving advice, arranging credit, and so forth—it may be that their view of the undertaking can be reconciled only with a true joint venture. To be certain of avoiding joint liability, nonoperators would have to form a statutory limited partnership that would effectively deny them any voice in operational matters. In Texas, nonoperators may wish to rely on the courts to find disclaimers of joint liability acceptable. Elsewhere, nonoperators will need to consider the matter carefully and structure their agreements so as to give themselves a degree of control appropriate to their aims and intended responsibilities.

Model Forms

As joint operating agreements became longer, more detailed, and more expensive to prepare, some standardization began to seem desirable. When every company and virtually every operator had a favorite form, agreeing to agree was a lengthy process often accompanied by confusion and carping. The situation was remedied in 1956 after a group of landmen and attorneys from several companies had completed its study of the industry's needs. The results of their efforts included a model form, which became available in 1965 and was slightly modified in 1967. Model Form Operating Agreement-1956 was then used widely until changing conditions in the industry required substantial revisions, which were completed in 1977. Model Form 610-1977 has since been superseded by Model Form 610-1982. AAPL (American Association of Petroleum Landmen) Model Form 610-1982 does not, of course, meet everyone's situation. The Rocky Mountain area, for example, has special forms that allow for the probable presence of federal leases. Canada has its own forms, and offshore activities often need specially drafted agreements. But the model form has proved

very useful, and it will be assumed in the general discussion that follows (fig. 9.4 at the end of the chapter).

Some standard provisions. The amended and reorganized Model Form of 1982 includes provisions that describe the lands and leases that make up the contract area, and it specifies the sharing of costs and revenues among the parties, including their rights to production. The parties' liabilities are set down, and an attempt is made to limit those of the nonoperators. A subsection also allows the parties to disclaim, if they wish, any intention of forming a partnership. Each lease owner is responsible for paying the royalties, overrides, and other production payments that burden his own leases, along with any rentals or shut-in well payments that may accrue under the terms of his leases.

The conditions for drilling the first well are laid down, the operator named, and provisions made for his removal should that become necessary. The operator's powers and obligations, together with the limits on his authority, are described. Special rights of the parties, like preferential right of purchase, are listed. A number of miscellaneous provisions cover matters like title, access, abandonment, notice, and so forth. A few terms and concepts not previously encountered in the present discussion are considered separately below.

AFEs. The operator may pay exploration expenses and bill nonoperators for their proportionate share. Or he may estimate his monthly operating expenses and ask for advance payment from nonoperators. In any case, before he starts to work, the operator will obtain nonoperators' consent to any proposed expenses by preparing an *AFE* (Authority for Expenditure) and sending it out for the nonoperators to sign. The AFE estimates the costs of whatever work the operator plans to do. AFEs, it should be noted, are prepared for all sorts of operational functions, not merely for those involved in the drilling of an initial well.

Subsequent operations. A joint operating agreement provides for operations subsequent to the initial test well—even if all the parties do not agree to such operations. *Nonconsent* with an agreed-upon penalty to a later operation proposed by one of the parties can be imposed if that operation takes place and is productive. (If it is not productive, the penalty cannot be applied.) The penalty for nonconsent usually works in one of two ways: as a percentage of costs or as exclusion from the operation. For example, consenting parties can recoup the costs attributable to the interest of nonconsenting parties out of the proceeds from the oil or gas that would otherwise go to the nonconsenting parties. However, those who consent will receive 200 or 300 percent of the nonconsenting parties' share of such costs. Once this penalty has been paid out, nonconsentors can come back in for their share of the profits. A more severe penalty would completely exclude nonconsentors from the operation, though they could, if they chose, come back in for other, later operations.

Accounting procedures. The accounting procedure attached to a joint operating agreement specifies the methods to be used by the operator in charging and accounting for all the expenses of operating the joint property. The procedure is therefore crucial to the daily use of the joint account. Over the years, this procedure has been standardized by the work of various groups, most recently that of the Council of Petroleum Accountants Societies of North America, or COPAS. The COPAS accounting procedure is available with options that meet the different problems found in the Midcontinent and on the West Coast. Operations in western Canada use a procedure known as PASWC, after the Petroleum Accountants Society of Western Canada.

Tax Considerations

Generally, each party to a joint operating agreement is taxed by the IRS as if he were drilling alone. This rule applies as long as each party's share of the costs is the same as his share of the working interest. In a consent/nonconsent arrangement, the parties who drill must take care to keep the full operating rights until payout is complete.

A word might also be said on the subject of prepayments for work performed later in, or after, the end of the tax year. Some operators require prepayments from their drilling partners to ensure the timely payment of drilling and completion costs. *Turnkey* drilling contracts in which the contractor furnishes all equipment and performs all work needed to place a well on production are also sometimes prepaid. Prepayments, however, have become rarer as the IRS has become more inclined to scrutinize drilling deductions. These days, to claim all drilling deductions successfully, operators usually need to demonstrate that work—sometimes only the staking of a well, but preferably the actual drilling—is going on at the drill site before the end of the tax year.

Figure 9.1. Dry hole contribution letter (Courtesy of Conoco)

Continental Oil Company
Western Hemisphere Petroleum Division
P.O. Box 2197
Houston, Texas 77001
(713) 225-1511

June 25, 1973

Signal Oil & Gas Company
1111 Fannin Street
Houston, Texas   77002

Attention: Mr. Joe Edwards

Gentlemen:

Subject: Dry Hole Contribution - Grand Isle Area, Block 65
Offshore Louisiana

You have advised of your intentions to drill a test well at a location
approximately 2200 feet from the East line and 600 feet from the North
line of Grand Isle Block 65, being OCS Lease No. 2158. Provided you
begin the test well by August 1, 1973, Continental Oil Company, Getty
Oil Company and Cities Service Oil Company, acting through their designated Operator, Continental Oil Company, will contribute dry hole money
as provided below and under the following conditions:

   1. That said test well be drilled to a vertical depth of 13,000'
      from the derrick floor unless salt water flow, heaving shale
      or an impenetrable formation is encountered which in the
      opinion of a reasonably prudent operator under the same or
      similar conditions would make further drilling impracticable
      or hazardous; or to such depth as there should be encountered
      abnormal pressure that would require a prudent operator to set
      protective casing prior to drilling further.

   2. During the drilling of said test well, you shall furnish free the
      following to:

                     Continental Oil Company
                     CAGC Marine Operations, Mr. J. H. Liddell
                     3010 General DeGaulle Drive
                     New Orleans, Louisiana
                     Telephone: Office: (504) 368-3000
                                Home: (504) 362-4500

Figure 9.1—*Continued*

Signal Oil & Gas Company
June 25, 1973
Page 2

(a) Daily drilling reports and all geological information
secured in the drilling of the well.

(b) Samples, cores and other information taken from or gained
by drilling the well.

(c) Notification of all coring and testing to be done, in sufficient time to have same witnessed if CGC so desires.

(d) Make and furnish the results of such tests of indicated
shows of oil and/or gas as are consistent in the industry
by prudent operators.

(e) Six (6) copies of all logs run in the well.

(f) Access of CGC representatives to use of your transportation facilities and access to the derrick floor, all at
the sole risk of CGC.

3. Provided said well is timely commenced and that operations are
prosecuted therein diligently and without undue delay, and the
well is plugged and abandoned without capabilities of re-entry
for producing purposes, Continental Oil Company, Getty Oil
Company and Cities Service Oil Company will pay you as a dry
hole contribution, a total sum not to exceed $120,000.00 calcu-
lated as follows:

$5.00 per foot for each vertical foot of hole
drilled and logged to a vertical depth of 10,000'
from the derrick floor;

$25.00 per foot for each vertical foot of hole
drilled and logged at a depth greater than 10,000'
to a vertical depth of 13,000'.

If you fail to commence and drill said test well as provided above, this
agreement at our option shall become null and void and we will be relieved
of any further obligation hereunder.

Figure 9.1—*Continued*

Signal Oil & Gas Company
June 25, 1973
Page   3

It is also agreed that Continental, as Operator for itself, Getty Oil Company and Cities Service Oil Company shall have the option to run a velocity survey in the well when it reaches total depth. If Continental elects to run such survey and you elect to join, Continental will supervise such survey with Signal, et al, and Continental, et al, each bearing 1/2 of all costs, risk and expense and each receiving all information gained. If you do not elect to join, Continental may at its option make such a survey at its sole cost risk and expense, retaining such information as its property and holding you harmless from damages which may result from said survey.

If you are agreeable to the terms of this letter agreement, please sign and return three (3) of the attached copies within fifteen (15) days from the date of this letter.

Yours very truly,

CONTINENTAL OIL COMPANY

By _Henry A. Hill_
   Henry A. Hill

AGREED TO this 28 day of
June, 1973.

SIGNAL OIL & GAS COMPANY

By _D. G. H._

Individually, and as Operator for the
SLAM Group, also comprised of:
The Louisiana Land and Exploration
   Company
Amerada Hess Corporation and
Marathon Oil Company

**Figure 9.2. AAPL Form 635, Farmout Agreement
(Courtesy of AAPL and Kraftbilt Products)**

AMERICAN ASSOCIATION OF PETROLEUM LANDMEN
APPROVED FORM   A.A.P.L. NO. 635
MAY BE ORDERED DIRECTLY FROM THE PUBLISHER
KRAFTBILT PRODUCTS,   BOX 800   TULSA, OK 74101

AAPL FORM 635
FARMOUT AGREEMENT

DATE:

TO: RE:

In consideration of the benefits to accrue to the parties hereto and the covenants and obligations to be kept by you, it is hereby mutually agreed as follows:

I ACREAGE:

We represent without Warranty of Title of any kind or character that we hold Oil and Gas Leases or Mineral Interests described as follows:

We agree to deliver to you such abstracts and other title papers as we have in our files at this time, and at your sole cost, risk and expense you agree to conduct such Title Examinations and secure such curative matter as is necessary to satisfy yourselves that Title is acceptable to you.

Figure 9.2—*Continued*

II OBLIGATIONS:

(A) TEST WELL: On or before the____day of_____, 19____, you agree to commence, or cause to be commenced the actual drilling of a well for oil and/or gas at the following location:

and you further agree to drill said Test Well with due diligence in a workmanlike manner to a depth sufficient to thoroughly test the following:

(B) COMPLETION OR ABANDONMENT: When the Test Well has reached its total depth, you agree:

   (1)   That if the Well can be completed as a producer of oil and/or gas to diligently prosecute the completion of said Well without unreasonable delays; or,

   (2)   If you determine to abandon the Well you will promptly furnish us with an appropriate electrical log acceptable to us and you further agree that you will not abandon the Well as a dry hole until you have furnished said electrical log to us and thereafter given us at least 48 hours notice of your intention to abandon, unless we consent to an earlier abandonment thereof. After consent has been given, you agree to promptly plug and abandon the Test Well in accordance with all the requirements of any governmental body having jurisdiction.

III FAILURE TO DRILL:

The only consequence of your failure to drill the proposed Test Well hereinabove provided for shall be the ipso facto cancellation of this Agreement in its entirety.

IV COMMITMENT:

UPON WRITTEN REQUEST, and after completion of the Test Well provided for hereinabove in accordance with all the terms and provisions of this Agreement to our satisfaction, we agree:

Figure 9.2 – *Continued*

V INFORMATION AND REPORTS:

As a further express Consideration for this Agreement, and not as a covenant only, you agree to furnish to:

the following:

1. (a) DAILY DRILLING REPORTS on the progress of the well which shall include drilling depth, information on all tests including character, thickness, name of any formation penetrated, shows of oil, gas or water, and detailed reports on all drillstem tests.

   (b) _____Certified Copies of all forms furnished to any governmental authority.

   (c) _____Copies of all electrical logging surveys.

   (d) _____Certified Copies of the well log upon completion.

   (e) _____Certified Copies of the plugging record, if any.

   (f) Samples of all cores and cuttings, if so requested.

2. Other Information Required:

VI PRODUCTION TESTS:

You agree to properly drillstem test any and all formations in which shows of oil and/or gas are encountered after notifying us of the proposed test and if we desire to be present during testing, you will delay such testing a reasonable amount of time in order to allow our representative to reach the well and witness the test, and you also agree to notify us immediately by telephone or telegraph as to the results of any such test. Notification shall be given to:

Name:
Address:
Telephone No.:
Night Telephone No.:

Figure 9.2 – *Continued*

It is understood that our representatives shall have access to the rig floor at all times and to any and all information concerning the Test Well.

VII DELAY RENTALS:

It is agreed that from and after the date of this Agreement we will pay any delay rentals which may become due on the Oil and Gas Leases subject to this Agreement until such time as the Assignment provided for in Section IV above has been executed, and thereafter bill you for _____ of the delay rental paid by us.

VIII CONSENT REQUIREMENT:

This Agreement is personal in nature and may not be assigned without our written consent being first obtained. When requesting consent to make an assignment of all or a portion of this Agreement you will advise the parties to whom the assignment will be made.

IX STATUS OF PARTIES:

In the drilling of the Test Well and otherwise complying with the terms and provisions of this Agreement, you are acting independently of us and not as a partner in any capacity, mining or otherwise. We shall have no responsibility whatsoever in connection with the drilling of said well and it shall be drilled at your sole cost, risk and expense. You further agree to hold us harmless from any and all debts, claims or damages incurred in connection with the performance of this Agreement.

In regard to all provisions of this Agreement, it is understood and agreed that Time is of the Essence.

X OTHER PROVISIONS:

Figure 9.2—*Continued*

If the terms and provisions of this Agreement in its entirety are acceptable to you, will you kindly indicate your approval by signing below in the space provided and returning _____ executed copies of this Agreement to us within _____ days. Failure to do so will result in the cancellation of this Agreement at our option.

_____

This Agreement is APPROVED

and ACCEPTED this _____ day

of _____ , 19___ .

_____

Figure 9.3. Farmout agreement letter
(Courtesy of Conoco and McMoran Offshore Exploration Co.)

Continental Oil Company
P. O. Box 2197
Houston, Texas 77001

March 5, 1979

McMoRan Offshore Exploration Company
P. O. Box 6800
Metairie, Louisiana   70009

Attention: Mr. C. M. Van Zandt, Jr.

Gentlemen:

Subject: Farmout Agreement, OCS Lease G-2552, West Cameron Area,
          South Addition, Block 538, Offshore Louisiana, C# 19892

1.   Continental Oil Company, Atlantic Richfield Company, Getty Oil Company
and Cities Service Company, hereinafter referred to as "CAGC" are the owners
and holders in equal proportions of the following oil and gas lease, hereinafter referred to as "the lease," situated Offshore Louisiana, to wit:

          OCS Lease No. G-2552, dated effective May 1, 1974, between
          the United States of America, acting through the Manager,
          New Orleans Outer Continental Shelf Office of the Bureau of
          Land Management, as Lessor, and CAGC, as Lessee, covering
          and affecting lands described as Block 538, West Cameron
          Area, South Addition, as shown on official leasing map,
          Louisiana Map No. 1B Outer Continental Shelf Leasing Map,
          containing 5,000 acres, more or less.

2.   By your acceptance hereof in the space provided below, it is hereby
mutually agreed by and between CAGC and McMoRan Offshore Exploration Company,
hereinafter referred to as "McMoRan," that McMoRan shall have the right to
acquire certain interests in the lease, as hereinafter provided, by completing the drilling of a certain well within the time and in the manner hereinafter set out, subject to the provisions hereof, to wit:

     A.   On or before April 15, 1979, McMoRan shall commence the actual
          drilling of an exploratory test well on the lease at a location
          of its choice, hereinafter called "first test well," and shall there-
          after drill said first test well at its sole cost, risk and expense
          with due diligence and dispatch, and in a good and workmanlike
          manner until it reaches the "objective depth," which is defined
          as 8,500 feet vertical measured depth subsea (-5,000 feet) or,
          as further set out herein, until conditions are encountered which
          would, in the opinion of a prudent operator render further drill-
          ing impractical.

Figure 9.3—*Continued*

McMoRan Offshore Exploration Company
March 5, 1979
Page 2

  B.   If, in the drilling of the test well, salt, salt water flow,
       heaving shale or other impenetrable substances or conditions,
       including loss of the hole from mechanical difficulties, are
       encountered, which in the opinion of a reasonably prudent oper-
       ator under the same or similar conditions would render further
       drilling impracticable or hazardous (hereinafter called "impene-
       trable conditions" or alternately "am impossible condition"),
       McMoRan shall, at its option, notify CAGC within thirty (30) days
       after abandonment of the first test well, of McMoRan's commitment
       to commence the actual drilling of a substitute well on the lease
       within sixty (60) days after abandonment of the first well and
       shall thereafter drill same under identical terms and conditions
       as provided for in the first test well.

  C.   Should the first test well (or any substitute therefor) reach the
       above described depth of 8,500 feet and result in a dry hole, or
       fail to reach said depth of 8,500 feet because of impenetrables or
       other conditions as described in Paragraph 2 B, McMoRan shall have
       the option to drill successive wells in an effort to complete a
       well as capable of producing oil and/or gas as approved by the
       U.S.G.S. provided that McMoRan, not later than thirty (30) days
       after abandonment of the last well drilled, shall notify CAGC that
       McMoRan commits to drill a successive well; and provided further
       that actual drilling of such successive well shall commence not
       later than sixty (60) days after abandonment of said last well
       drilled. Each successive well shall be drilled in accordance with
       the terms and conditions specified in Paragraph 2 A for the first
       test well.

3.   During the drilling of all wells on OCS-G 2552, McMoRan shall furnish,
free of charge, the following to:
                              Mr. Mal Liddle
                              Continental Oil Company
                              Louisiana Savings Building
                              901 Lakeshore Drive
                              Lake Charles, Louisiana 70601
                              Telephone: Office (318) 491-5211
                                          Home   (318) 855-2557

  A.   Daily drilling reports and all geological information secured in the
       drilling of any well.

Figure 9.3 — *Continued*

McMoRan Offshore Exploration Company
March 5, 1979
Page 3

        B.   Samples, cores and other information taken from or gained by drilling any well.

        C.   Notification of all coring and testing to be done in sufficient time to have same witnessed if CAGC so desires.

        D.   Make and furnish the results of such tests of indicated shows of oil and/or gas as are consistent with practices in the industry by prudent operators.

        E.   Seven (7) copies of all logs run in any well.

        F.   Access of CAGC representatives to use of McMoRan transportation facilities and access to the derrick floor, all at the sole risk of CAGC.

        G.   "Disposition Information" as to whether McMoRan plans to plug and abandon said well, or to complete it for production, or some other alternative. The disposition information shall be detailed and as complete as possible, including the estimated costs of completion and producing facilities.

4.   All information (other than samples) furnished to CAGC relative to drilling said test well or wells shall be in writing or be confirmed in writing.

5.   Should McMoRan drill said test well to the objective depth and encounter production in paying quantities, as approved by the U.S.G.S. under OCS Order No. 4, then in that event McMoRan shall receive within thirty (30) days from rig release on the test well, an assignment of CAGC interest in the lease according to the terms below and at the option of CAGC:

        A.   One hundred percent (100%) of their right, title and interest in OCS-G 2552 subject to the retention of a 1/12th of 6/6ths overriding royalty interest by CAGC, said overriding royalty to be free and clear of all cost and expense except for its proportionate share of taxes on production; or

        B.   An undivided seventy percent (70%) of their right, title and interest in the lease; and

                One hundred percent (100%) interest in the test well subject to CAGC retaining a 1/12th of 6/6ths overriding royalty

Figure 9.3 – *Continued*

McMoRan Offshore Exploration Company
March 5, 1979
Page 4

        until payout. "Payout" is defined as that point in time
when McMoRan has, from all the production from the test
well, after the deduction of lessor's royalty, operating
expenses, CAGC's overriding royalty and taxes on production,
recovered the cost of drilling, testing and completing the
test well through the wellhead. CAGC shall elect within
thirty (30) days after being notified that payout has been
achieved to:

       (i)   retain 1/12th of 6/6ths overriding royalty interest
           in the well; or

      (ii)   convert said overriding royalty interest in the well
           to an undivided thirty (30) percent interest in the
           well, the production therefrom and the equipment
           thereon; or

  C.   An assignment of all of CAGC's right, title and interest in the
      subject lease, subject to the reservation of a production payment
      to CAGC in the amount of five million dollars ($5,000,000) payable
      out of ten percent (10%) of the oil, gas and condensate produced
      and saved from the subject lease, after deducting the propor-
      tionate share of ten percent (10%) of the lease royalty,
      operating expenses and production taxes.

Said assignment to McMoRan shall be without warranty of title expressed
or implied, and subject to the approval of the Bureau of Land Management.

6. A.   In the event McMoRan earns an interest in the lease as provided in
      Paragraph 5 above, McMoRan and CAGC shall enter into an operating
      agreement naming McMoRan as operator, on a mutually agreeable form.
      Such agreement shall provide for "non-consent" operations in which
      fewer than all parties participate, the participants shall bear
      all expenses and shall own all the production from the well in
      question until, after deducting Lessor's royalty, applicable taxes,
      and operating expenses, they have recovered 600% of the cost of
      such operations.

   B.   The Accounting Procedure attached hereto and made a part hereof as
      Exhibit "A" shall be used in said operating agreement.

Figure 9.3— *Continued*

McMoRan Offshore Exploration Company
March 5, 1979
Page 5

    C.   McMoRan recognizes that CAGC are now under a joint agreement which
        shall continue to cover operations between CAGC insofar as practi-
        cal and McMoRan realizes that the interest as between CAGC may
        change pursuant to said agreement.

7.   All notices to be given hereunder, except those specified in Paragraph 3
above, shall be given to the parties at the following addresses:

                 Continental Oil Company
                 P. O. Box 2197
                 Houston, Texas   77001

                   Attention: Mr. H. A. Hill

                 McMoRan Offshore Exploration Company
                 P. O. Box 6800
                 Metairie, Louisiana   70009

                   Attention: Mr. C. M. Van Zandt, Jr.

Continental Oil Company will receive all notices and make all replies on behalf
of CAGC.

8.   Any assignment of rights under (a) this agreement, or (b) the assignment
earned pursuant to this agreement, shall not be binding on CAGC until CAGC
assents thereto in writing. If more than one party holds rights which derive
from (a) or (b) above, they shall name one party to give and receive notices
on behalf of all.

9.   Continental, as Operator for CAGC, shall make a good faith effort to
pay any delay rental or similar lease payment falling due subsequent to the
date of this agreement and prior to McMoRan's earning an interest in the lease,
and shall be reimbursed in full therefor by McMoRan. CAGC shall incur no
liability for failure to make any such payment if Continental acts in good
faith and follows its usual procedures with regard thereto. Upon McMoRan's
earning an interest in the lease, the expense of delay rentals and similar
lease payments shall be borne proportionately in accordance therewith, and
such payments shall be made by McMoRan as operator.

Figure 9.3—*Continued*

McMoRan Offshore Exploration Company
March 5, 1979
Page 6

10.   McMoRan and CAGC hereby consent as to this Farmout Agreement to operate
under the tax partnership provisions attached hereto as Exhibit "B."

This agreement may be executed in counterparts, which shall be considered
collectively as if all executing parties signed one and the same copy.

If the above letter correctly states your understanding of our agreement,
please execute in the space provided and return five (5) copies to Continental
Oil Company at the above address.

Yours very truly,

CONTINENTAL OIL COMPANY   ACCEPTED AND AGREED TO this _____

                                           day of _____, 1979.

By_____

                                           MCMORAN OFFSHORE EXPLORATION COMPANY

ATLANTIC RICHFIELD COMPANY

By_____   By_____

GETTY OIL COMPANY

By_____

CITIES SERVICE COMPANY

By_____

Figure 9.4. AAPL Form 610-1982, Model Form Operating Agreement
(Courtesy of AAPL)

A.A.P.L. FORM 610-1982

MODEL FORM OPERATING AGREEMENT

OPERATING AGREEMENT

DATED

——————— , 19 —— ,

OPERATOR _____

CONTRACT AREA _____

_____

_____

COUNTY OR PARISH OF _____ STATE OF _____

Figure 9.4 — *Continued*

GUIDANCE IN THE PREPARATION OF THIS AGREEMENT:

1. Title Page - Fill in blanks as applicable.

2. Preamble, Page 1 - Enter name of Operator.

3. Article II - Exhibits:
    (a) Indicate Exhibits to be attached.
    (b) If it is desired that no reference be made to non-discrimination, the reference to Exhibit ''F'' should be deleted.

4. Article III.B. - Interests of Parties in Costs and Production - Enter royalty fraction as agreed to by parties.

5. Article IV.A. - Title Examination - Select option as agreed to by the parties.

6. Article IV.B. - Loss of Title - If ''Joint Loss'' of Title is desired, the following changes should be made:
    (a) Delete Articles IV.B.1 and IV.B.2.
    (b) Article IV.B.3 - Delete phrase ''other than those set forth in Articles IV.B.1 and IV.B.2 above.''
    (c) Article VII.E. - Change reference at end of the first grammatical paragraph from ''Article IV.B.2'' to ''Article IV.B.3.''
    (d) Article X. - Add as the concluding sentence - ''All claims or suits involving title to any interest subject to this agreement shall be treated as a claim or a suit against all parties hereto.''

7. Article V - Operator - Enter name of Operator.

8. Article VI.A - Initial Well:
    (a) Date of commencement of drilling.
    (b) Location of well.
    (c) Obligation depth.

9. Article VI.B.2.(b) - Subsequent Operations - Enter penalty percentage as agreed to by parties.

10. Article VI.C. - Taking Production in Kind - If a Gas Balancing Agreement is not in existence nor attached hereto as Exhibit ''E'', then use Alternate Page 8.

11. Article VII.D.1. - Limitation of Expenditures - Select option as agreed to by parties.

12. Article VII.D.3. - Limitation of Expenditures - Enter limitation of expenditure of Operator for single project and amount above which Operator may furnish information AFE.

13. Article IX. - Internal Revenue Code Election - Delete this article in the event the agreement is a Tax Partnership and Exhibit ''G'' is attached.

14. Article X. - Claims and Lawsuits - Enter claim limit as agreed to by parties.

15. Article XIII. - Term of Agreement:
    (a) Select Option as agreed to by parties.
    (b) If Option No. 2 is selected, enter agreed number of days in two (2) blanks.

16. Article XIV.B - Governing Law - Enter state as agreed to by parties.

17. Signature Page - Enter effective date.

Figure 9.4 – *Continued*

1 OPERATING AGREEMENT

3 THIS AGREEMENT, entered into by and between_____

4 _____, hereinafter designated and
5 referred to as ''Operator'', and the signatory party or parties other than Operator, sometimes hereinafter referred to individually herein
6 as ''Non-Operator'', and collectively as ''Non-Operators''.

8 WITNESSETH:

10 WHEREAS, the parties to this agreement are owners of oil and gas leases and/or oil and gas interests in the land identified in
11 Exhibit ''A'', and the parties hereto have reached an agreement to explore and develop these leases and/or oil and gas interests for the
12 production of oil and gas to the extent and as hereinafter provided,

14 NOW, THEREFORE, it is agreed as follows:

16 ARTICLE I.
17 DEFINITIONS

19 As used in this agreement, the following words and terms shall have the meanings here ascribed to them:
20 A. The term ''oil and gas'' shall mean oil, gas, casinghead gas, gas condensate, and all other liquid or gaseous hydrocarbons
21 and other marketable substances produced therewith, unless an intent to limit the inclusiveness of this term is specifically stated.
22 B. The terms ''oil and gas lease'', ''lease'' and ''leasehold'' shall mean the oil and gas leases covering tracts of land
23 lying within the Contract Area which are owned by the parties to this agreement.
24 C. The term ''oil and gas interests'' shall mean unleased fee and mineral interests in tracts of land lying within the
25 Contract Area which are owned by parties to this agreement.
26 D. The term ''Contract Area'' shall mean all of the lands, oil and gas leasehold interests and oil and gas interests intended to be
27 developed and operated for oil and gas purposes under this agreement. Such lands, oil and gas leasehold interests and oil and gas interests
28 are described in Exhibit ''A''.
29 E. The term ''drilling unit'' shall mean the area fixed for the drilling of one well by order or rule of any state or
30 federal body having authority. If a drilling unit is not fixed by any such rule or order, a drilling unit shall be the drilling unit as establish-
31 ed by the pattern of drilling in the Contract Area or as fixed by express agreement of the Drilling Parties.
32 F. The term ''drillsite'' shall mean the oil and gas lease or interest on which a proposed well is to be located.
33 G. The terms ''Drilling Party'' and ''Consenting Party'' shall mean a party who agrees to join in and pay its share of the cost of
34 any operation conducted under the provisions of this agreement.
35 H. The terms ''Non-Drilling Party'' and ''Non-Consenting Party'' shall mean a party who elects not to participate
36 in a proposed operation.

38 Unless the context otherwise clearly indicates, words used in the singular include the plural, the plural includes the
39 singular, and the neuter gender includes the masculine and the feminine.

41 ARTICLE II.
42 EXHIBITS

44 The following exhibits, as indicated below and attached hereto, are incorporated in and made a part hereof:
45 ☐ A. Exhibit ''A'', shall include the following information:
46   (1) Identification of lands subject to this agreement,
47   (2) Restrictions, if any, as to depths, formations, or substances,
48   (3) Percentages or fractional interests of parties to this agreement,
49   (4) Oil and gas leases and/or oil and gas interests subject to this agreement,
50   (5) Addresses of parties for notice purposes.

Figure 9.4—*Continued*

---

51   ☐ B. Exhibit "B", Form of Lease.
52   ☐ C. Exhibit "C", Accounting Procedure.
53   ☐ D. Exhibit "D", Insurance.
54   ☐ E. Exhibit "E", Gas Balancing Agreement.
55   ☐ F. Exhibit "F", Non-Discrimination and Certification of Non-Segregated Facilities.
56   ☐ G. Exhibit "G", Tax Partnership.
57   If any provision of any exhibit, except Exhibits "E" and "G", is inconsistent with any provision contained in the body
58   of this agreement, the provisions in the body of this agreement shall prevail.

1   ARTICLE III.
2   INTERESTS OF PARTIES
3
4   A. Oil and Gas Interests:
5
6   If any party owns an oil and gas interest in the Contract Area, that interest shall be treated for all purposes of this agreement
7   and during the term hereof as if it were covered by the form of oil and gas lease attached hereto as Exhibit "B", and the owner thereof
8   shall be deemed to own both the royalty interest reserved in such lease and the interest of the lessee thereunder.
9
10   B. Interests of Parties in Costs and Production:
11
12   Unless changed by other provisions, all costs and liabilities incurred in operations under this agreement shall be borne and
13   paid, and all equipment and materials acquired in operations on the Contract Area shall be owned, by the parties as their interests are set
14   forth in Exhibit "A". In the same manner, the parties shall also own all production of oil and gas from the Contract Area subject to the
15   payment of royalties to the extent of_____which shall be borne as hereinafter set forth.
16
17   Regardless of which party has contributed the lease(s) and/or oil and gas interest(s) hereto on which royalty is due and
18   payable, each party entitled to receive a share of production of oil and gas from the Contract Area shall bear and shall pay or deliver, or
19   cause to be paid or delivered, to the extent of its interest in such production, the royalty amount stipulated hereinabove and shall hold the
20   other parties free from any liability therefor. No party shall ever be responsible, however, on a price basis higher than the price received
21   by such party, to any other party's lessor or royalty owner, and if any such other party's lessor or royalty owner should demand and
22   receive settlement on a higher price basis, the party contributing the affected lease shall bear the additional royalty burden attributable to
23   such higher price.
24
25   Nothing contained in this Article III.B. shall be deemed an assignment or cross-assignment of interests covered hereby.
26
27   C. Excess Royalties, Overriding Royalties and Other Payments:
28
29   Unless changed by other provisions, if the interest of any party in any lease covered hereby is subject to any royalty,
30   overriding royalty, production payment or other burden on production in excess of the amount stipulated in Article III.B., such party so
31   burdened shall assume and alone bear all such excess obligations and shall indemnify and hold the other parties hereto harmless from any
32   and all claims and demands for payment asserted by owners of such excess burden.
33
34   D. Subsequently Created Interests:
35
36   If any party should hereafter create an overriding royalty, production payment or other burden payable out of production
37   attributable to its working interest hereunder, or if such a burden existed prior to this agreement and is not set forth in Exhibit "A", or
38   was not disclosed in writing to all other parties prior to the execution of this agreement by all parties, or is not a jointly acknowledged and
39   accepted obligation of all parties (any such interest being hereinafter referred to as "subsequently created interest" irrespective of the
40   timing of its creation and the party out of whose working interest the subsequently created interest is derived being hereinafter referred
41   to as "burdened party"), and:

Figure 9.4—*Continued*

---

1. If the burdened party is required under this agreement to assign or relinquish to any other party, or parties, all or a portion of its working interest and/or the production attributable thereto, said other party, or parties, shall receive said assignment and/or production free and clear of said subsequently created interest and the burdened party shall indemnify and save said other party, or parties, harmless from any and all claims and demands for payment asserted by owners of the subsequently created interest; and,

2. If the burdened party fails to pay, when due, its share of expenses chargeable hereunder, all provisions of Article VII.B. shall be enforceable against the subsequently created interest in the same manner as they are enforceable against the working interest of the burdened party.

ARTICLE IV.

TITLES

A. Title Examination:

Title examination shall be made on the drillsite of any proposed well prior to commencement of drilling operations or, if the Drilling Parties so request, title examination shall be made on the leases and/or oil and gas interests included, or planned to be included, in the drilling unit around such well. The opinion will include the ownership of the working interest, minerals, royalty, overriding royalty and production payments under the applicable leases. At the time a well is proposed, each party contributing leases and/or oil and gas interests to the drillsite, or to be included in such drilling unit, shall furnish to Operator all abstracts (including federal lease status reports), title opinions, title papers and curative material in its possession free of charge. All such information not in the possession of or made available to Operator by the parties, but necessary for the examination of the title, shall be obtained by Operator. Operator shall cause title to be examined by attorneys on its staff or by outside attorneys. Copies of all title opinions shall be furnished to each party hereto. The cost incurred by Operator in this title program shall be borne as follows:

☐ Option No. 1: Costs incurred by Operator in procuring abstracts and title examination (including preliminary, supplemental, shut-in gas royalty opinions and division order title opinions) shall be a part of the administrative overhead as provided in Exhibit "C", and shall not be a direct charge, whether performed by Operator's staff attorneys or by outside attorneys.

☐ Option No. 2: Costs incurred by Operator in procuring abstracts and fees paid outside attorneys for title examination (including preliminary, supplemental, shut-in gas royalty opinions and division order title opinions) shall be borne by the Drilling Parties in the proportion that the interest of each Drilling Party bears to the total interest of all Drilling Parties as such interests appear in Exhibit "A". Operator shall make no charge for services rendered by its staff attorneys or other personnel in the performance of the above functions.

Each party shall be responsible for securing curative matter and pooling amendments or agreements required in connection with leases or oil and gas interests contributed by such party. Operator shall be responsible for the preparation and recording of pooling designations or declarations as well as the conduct of hearings before governmental agencies for the securing of spacing or pooling orders. This shall not prevent any party from appearing on its own behalf at any such hearing.

No well shall be drilled on the Contract Area until after (1) the title to the drillsite or drilling unit has been examined as above provided, and (2) the title has been approved by the examining attorney or title has been accepted by all of the parties who are to participate in the drilling of the well.

B. Loss of Title:

1. Failure of Title: Should any oil and gas interest or lease, or interest therein, be lost through failure of title, which loss results in a reduction of interest from that shown on Exhibit "A", the party contributing the affected lease or interest shall have ninety (90) days from final determination of title failure to acquire a new lease or other instrument curing the entirety of the title failure, which acquisition will not be subject to Article VIII.B., and failing to do so, this agreement, nevertheless, shall continue in force as to all remaining oil and gas leases and interests: and,

Figure 9.4— *Continued*

(a) The party whose oil and gas lease or interest is affected by the title failure shall bear alone the entire loss and it shall not be entitled to recover from Operator or the other parties any development or operating costs which it may have theretofore paid or incurred, but there shall be no additional liability on its part to the other parties hereto by reason of such title failure;

(b) There shall be no retroactive adjustment of expenses incurred or revenues received from the operation of the interest which has been lost, but the interests of the parties shall be revised on an acreage basis, as of the time it is determined finally that title failure has occurred, so that the interest of the party whose lease or interest is affected by the title failure will thereafter be reduced in the Contract Area by the amount of the interest lost;

(c) If the proportionate interest of the other parties hereto in any producing well theretofore drilled on the Contract Area is increased by reason of the title failure, the party whose title has failed shall receive the proceeds attributable to the increase in such interest (less costs and burdens attributable thereto) until it has been reimbursed for unrecovered costs paid by it in connection with such well;

(d) Should any person not a party to this agreement, who is determined to be the owner of any interest in the title which has failed, pay in any manner any part of the cost of operation, development, or equipment, such amount shall be paid to the party or parties who bore the costs which are so refunded;

(e) Any liability to account to a third party for prior production of oil and gas which arises by reason of title failure shall be borne by the party or parties whose title failed in the same proportions in which they shared in such prior production; and,

(f) No charge shall be made to the joint account for legal expenses, fees or salaries, in connection with the defense of the interest claimed by any party hereto, it being the intention of the parties hereto that each shall defend title to its interest and bear all expenses in connection therewith.

2. <u>Loss by Non-Payment or Erroneous Payment of Amount Due</u>: If, through mistake or oversight, any rental, shut-in well payment, minimum royalty or royalty payment, is not paid or is erroneously paid, and as a result a lease or interest therein terminates, there shall be no monetary liability against the party who failed to make such payment. Unless the party who failed to make the required payment secures a new lease covering the same interest within ninety (90) days from the discovery of the failure to make proper payment, which acquisition will not be subject to Article VIII.B., the interests of the parties shall be revised on an acreage basis, effective as of the date of termination of the lease involved, and the party who failed to make proper payment will no longer be credited with an interest in the Contract Area on account of ownership of the lease or interest which has terminated. In the event the party who failed to make the required payment shall not have been fully reimbursed, at the time of the loss, from the proceeds of the sale of oil and gas attributable to the lost interest, calculated on an acreage basis, for the development and operating costs theretofore paid on account of such interest, it shall be reimbursed for unrecovered actual costs theretofore paid by it (but not for its share of the cost of any dry hole previously drilled or wells previously abandoned) from so much of the following as is necessary to effect reimbursement:

(a) Proceeds of oil and gas, less operating expenses, theretofore accrued to the credit of the lost interest, on an acreage basis, up to the amount of unrecovered costs;

(b) Proceeds, less operating expenses, thereafter accrued attributable to the lost interest on an acreage basis, of that portion of oil and gas thereafter produced and marketed (excluding production from any wells thereafter drilled) which, in the absence of such lease termination, would be attributable to the lost interest on an acreage basis, up to the amount of unrecovered costs, the proceeds of said portion of the oil and gas to be contributed by the other parties in proportion to their respective interests; and,

(c) Any monies, up to the amount of unrecovered costs, that may be paid by any party who is, or becomes, the owner of the interest lost, for the privilege of participating in the Contract Area or becoming a party to this agreement.

3. <u>Other Losses</u>: All losses incurred, other than those set forth in Articles IV.B.1. and IV.B.2. above, shall be joint losses and shall be borne by all parties in proportion to their interests. There shall be no readjustment of interests in the remaining portion of the Contract Area.

Figure 9.4–*Continued*

1	ARTICLE V.
2	OPERATOR
3	
4	A. Designation and Responsibilities of Operator:

5

6 _____shall be the
7 Operator of the Contract Area, and shall conduct and direct and have full control of all operations on the Contract Area as permitted and
8 required by, and within the limits of this agreement. It shall conduct all such operations in a good and workmanlike manner, but it shall
9 have no liability as Operator to the other parties for losses sustained or liabilities incurred, except such as may result from gross
10 negligence or willful misconduct.

11

12 B. Resignation or Removal of Operator and Selection of Successor:

13

14   1. Resignation or Removal of Operator: Operator may resign at any time by giving written notice thereof to Non-Operators.
15 If Operator terminates its legal existence, no longer owns an interest hereunder in the Contract Area, or is no longer capable of serving as
16 Operator, Operator shall be deemed to have resigned without any action by Non-Operators, except the selection of a successor. Operator
17 may be removed if it fails or refuses to carry out its duties hereunder, or becomes insolvent, bankrupt or is placed in receivership, by the
18 affirmative vote of two (2) or more Non-Operators owning a majority interest based on ownership as shown on Exhibit "A" remaining
19 after excluding the voting interest of Operator. Such resignation or removal shall not become effective until 7:00 o'clock A.M. on the
20 first day of the calendar month following the expiration of ninety (90) days after the giving of notice of resignation by Operator or action
21 by the Non-Operators to remove Operator, unless a successor Operator has been selected and assumes the duties of Operator at an earlier
22 date. Operator, after effective date of resignation or removal, shall be bound by the terms hereof as a Non-Operator. A change of a cor-
23 porate name or structure of Operator or transfer of Operator's interest to any single subsidiary, parent or successor corporation shall not
24 be the basis for removal of Operator.

25

26   2. Selection of Successor Operator: Upon the resignation or removal of Operator, a successor Operator shall be selected by
27 the parties. The successor Operator shall be selected from the parties owning an interest in the Contract Area at the time such successor
28 Operator is selected. The successor Operator shall be selected by the affirmative vote of two (2) or more parties owning a majority interest
29 based on ownership as shown on Exhibit "A"; provided, however, if an Operator which has been removed fails to vote or votes only to
30 succeed itself, the successor Operator shall be selected by the affirmative vote of two (2) or more parties owning a majority interest based
31 on ownership as shown on Exhibit "A" remaining after excluding the voting interest of the Operator that was removed.

32

33 C. Employees:

34

35   The number of employees used by Operator in conducting operations hereunder, their selection, and the hours of labor and the
36 compensation for services performed shall be determined by Operator, and all such employees shall be the employees of Operator.

37

38 D. Drilling Contracts:

39

40   All wells drilled on the Contract Area shall be drilled on a competitive contract basis at the usual rates prevailing in the area. If it so
41 desires, Operator may employ its own tools and equipment in the drilling of wells, but its charges therefor shall not exceed the prevailing
42 rates in the area and the rate of such charges shall be agreed upon by the parties in writing before drilling operations are commenced, and
43 such work shall be performed by Operator under the same terms and conditions as are customary and usual in the area in contracts of in-
44 dependent contractors who are doing work of a similar nature.

45

46

47

48

Figure 9.4 — *Continued*

49

50

51

52

ARTICLE VI.

DRILLING AND DEVELOPMENT

A. Initial Well:

53

54   On or before the_____day of_____ , 19_____ , Operator shall commence the drilling of a well for

55   oil and gas at the following location:

56

57

58

59

60   and shall thereafter continue the drilling of the well with due diligence to

61

62

63

64

65   unless granite or other practically impenetrable substance or condition in the hole, which renders further drilling impractical, is en-

66   countered at a lesser depth, or unless all parties agree to complete or abandon the well at a lesser depth.

67

68   Operator shall make reasonable tests of all formations encountered during drilling which give indication of containing oil and

69   gas in quantities sufficient to test, unless this agreement shall be limited in its application to a specific formation or formations, in which

70   event Operator shall be required to test only the formation or formations to which this agreement may apply.

1   If, in Operator's judgment, the well will not produce oil or gas in paying quantities, and it wishes to plug and abandon the

2   well as a dry hole, the provisions of Article VI.E.1. shall thereafter apply.

3

4

5

6

7

B. Subsequent Operations:

8   1. Proposed Operations: Should any party hereto desire to drill any well on the Contract Area other than the well provided

9   for in Article VI.A., or to rework, deepen or plug back a dry hole drilled at the joint expense of all parties or a well jointly owned by all

10   the parties and not then producing in paying quantities, the party desiring to drill, rework, deepen or plug back such a well shall give the

11   other parties written notice of the proposed operation, specifying the work to be performed, the location, proposed depth, objective forma-

12   tion and the estimated cost of the operation. The parties receiving such a notice shall have thirty (30) days after receipt of the notice

13   within which to notify the party wishing to do the work whether they elect to participate in the cost of the proposed operation. If a drill-

14   ing rig is on location, notice of a proposal to rework, plug back or drill deeper may be given by telephone and the response period shall be

15   limited to forty-eight (48) hours, exclusive of Saturday, Sunday and legal holidays. Failure of a party receiving such notice to reply within

16   the period above fixed shall constitute an election by that party not to participate in the cost of the proposed operation. Any notice or

17   response given by telephone shall be promptly confirmed in writing.

18

19

20

21   If all parties elect to participate in such a proposed operation, Operator shall, within ninety (90) days after expiration of the notice

22   period of thirty (30) days (or as promptly as possible after the expiration of the forty-eight (48) hour period when a drilling rig is on loca-

23   tion, as the case may be), actually commence the proposed operation and complete it with due diligence at the risk and expense of all par-

24   ties hereto; provided, however, said commencement date may be extended upon written notice of same by Operator to the other parties,

25   for a period of up to thirty (30) additional days if, in the sole opinion of Operator, such additional time is reasonably necessary to obtain

Figure 9.4—*Continued*

---

26 permits from governmental authorities, surface rights (including rights-of-way) or appropriate drilling equipment, or to complete title ex-
27 amination or curative matter required for title approval or acceptance. Notwithstanding the force majeure provisions of Article XI, if the
28 actual operation has not been commenced within the time provided (including any extension thereof as specifically permitted herein) and
29 if any party hereto still desires to conduct said operation, written notice proposing same must be resubmitted to the other parties in accor-
30 dance with the provisions hereof as if no prior proposal had been made.
31
32
33
34   2. Operations by Less than All Parties: If any party receiving such notice as provided in Article VI.B.1. or VII.D.1. (Option
35 No. 2) elects not to participate in the proposed operation, then, in order to be entitled to the benefits of this Article, the party or parties
36 giving the notice and such other parties as shall elect to participate in the operation shall, within ninety (90) days after the expiration of
37 the notice period of thirty (30) days (or as promptly as possible after the expiration of the forty-eight (48) hour period when a drilling rig is
38 on location, as the case may be) actually commence the proposed operation and complete it with due diligence. Operator shall perform all
39 work for the account of the Consenting Parties; provided, however, if no drilling rig or other equipment is on location, and if Operator is
40 a Non-Consenting Party, the Consenting Parties shall either: (a) request Operator to perform the work required by such proposed opera-
41 tion for the account of the Consenting Parties, or (b) designate one (1) of the Consenting Parties as Operator to perform such work. Con-
42 senting Parties, when conducting operations on the Contract Area pursuant to this Article VI.B.2., shall comply with all terms and con-
43 ditions of this agreement.
44
45
46
47   If less than all parties approve any proposed operation, the proposing party, immediately after the expiration of the applicable
48 notice period, shall advise the Consenting Parties of the total interest of the parties approving such operation and its recommendation as
49 to whether the Consenting Parties should proceed with the operation as proposed. Each Consenting Party, within forty-eight (48) hours
50 (exclusive of Saturday, Sunday and legal holidays) after receipt of such notice, shall advise the proposing party of its desire to (a) limit par-
51 ticipation to such party's interest as shown on Exhibit ''A'' or (b) carry its proportionate part of Non-Consenting Parties' interests, and
52 failure to advise the proposing party shall be deemed an election under (a). In the event a drilling rig is on location, the time permitted for
53 such a response shall not exceed a total of forty-eight (48) hours (<u>inclusive</u> of Saturday, Sunday and legal holidays). The proposing party,
54 at its election, may withdraw such proposal if there is insufficient participation and shall promptly notify all parties of such decision.
55
56
57
58   The entire cost and risk of conducting such operations shall be borne by the Consenting Parties in the proportions they have
59 elected to bear same under the terms of the preceding paragraph. Consenting Parties shall keep the leasehold estates involved in such
60 operations free and clear of all liens and encumbrances of every kind created by or arising from the operations of the Consenting Parties.
61 If such an operation results in a dry hole, the Consenting Parties shall plug and abandon the well and restore the surface location at their
62 sole cost, risk and expense. If any well drilled, reworked, deepened or plugged back under the provisions of this Article results in a pro-
63 ducer of oil and/or gas in paying quantities, the Consenting Parties shall complete and equip the well to produce at their sole cost and risk,
1   and the well shall then be turned over to Operator and shall be operated by it at the expense and for the account of the Consenting Par-
2   ties. Upon commencement of operations for the drilling, reworking, deepening or plugging back of any such well by Consenting Parties
3   in accordance with the provisions of this Article, each Non-Consenting Party shall be deemed to have relinquished to Consenting Parties,
4   and the Consenting Parties shall own and be entitled to receive, in proportion to their respective interests, all of such Non-Consenting
5   Party's interest in the well and share of production therefrom until the proceeds of the sale of such share, calculated at the well, or
6   market value thereof if such share is not sold, (after deducting production taxes, excise taxes, royalty, overriding royalty and other in-
7   terests not excepted by Article III.D. payable out of or measured by the production from such well accruing with respect to such interest
8   until it reverts) shall equal the total of the following:
9
10
11

Figure 9.4— *Continued*

12   (a) 100% of each such Non-Consenting Party's share of the cost of any newly acquired surface equipment beyond the wellhead
13   connections (including, but not limited to, stock tanks, separators, treaters, pumping equipment and piping), plus 100% of each such
14   Non-Consenting Party's share of the cost of operation of the well commencing with first production and continuing until each such Non-
15   Consenting Party's relinquished interest shall revert to it under other provisions of this Article, it being agreed that each Non-
16   Consenting Party's share of such costs and equipment will be that interest which would have been chargeable to such Non-Consenting
17   Party had it participated in the well from the beginning of the operations; and
18
19
20
21   (b) _____% of that portion of the costs and expenses of drilling, reworking, deepening, plugging back, testing and completing,
22   after deducting any cash contributions received under Article VIII.C., and _____% of that portion of the cost of newly acquired equip-
23   ment in the well (to and including the wellhead connections), which would have been chargeable to such Non-Consenting Party if it had
24   participated therein.
25
26
27
28   An election not to participate in the drilling or the deepening of a well shall be deemed an election not to participate in any re-
29   working or plugging back operation proposed in such a well, or portion thereof, to which the initial Non-Consent election applied that is
30   conducted at any time prior to full recovery by the Consenting Parties of the Non-Consenting Party's recoupment account. Any such
31   reworking or plugging back operation conducted during the recoupment period shall be deemed part of the cost of operation of said well
32   and there shall be added to the sums to be recouped by the Consenting Parties one hundred percent (100%) of that portion of the costs of
33   the reworking or plugging back operation which would have been chargeable to such Non-Consenting Party had it participated therein. If
34   such a reworking or plugging back operation is proposed during such recoupment period, the provisions of this Article VI.B. shall be ap-
35   plicable as between said Consenting Parties in said well.
36
37
38
39   During the period of time Consenting Parties are entitled to receive Non-Consenting Party's share of production, or the
40   proceeds therefrom, Consenting Parties shall be responsible for the payment of all production, severance, excise, gathering and other
41   taxes, and all royalty, overriding royalty and other burdens applicable to Non-Consenting Party's share of production not excepted by Ar-
42   ticle III.D.
43
44
45
46   In the case of any reworking, plugging back or deeper drilling operation, the Consenting Parties shall be permitted to use, free
47   of cost, all casing, tubing and other equipment in the well, but the ownership of all such equipment shall remain unchanged; and upon
48   abandonment of a well after such reworking, plugging back or deeper drilling, the Consenting Parties shall account for all such equip-
49   ment to the owners thereof, with each party receiving its proportionate part in kind or in value, less cost of salvage.
50
51
52
53   Within sixty (60) days after the completion of any operation under this Article, the party conducting the operations for the
54   Consenting Parties shall furnish each Non-Consenting Party with an inventory of the equipment in and connected to the well, and an
55   itemized statement of the cost of drilling, deepening, plugging back, testing, completing, and equipping the well for production; or, at its
56   option, the operating party, in lieu of an itemized statement of such costs of operation, may submit a detailed statement of monthly bill-
57   ings. Each month thereafter, during the time the Consenting Parties are being reimbursed as provided above, the party conducting the
58   operations for the Consenting Parties shall furnish the Non-Consenting Parties with an itemized statement of all costs and liabilities in-
59   curred in the operation of the well, together with a statement of the quantity of oil and gas produced from it and the amount of proceeds
60   realized from the sale of the well's working interest production during the preceding month. In determining the quantity of oil and gas

Figure 9.4 — *Continued*

61 produced during any month. Consenting Parties shall use industry accepted methods such as, but not limited to, metering or periodic
62 well tests. Any amount realized from the sale or other disposition of equipment newly acquired in connection with any such operation
63 which would have been owned by a Non-Consenting Party had it participated therein shall be credited against the total unreturned costs
64 of the work done and of the equipment purchased in determining when the interest of such Non-Consenting Party shall revert to it as
65 above provided; and if there is a credit balance, it shall be paid to such Non-Consenting Party.

1   If and when the Consenting Parties recover from a Non-Consenting Party's relinquished interest the amounts provided for above,
2 the relinquished interests of such Non-Consenting Party shall automatically revert to it, and, from and after such reversion, such Non-
3 Consenting Party shall own the same interest in such well, the material and equipment in or pertaining thereto, and the production
4 therefrom as such Non-Consenting Party would have been entitled to had it participated in the drilling, reworking, deepening or plugging
5 back of said well. Thereafter, such Non-Consenting Party shall be charged with and shall pay its proportionate part of the further costs of
6 the operation of said well in accordance with the terms of this agreement and the Accounting Procedure attached hereto.
7
8
9
10.   Notwithstanding the provisions of this Article VI.B.2., it is agreed that without the mutual consent of all parties, no wells shall
11 be completed in or produced from a source of supply from which a well located elsewhere on the Contract Area is producing, unless such
12 well conforms to the then-existing well spacing pattern for such source of supply.
13
14
15
16   The provisions of this Article shall have no application whatsoever to the drilling of the initial well described in Article VI.A.
17 except (a) as to Article VII.D.1. (Option No. 2), if selected, or (b) as to the reworking, deepening and plugging back of such initial well
18 after it has been drilled to the depth specified in Article VI.A. if it shall thereafter prove to be a dry hole or, if initially completed for pro-
19 duction, ceases to produce in paying quantities.
20
21
22
23   3. Stand-By Time: When a well which has been drilled or deepened has reached its authorized depth and all tests have been
24 completed, and the results thereof furnished to the parties, stand-by costs incurred pending response to a party's notice proposing a
25 reworking, deepening, plugging back or completing operation in such a well shall be charged and borne as part of the drilling or deepen-
26 ing operation just completed. Stand-by costs subsequent to all parties responding, or expiration of the response time permitted, whichever
27 first occurs, and prior to agreement as to the participating interests of all Consenting Parties pursuant to the terms of the second gram-
28 matical paragraph of Article VI.B.2, shall be charged to and borne as part of the proposed operation, but if the proposal is subsequently
29 withdrawn because of insufficient participation, such stand-by costs shall be allocated between the Consenting Parties in the proportion
30 each Consenting Party's interest as shown on Exhibit "A" bears to the total interest as shown on Exhibit "A" of all Consenting Par-
31 ties.
32
33
34
35   4. Sidetracking: Except as hereinafter provided, those provisions of this agreement applicable to a "deepening" operation shall
36 also be applicable to any proposal to directionally control and intentionally deviate a well from vertical so as to change the bottom hole
37 location (herein called "sidetracking"), unless done to straighten the hole or to drill around junk in the hole or because of other
38 mechanical difficulties. Any party having the right to participate in a proposed sidetracking operation that does not own an interest in the
39 affected well bore at the time of the notice shall, upon electing to participate, tender to the well bore owners its proportionate share (equal
40 to its interest in the sidetracking operation) of the value of that portion of the existing well bore to be utilized as follows:
41
42
43
44   (a) If the proposal is for sidetracking an existing dry hole, reimbursement shall be on the basis of the actual costs incurred in
45 the initial drilling of the well down to the depth at which the sidetracking operation is initiated.

Figure 9.4 – *Continued*

46
47
48
49 (b) If the proposal is for sidetracking a well which has previously produced, reimbursement shall be on the basis of the well's
50 salvable materials and equipment down to the depth at which the sidetracking operation is initiated, determined in accordance with the
51 provisions of Exhibit "C", less the estimated cost of salvaging and the estimated cost of plugging and abandoning.
52
53
54
55 In the event that notice for a sidetracking operation is given while the drilling rig to be utilized is on location, the response period
56 shall be limited to forty-eight (48) hours, exclusive of Saturday, Sunday and legal holidays; provided, however, any party may request and
57 receive up to eight (8) additional days after expiration of the forty-eight (48) hours within which to respond by paying for all stand-by time
58 incurred during such extended response period. If more than one party elects to take such additional time to respond to the notice, stand-
59 by costs shall be allocated between the parties taking additional time to respond on a day-to-day basis in the proportion each electing par-
60 ty's interest as shown on Exhibit "A" bears to the total interest as shown on Exhibit "A" of all the electing parties. In all other in-
61 stances the response period to a proposal for sidetracking shall be limited to thirty (30) days.
62
63
64
65 C.   TAKING PRODUCTION IN KIND:
66
67 Each party shall take in kind or separately dispose of its proportionate share of all oil and gas produced from the Contract Area,
68 exclusive of production which may be used in development and producing operations and in preparing and treating oil and gas for
69 marketing purposes and production unavoidably lost. Any extra expenditure incurred in the taking in kind or separate disposition by any
70 party of its proportionate share of the production shall be borne by such party. Any party taking its share of production in kind shall be
1   required to pay for only its proportionate share of such part of Operator's surface facilities which it uses.
2
3   Each party shall execute such division orders and contracts as may be necessary for the sale of its interest in production from
4   the Contract Area, and, except as provided in Article VII.B., shall be entitled to receive payment directly from the purchaser thereof for
5   its share of all production.
6
7   In the event any party shall fail to make the arrangements necessary to take in kind or separately dispose of its proportionate share of
8   the oil produced from the Contract Area, Operator shall have the right, subject to the revocation at will by the party owning it, but not
9   the obligation, to purchase such oil or sell it to others at any time and from time to time, for the account of the non-taking party at the
10 best price obtainable in the area for such production. Any such purchase or sale by Operator shall be subject always to the right of the
11 owner of the production to exercise at any time its right to take in kind, or separately dispose of, its share of all oil not previously
12 delivered to a purchaser. Any purchase or sale by Operator of any other party's share of oil shall be only for such reasonable periods of
13 time as are consistent with the minimum needs of the industry under the particular circumstances, but in no event for a period in excess
14 of one (1) year.
15
16 In the event one or more parties' separate disposition of its share of the gas causes split-stream deliveries to separate pipelines and/or
17 deliveries which on a day-to-day basis for any reason are not exactly equal to a party's respective proportionate share of total gas sales to
18 be allocated to it, the balancing or accounting between the respective accounts of the parties shall be in accordance with any gas balancing
19 agreement between the parties hereto, whether such an agreement is attached as Exhibit "E", or is a separate agreement.
20
21 D.   Access to Contract Area and Information:
22
23 Each party shall have access to the Contract Area at all reasonable times, at its sole cost and risk to inspect or observe operations,
24 and shall have access at reasonable times to information pertaining to the development or operation thereof, including Operator's books
25 and records relating thereto. Operator, upon request, shall furnish each of the other parties with copies of all forms or reports filed with
26 governmental agencies, daily drilling reports, well logs, tank tables, daily gauge and run tickets and reports of stock on hand at the first of

Figure 9.4— *Continued*

27 each month, and shall make available samples of any cores or cuttings taken from any well drilled on the Contract Area. The cost of
28 gathering and furnishing information to Non-Operator, other than that specified above, shall be charged to the Non-Operator that re-
29 quests the information.
30
31 E. Abandonment of Wells:
32
33   1. <u>Abandonment of Dry Holes:</u> Except for any well drilled or deepened pursuant to Article VI.B.2., any well which has been
34 drilled or deepened under the terms of this agreement and is proposed to be completed as a dry hole shall not be plugged and abandoned
35 without the consent of all parties. Should Operator, after diligent effort, be unable to contact any party, or should any party fail to reply
36 within forty-eight (48) hours (exclusive of Saturday, Sunday and legal holidays) after receipt of notice of the proposal to plug and abandon
37 such well, such party shall be deemed to have consented to the proposed abandonment. All such wells shall be plugged and abandoned in
38 accordance with applicable regulations and at the cost, risk and expense of the parties who participated in the cost of drilling or deepening
39 such well. Any party who objects to plugging and abandoning such well shall have the right to take over the well and conduct further
40 operations in search of oil and/or gas subject to the provisions of Article VI.B.
41
42   2. <u>Abandonment of Wells that have Produced:</u> Except for any well in which a Non-Consent operation has been conducted
43 hereunder for which the Consenting Parties have not been fully reimbursed as herein provided, any well which has been completed as a
44 producer shall not be plugged and abandoned without the consent of all parties. If all parties consent to such abandonment, the well shall
45 be plugged and abandoned in accordance with applicable regulations and at the cost, risk and expense of all the parties hereto. If, within
46 thirty (30) days after receipt of notice of the proposed abandonment of any well, all parties do not agree to the abandonment of such well,
47 those wishing to continue its operation from the interval(s) of the formation(s) then open to production shall tender to each of the other
48 parties its proportionate share of the value of the well's salvable material and equipment, determined in accordance with the provisions of
49 Exhibit "C", less the estimated cost of salvaging and the estimated cost of plugging and abandoning. Each abandoning party shall assign
50 the non-abandoning parties, without warranty, express or implied, as to title or as to quantity, or fitness for use of the equipment and
51 material, all of its interest in the well and related equipment, together with its interest in the leasehold estate as to, but only as to, the in-
52 terval or intervals of the formation or formations then open to production. If the interest of the abandoning party is or includes an oil and
53 gas interest, such party shall execute and deliver to the non-abandoning party or parties an oil and gas lease, limited to the interval or in-
54 tervals of the formation or formations then open to production, for a term of one (1) year and so long thereafter as oil and/or gas is pro-
55 duced from the interval or intervals of the formation or formations covered thereby, such lease to be on the form attached as Exhibit
1 required to pay for only its proportionate share of such part of Operator's surface facilities which it uses.
2
3   Each party shall execute such division orders and contracts as may be necessary for the sale of its interest in production from
4 the Contract Area, and, except as provided in Article VII.B., shall be entitled to receive payment directly from the purchaser thereof for
5 its share of all production.
6
7   In the event any party shall fail to make the arrangements necessary to take in kind or separately dispose of its proportionate share of
8 the oil and gas produced from the Contract Area, Operator shall have the right, subject to the revocation at will by the party owning it,
9 but not the obligation, to purchase such oil and gas or sell it to others at any time and from time to time, for the account of the non-
10 taking party at the best price obtainable in the area for such production. Any such purchase or sale by Operator shall be subject always to
11 the right of the owner of the production to exercise at any time its right to take in kind, or separately dispose of, its share of all oil and gas
12 not previously delivered to a purchaser. Any purchase or sale by Operator of any other party's share of oil and gas shall be only for such
13 reasonable periods of time as are consistent with the minimum needs of the industry under the particular circumstances, but in no event
14 for a period in excess of one (1) year. Notwithstanding the foregoing, Operator shall not make a sale, including one into interstate com-
15 merce, of any other party's share of gas production without first giving such other party thirty (30) days notice of such intended sale.
16
17 D. Access to Contract Area and Information:
18
19   Each party shall have access to the Contract Area at all reasonable times, at its sole cost and risk to inspect or observe operations,
20 and shall have access at reasonable times to information pertaining to the development or operation thereof, including Operator's books
21 and records relating thereto. Operator, upon request, shall furnish each of the other parties with copies of all forms or reports filed with
22 governmental agencies, daily drilling reports, well logs, tank tables, daily gauge and run tickets and reports of stock on hand at the first of

Figure 9.4 — *Continued*

23 each month, and shall make available samples of any cores or cuttings taken from any well drilled on the Contract Area. The cost of
24 gathering and furnishing information to Non-Operator, other than that specified above, shall be charged to the Non-Operator that re-
25 quests the information.
26
27 **E. Abandonment of Wells:**
28
29   1. Abandonment of Dry Holes: Except for any well drilled or deepened pursuant to Article VI.B.2., any well which has been
30 drilled or deepened under the terms of this agreement and is proposed to be completed as a dry hole shall not be plugged and abandoned
31 without the consent of all parties. Should Operator, after diligent effort, be unable to contact any party, or should any party fail to reply
32 within forty-eight (48) hours (exclusive of Saturday, Sunday and legal holidays) after receipt of notice of the proposal to plug and abandon
33 such well, such party shall be deemed to have consented to the proposed abandonment. All such wells shall be plugged and abandoned in
34 accordance with applicable regulations and at the cost, risk and expense of the parties who participated in the cost of drilling or deepening
35 such well. Any party who objects to plugging and abandoning such well shall have the right to take over the well and conduct further
36 operations in search of oil and/or gas subject to the provisions of Article VI.B.
37
38   2. Abandonment of Wells that have Produced: Except for any well in which a Non-Consent operation has been conducted
39 hereunder for which the Consenting Parties have not been fully reimbursed as herein provided, any well which has been completed as a
40 producer shall not be plugged and abandoned without the consent of all parties. If all parties consent to such abandonment, the well shall
41 be plugged and abandoned in accordance with applicable regulations and at the cost, risk and expense of all the parties hereto. If, within
42 thirty (30) days after receipt of notice of the proposed abandonment of any well, all parties do not agree to the abandonment of such well,
43 those wishing to continue its operation from the interval(s) of the formation(s) then open to production shall tender to each of the other
44 parties its proportionate share of the value of the well's salvable material and equipment, determined in accordance with the provisions of
45 Exhibit ''C'', less the estimated cost of salvaging and the estimated cost of plugging and abandoning. Each abandoning party shall assign
46 the non-abandoning parties, without warranty, express or implied, as to title or as to quantity, or fitness for use of the equipment and
47 material, all of its interest in the well and related equipment, together with its interest in the leasehold estate as to, but only as to, the in-
48 terval or intervals of the formation or formations then open to production. If the interest of the abandoning party is or includes an oil and
49 gas interest, such party shall execute and deliver to the non-abandoning party or parties an oil and gas lease, limited to the interval or in-
50 tervals of the formation or formations then open to production, for a term of one (1) year and so long thereafter as oil and/or gas is pro-
51 duced from the interval or intervals of the formation or formations covered thereby, such lease to be on the form attached as Exhibit
1   ''B''. The assignments or leases so limited shall encompass the ''drilling unit'' upon which the well is located. The payments by, and the
2   assignments or leases to, the assignees shall be in a ratio based upon the relationship of their respective percentage of participation in the
3   Contract Area to the aggregate of the percentages of participation in the Contract Area of all assignees. There shall be no readjustment of
4   interests in the remaining portion of the Contract Area.
5
6   Thereafter, abandoning parties shall have no further responsibility, liability, or interest in the operation of or production from
7   the well in the interval or intervals then open other than the royalties retained in any lease made under the terms of this Article. Upon re-
8   quest, Operator shall continue to operate the assigned well for the account of the non-abandoning parties at the rates and charges con-
9   templated by this agreement, plus any additional cost and charges which may arise as the result of the separate ownership of the assigned
10 well. Upon proposed abandonment of the producing interval(s) assigned or leased, the assignor or lessor shall then have the option to
11 repurchase its prior interest in the well (using the same valuation formula) and participate in further operations therein subject to the pro-
12 visions hereof.
13
14   3. Abandonment of Non-Consent Operations: The provisions of Article VI.E.1. or VI.E.2. above shall be applicable as between
15 Consenting Parties in the event of the proposed abandonment of any well excepted from said Articles; provided, however, no well shall be
16 permanently plugged and abandoned unless and until all parties having the right to conduct further operations therein have been notified
17 of the proposed abandonment and afforded the opportunity to elect to take over the well in accordance with the provisions of this Article
18 VI.E.
19

Figure 9.4—*Continued*

20	ARTICLE VII.
21	EXPENDITURES AND LIABILITY OF PARTIES
22	
23	A. Liability of Parties:
24	

25   The liability of the parties shall be several, not joint or collective. Each party shall be responsible only for its obligations, and
26 shall be liable only for its proportionate share of the costs of developing and operating the Contract Area. Accordingly, the liens granted
27 among the parties in Article VII.B. are given to secure only the debts of each severally. It is not the intention of the parties to create, nor
28 shall this agreement be construed as creating, a mining or other partnership or association, or to render the parties liable as partners.
29

30 B. Liens and Payment Defaults:
31

32   Each Non-Operator grants to Operator a lien upon its oil and gas rights in the Contract Area, and a security interest in its share
33 of oil and/or gas when extracted and its interest in all equipment, to secure payment of its share of expense, together with interest thereon
34 at the rate provided in Exhibit "C". To the extent that Operator has a security interest under the Uniform Commercial Code of the
35 state, Operator shall be entitled to exercise the rights and remedies of a secured party under the Code. The bringing of a suit and the ob-
36 taining of judgment by Operator for the secured indebtedness shall not be deemed an election of remedies or otherwise affect the lien
37 rights or security interest as security for the payment thereof. In addition, upon default by any Non-Operator in the payment of its share
38 of expense, Operator shall have the right, without prejudice to other rights or remedies, to collect from the purchaser the proceeds from
39 the sale of such Non-Operator's share of oil and/or gas until the amount owed by such Non-Operator, plus interest, has been paid. Each
40 purchaser shall be entitled to rely upon Operator's written statement concerning the amount of any default. Operator grants a like lien
41 and security interest to the Non-Operators to secure payment of Operator's proportionate share of expense.
42

43   If any party fails or is unable to pay its share of expense within sixty (60) days after rendition of a statement therefor by
44 Operator, the non-defaulting parties, including Operator, shall, upon request by Operator, pay the unpaid amount in the proportion that
45 the interest of each such party bears to the interest of all such parties. Each party so paying its share of the unpaid amount shall, to obtain
46 reimbursement thereof, be subrogated to the security rights described in the foregoing paragraph.
47

48 C. Payments and Accounting:
49

50   Except as herein otherwise specifically provided, Operator shall promptly pay and discharge expenses incurred in the development
51 and operation of the Contract Area pursuant to this agreement and shall charge each of the parties hereto with their respective propor-
52 tionate shares upon the expense basis provided in Exhibit "C". Operator shall keep an accurate record of the joint account hereunder,
53 showing expenses incurred and charges and credits made and received.
54

55   Operator, at its election, shall have the right from time to time to demand and receive from the other parties payment in advance
56 of their respective shares of the estimated amount of the expense to be incurred in operations hereunder during the next succeeding
57 month, which right may be exercised only by submission to each such party of an itemized statement of such estimated expense, together
58 with an invoice for its share thereof. Each such statement and invoice for the payment in advance of estimated expense shall be submitted
59 on or before the 20th day of the next preceding month. Each party shall pay to Operator its proportionate share of such estimate within
60 fifteen (15) days after such estimate and invoice is received. If any party fails to pay its share of said estimate within said time, the amount
61 due shall bear interest as provided in Exhibit "C" until paid. Proper adjustment shall be made monthly between advances and actual ex-
62 pense to the end that each party shall bear and pay its proportionate share of actual expenses incurred, and no more.
63

64 D. Limitation of Expenditures:
65

66   1. Drill or Deepen: Without the consent of all parties, no well shall be drilled or deepened, except any well drilled or deepened
67 pursuant to the provisions of Article VI.B.2. of this agreement. Consent to the drilling or deepening shall include:

1   ☐   Option No. 1: All necessary expenditures for the drilling or deepening, testing, completing and equipping of the well, including
2 necessary tankage and/or surface facilities.

Figure 9.4 — *Continued*

□   Option No. 2: All necessary expenditures for the drilling or deepening and testing of the well. When such well has reached its authorized depth, and all tests have been completed, and the results thereof furnished to the parties, Operator shall give immediate notice to the Non-Operators who have the right to participate in the completion costs. The parties receiving such notice shall have forty-eight (48) hours (exclusive of Saturday, Sunday and legal holidays) in which to elect to participate in the setting of casing and the completion attempt. Such election, when made, shall include consent to all necessary expenditures for the completing and equipping of such well, including necessary tankage and/or surface facilities. Failure of any party receiving such notice to reply within the period above fixed shall constitute an election by that party not to participate in the cost of the completion attempt. If one or more, but less than all of the parties, elect to set pipe and to attempt a completion, the provisions of Article VI.B.2. hereof (the phrase "reworking, deepening or plugging back" as contained in Article VI.B.2. shall be deemed to include "completing") shall apply to the operations thereafter conducted by less than all parties.

2. <u>Rework or Plug Back</u>: Without the consent of all parties, no well shall be reworked or plugged back except a well reworked or plugged back pursuant to the provisions of Article VI.B.2. of this agreement. Consent to the reworking or plugging back of a well shall include all necessary expenditures in conducting such operations and completing and equipping of said well, including necessary tankage and/or surface facilities.

3. <u>Other Operations</u>: Without the consent of all parties, Operator shall not undertake any single project reasonably estimated to require an expenditure in excess of_____Dollars ($_____) except in connection with a well, the drilling, reworking, deepening, completing, recompleting, or plugging back of which has been previously authorized by or pursuant to this agreement; provided, however, that, in case of explosion, fire, flood or other sudden emergency, whether of the same or different nature, Operator may take such steps and incur such expenses as in its opinion are required to deal with the emergency to safeguard life and property but Operator, as promptly as possible, shall report the emergency to the other parties. If Operator prepares an authority for expenditure (AFE) for its own use, Operator shall furnish any Non-Operator so requesting an information copy thereof for any single project costing in excess of_____ Dollars ($_____) but less than the amount first set forth above in this paragraph.

E.   Rentals, Shut-in Well Payments and Minimum Royalties:

Rentals, shut-in well payments and minimum royalties which may be required under the terms of any lease shall be paid by the party or parties who subjected such lease to this agreement at its or their expense. In the event two or more parties own and have contributed interests in the same lease to this agreement, such parties may designate one of such parties to make said payments for and on behalf of all such parties. Any party may request, and shall be entitled to receive, proper evidence of all such payments. In the event of failure to make proper payment of any rental, shut-in well payment or minimum royalty through mistake or oversight where such payment is required to continue the lease in force, any loss which results from such non-payment shall be borne in accordance with the provisions of Article IV.B.2.

Operator shall notify Non-Operator of the anticipated completion of a shut-in gas well, or the shutting in or return to production of a producing gas well, at least five (5) days (excluding Saturday, Sunday and legal holidays), or at the earliest opportunity permitted by circumstances, prior to taking such action, but assumes no liability for failure to do so. In the event of failure by Operator to so notify Non-Operator, the loss of any lease contributed hereto by Non-Operator for failure to make timely payments of any shut-in well payment shall be borne jointly by the parties hereto under the provisions of Article IV.B.3.

F.   Taxes:

Beginning with the first calendar year after the effective date hereof, Operator shall render for ad valorem taxation all property subject to this agreement which by law should be rendered for such taxes, and it shall pay all such taxes assessed thereon before they become delinquent. Prior to the rendition date, each Non-Operator shall furnish Operator information as to burdens (to include, but not be limited to, royalties, overriding royalties and production payments) on leases and oil and gas interests contributed by such Non-Operator. If the assessed valuation of any leasehold estate is reduced by reason of its being subject to outstanding excess royalties, overriding royalties or production payments, the reduction in ad valorem taxes resulting therefrom shall inure to the benefit of the owner or

Figure 9.4 – *Continued*

54 owners of such leasehold estate, and Operator shall adjust the charge to such owner or owners so as to reflect the benefit of such reduc-
55 tion. If the ad valorem taxes are based in whole or in part upon separate valuations of each party's working interest, then notwithstanding
56 anything to the contrary herein, charges to the joint account shall be made and paid by the parties hereto in accordance with the tax
57 value generated by each party's working interest. Operator shall bill the other parties for their proportionate shares of all tax payments in
58 the manner provided in Exhibit "C".
59
60   If Operator considers any tax assessment improper, Operator may, at its discretion, protest within the time and manner
61 prescribed by law, and prosecute the protest to a final determination, unless all parties agree to abandon the protest prior to final deter-
62 mination. During the pendency of administrative or judicial proceedings, Operator may elect to pay, under protest. all such taxes and any
63 interest and penalty. When any such protested assessment shall have been finally determined, Operator shall pay the tax for the joint ac-
64 count, together with any interest and penalty accrued, and the total cost shall then be assessed against the parties, and be paid by them, as
65 provided in Exhibit "C".
66
67   Each party shall pay or cause to be paid all production, severance, excise, gathering and other taxes imposed upon or with respect to
68 the production or handling of such party's share of oil and/or gas produced under the terms of this agreement.
69
70

1 G. Insurance:
2
3   At all times while operations are conducted hereunder, Operator shall comply with the workmen's compensation law of
4 the state where the operations are being conducted; provided, however, that Operator may be a self-insurer for liability under said com-
5 pensation laws in which event the only charge that shall be made to the joint account shall be as provided in Exhibit "C". Operator shall
6 also carry or provide insurance for the benefit of the joint account of the parties as outlined in Exhibit "D", attached to and made a part
7 hereof. Operator shall require all contractors engaged in work on or for the Contract Area to comply with the workmen's compensation
8 law of the state where the operations are being conducted and to maintain such other insurance as Operator may require.
9
10   In the event automobile public liability insurance is specified in said Exhibit "D", or subsequently receives the approval of the
11 parties, no direct charge shall be made by Operator for premiums paid for such insurance for Operator's automotive equipment.
12
13   ARTICLE VIII.
14   ACQUISITION, MAINTENANCE OR TRANSFER OF INTEREST
15
16 A. Surrender of Leases:
17
18   The leases covered by this agreement, insofar as they embrace acreage in the Contract Area, shall not be surrendered in whole
19 or in part unless all parties consent thereto.
20
21   However, should any party desire to surrender its interest in any lease or in any portion thereof, and the other parties do not
22 agree or consent thereto, the party desiring to surrender shall assign, without express or implied warranty of title, all of its interest in
23 such lease, or portion thereof, and any well, material and equipment which may be located thereon and any rights in production
24 thereafter secured, to the parties not consenting to such surrender. If the interest of the assigning party is or includes an oil and gas in-
25 terest, the assigning party shall execute and deliver to the party or parties not consenting to such surrender an oil and gas lease covering
26 such oil and gas interest for a term of one (1) year and so long thereafter as oil and/or gas is produced from the land covered thereby, such
27 lease to be on the form attached hereto as Exhibit "B". Upon such assignment or lease, the assigning party shall be relieved from all
28 obligations thereafter accruing, but not theretofore accrued, with respect to the interest assigned or leased and the operation of any well
29 attributable thereto, and the assigning party shall have no further interest in the assigned or leased premises and its equipment and pro-
30 duction other than the royalties retained in any lease made under the terms of this Article. The party assignee or lessee shall pay to the
31 party assignor or lessor the reasonable salvage value of the latter's interest in any wells and equipment attributable to the assigned or leas-
32 ed acreage. The value of all material shall be determined in accordance with the provisions of Exhibit "C", less the estimated cost of
33 salvaging and the estimated cost of plugging and abandoning. If the assignment or lease is in favor of more than one party, the interest
34 shall be shared by such parties in the proportions that the interest of each bears to the total interest of all such parties.

Figure 9.4—*Continued*

35
36   Any assignment, lease or surrender made under this provision shall not reduce or change the assignor's, lessor's or surrendering
37 party's interest as it was immediately before the assignment, lease or surrender in the balance of the Contract Area; and the acreage
38 assigned, leased or surrendered, and subsequent operations thereon, shall not thereafter be subject to the terms and provisions of this
39 agreement.
40
41 **B. Renewal or Extension of Leases:**
42
43   If any party secures a renewal of any oil and gas lease subject to this agreement, all other parties shall be notified promptly, and
44 shall have the right for a period of thirty (30) days following receipt of such notice in which to elect to participate in the ownership of the
45 renewal lease, insofar as such lease affects lands within the Contract Area, by paying to the party who acquired it their several proper pro-
46 portionate shares of the acquisition cost allocated to that part of such lease within the Contract Area, which shall be in proportion to the
47 interests held at that time by the parties in the Contract Area.
48
49   If some, but less than all, of the parties elect to participate in the purchase of a renewal lease, it shall be owned by the parties
50 who elect to participate therein, in a ratio based upon the relationship of their respective percentage of participation in the Contract Area
51 to the aggregate of the percentages of participation in the Contract Area of all parties participating in the purchase of such renewal lease.
52 Any renewal lease in which less than all parties elect to participate shall not be subject to this agreement.
53
54   Each party who participates in the purchase of a renewal lease shall be given an assignment of its proportionate interest therein
55 by the acquiring party.
56
57   The provisions of this Article shall apply to renewal leases whether they are for the entire interest covered by the expiring lease
58 or cover only a portion of its area or an interest therein. Any renewal lease taken before the expiration of its predecessor lease, or taken or
59 contracted for within six (6) months after the expiration of the existing lease shall be subject to this provision; but any lease taken or con-
60 tracted for more than six (6) months after the expiration of an existing lease shall not be deemed a renewal lease and shall not be subject to
61 the provisions of this agreement.
62
63   The provisions in this Article shall also be applicable to extensions of oil and gas leases.
64
65 **C. Acreage or Cash Contributions:**
66
67   While this agreement is in force, if any party contracts for a contribution of cash towards the drilling of a well or any other
68 operation on the Contract Area, such contribution shall be paid to the party who conducted the drilling or other operation and shall be
69 applied by it against the cost of such drilling or other operation. If the contribution be in the form of acreage, the party to whom the con-
70 tribution is made shall promptly tender an assignment of the acreage, without warranty of title, to the Drilling Parties in the proportions
1 said Drilling Parties shared the cost of drilling the well. Such acreage shall become a separate Contract Area and, to the extent possible, be
2 governed by provisions identical to this agreement. Each party shall promptly notify all other parties of any acreage or cash contributions
3 it may obtain in support of any well or any other operation on the Contract Area. The above provisions shall also be applicable to op-
4 tional rights to earn acreage outside the Contract Area which are in support of a well drilled inside the Contract Area.
5
6   If any party contracts for any consideration relating to disposition of such party's share of substances produced hereunder, such
7 consideration shall not be deemed a contribution as contemplated in this Article VIII.C.
8
9 **D. Maintenance of Uniform Interest:**
10
11   For the purpose of maintaining uniformity of ownership in the oil and gas leasehold interests covered by this agreement, no
12 party shall sell, encumber, transfer or make other disposition of its interest in the leases embraced within the Contract Area and in wells,
13 equipment and production unless such disposition covers either:
14
15   1. the entire interest of the party in all leases and equipment and production; or
16

Figure 9.4 – *Continued*

17   2. an equal undivided interest in all leases and equipment and production in the Contract Area.
18

19   Every such sale, encumbrance, transfer or other disposition made by any party shall be made expressly subject to this agreement
20   and shall be made without prejudice to the right of the other parties.
21

22   If, at any time the interest of any party is divided among and owned by four or more co-owners, Operator, at its discretion, may
23   require such co-owners to appoint a single trustee or agent with full authority to receive notices, approve expenditures, receive billings for
24   and approve and pay such party's share of the joint expenses, and to deal generally with, and with power to bind, the co-owners of such
25   party's interest within the scope of the operations embraced in this agreement; however, all such co-owners shall have the right to enter
26   into and execute all contracts or agreements for the disposition of their respective shares of the oil and gas produced from the Contract
27   Area and they shall have the right to receive, separately, payment of the sale proceeds thereof.
28

29   **E.   Waiver of Rights to Partition:**
30

31   If permitted by the laws of the state or states in which the property covered hereby is located, each party hereto owning an
32   undivided interest in the Contract Area waives any and all rights it may have to partition and have set aside to it in severalty its undivided
33   interest therein.
34

35   **F.   Preferential Right to Purchase:**
36

37   Should any party desire to sell all or any part of its interests under this agreement, or its rights and interests in the Contract
38   Area, it shall promptly give written notice to the other parties, with full information concerning its proposed sale, which shall include the
39   name and address of the prospective purchaser (who must be ready, willing and able to purchase), the purchase price, and all other terms
40   of the offer. The other parties shall then have an optional prior right, for a period of ten (10) days after receipt of the notice, to purchase
41   on the same terms and conditions the interest which the other party proposes to sell; and, if this optional right is exercised, the purchas-
42   ing parties shall share the purchased interest in the proportions that the interest of each bears to the total interest of all purchasing par-
43   ties. However, there shall be no preferential right to purchase in those cases where any party wishes to mortgage its interests, or to
44   dispose of its interests by merger, reorganization, consolidation, or sale of all or substantially all of its assets to a subsidiary or parent com-
45   pany or to a subsidiary of a parent company, or to any company in which any one party owns a majority of the stock.
46

47   **ARTICLE IX.**
48   **INTERNAL REVENUE CODE ELECTION**
49

50   This agreement is not intended to create, and shall not be construed to create, a relationship of partnership or an association
51   for profit between or among the parties hereto. Notwithstanding any provision herein that the rights and liabilities hereunder are several
52   and not joint or collective, or that this agreement and operations hereunder shall not constitute a partnership, if, for federal income tax
53   purposes, this agreement and the operations hereunder are regarded as a partnership, each party hereby affected elects to be excluded
54   from the application of all of the provisions of Subchapter "K", Chapter 1, Subtitle "A", of the Internal Revenue Code of 1954, as per-
55   mitted and authorized by Section 761 of the Code and the regulations promulgated thereunder. Operator is authorized and directed to ex-
56   ecute on behalf of each party hereby affected such evidence of this election as may be required by the Secretary of the Treasury of the
57   United States or the Federal Internal Revenue Service, including specifically, but not by way of limitation, all of the returns statements,
58   and the data required by Federal Regulations 1.761. Should there be any requirement that each party hereby affected give further
59   evidence of this election, each such party shall execute such documents and furnish such other evidence as may be required by the
60   Federal Internal Revenue Service or as may be necessary to evidence this election. No such party shall give any notices or take any other
61   action inconsistent with the election made hereby. If any present or future income tax laws of the state or states in which the Contract
62   Area is located or any future income tax laws of the United States contain provisions similar to those in Subchapter "K", Chapter 1,
63   Subtitle "A", of the Internal Revenue Code of 1954, under which an election similar to that provided by Section 761 of the Code is per-
64   mitted, each party hereby affected shall make such election as may be permitted or required by such laws. In making the foregoing elec-
65   tion, each such party states that the income derived by such party from operations hereunder can be adequately determined without the
66   computation of partnership taxable income.

Figure 9.4—*Continued*

ARTICLE X.

CLAIMS AND LAWSUITS

Operator may settle any single uninsured third party damage claim or suit arising from operations hereunder if the expenditure does not exceed_____Dollars ($_____) and if the payment is in complete settlement of such claim or suit. If the amount required for settlement exceeds the above amount, the parties hereto shall assume and take over the further handling of the claim or suit, unless such authority is delegated to Operator. All costs and expenses of handling, settling, or otherwise discharging such claim or suit shall be at the joint expense of the parties participating in the operation from which the claim or suit arises. If a claim is made against any party or if any party is sued on account of any matter arising from operations hereunder over which such individual has no control because of the rights given Operator by this agreement, such party shall immediately notify all other parties, and the claim or suit shall be treated as any other claim or suit involving operations hereunder.

ARTICLE XI.

FORCE MAJEURE

If any party is rendered unable, wholly or in part, by force majeure to carry out its obligations under this agreement, other than the obligation to make money payments, that party shall give to all other parties prompt written notice of the force majeure with reasonably full particulars concerning it; thereupon, the obligations of the party giving the notice, so far as they are affected by the force majeure, shall be suspended during, but no longer than, the continuance of the force majeure. The affected party shall use all reasonable diligence to remove the force majeure situation as quickly as practicable.

The requirement that any force majeure shall be remedied with all reasonable dispatch shall not require the settlement of strikes, lockouts, or other labor difficulty by the party involved, contrary to its wishes; how all such difficulties shall be handled shall be entirely within the discretion of the party concerned.

The term "force majeure", as here employed, shall mean an act of God, strike, lockout, or other industrial disturbance, act of the public enemy, war, blockade, public riot, lightning, fire, storm, flood, explosion, governmental action, governmental delay, restraint or inaction, unavailability of equipment, and any other cause, whether of the kind specifically enumerated above or otherwise, which is not reasonably within the control of the party claiming suspension.

ARTICLE XII.

NOTICES

All notices authorized or required between the parties and required by any of the provisions of this agreement, unless otherwise specifically provided, shall be given in writing by mail or telegram, postage or charges prepaid, or by telex or telecopier and addressed to the parties to whom the notice is given at the addresses listed on Exhibit "A". The originating notice given under any provision hereof shall be deemed given only when received by the party to whom such notice is directed, and the time for such party to give any notice in response thereto shall run from the date the originating notice is received. The second or any responsive notice shall be deemed given when deposited in the mail or with the telegraph company, with postage or charges prepaid, or sent by telex or telecopier. Each party shall have the right to change its address at any time, and from time to time, by giving written notice thereof to all other parties.

ARTICLE XIII.

TERM OF AGREEMENT

This agreement shall remain in full force and effect as to the oil and gas leases and/or oil and gas interests subject hereto for the period of time selected below; provided, however, no party hereto shall ever be construed as having any right, title or interest in or to any lease or oil and gas interest contributed by any other party beyond the term of this agreement.

Figure 9.4— *Continued*

50   □   Option No. 1: So long as any of the oil and gas leases subject to this agreement remain or are continued in force as to any part
51 of the Contract Area, whether by production, extension, renewal or otherwise.
52

53   □   Option No. 2: In the event the well described in Article VI.A., or any subsequent well drilled under any provision of this
54 agreement, results in production of oil and/or gas in paying quantities, this agreement shall continue in force so long as any such well or
55 wells produce, or are capable of production, and for an additional period of _____ days from cessation of all production; provided,
56 however, if, prior to the expiration of such additional period, one or more of the parties hereto are engaged in drilling, reworking, deepen-
57 ing, plugging back, testing or attempting to complete a well or wells hereunder, this agreement shall continue in force until such opera-
58 tions have been completed and if production results therefrom, this agreement shall continue in force as provided herein. In the event the
59 well described in Article VI.A., or any subsequent well drilled hereunder, results in a dry hole, and no other well is producing, or capable
60 of producing oil and/or gas from the Contract Area, this agreement shall terminate unless drilling, deepening, plugging back or rework-
61 ing operations are commenced within _____ days from the date of abandonment of said well.
62

63   It is agreed, however, that the termination of this agreement shall not relieve any party hereto from any liability which has
64 accrued or attached prior to the date of such termination.
65

1   ARTICLE XIV.
2   COMPLIANCE WITH LAWS AND REGULATIONS
3

4 **A. Laws, Regulations and Orders:**
5

6   This agreement shall be subject to the conservation laws of the state in which the Contract Area is located, to the valid rules,
7 regulations, and orders of any duly constituted regulatory body of said state; and to all other applicable federal, state, and local laws, or-
8 dinances, rules, regulations, and orders.
9

10 **B. Governing Law:**
11

12   This agreement and all matters pertaining hereto, including, but not limited to, matters of performance, non-performance, breach,
13 remedies, procedures, rights, duties and interpretation or construction, shall be governed and determined by the law of the state in which
14 the Contract Area is located. If the Contract Area is in two or more states, the law of the state of _____
15 shall govern.
16

17 **C. Regulatory Agencies:**
18

19   Nothing herein contained shall grant, or be construed to grant, Operator the right or authority to waive or release any rights,
20 privileges, or obligations which Non-Operators may have under federal or state laws or under rules, regulations or orders promulgated
21 under such laws in reference to oil, gas and mineral operations, including the location, operation, or production of wells, on tracts offset-
22 ting or adjacent to the Contract Area.
23

24   With respect to operations hereunder, Non-Operators agree to release Operator from any and all losses, damages, injuries, claims
25 and causes of action arising out of, incident to or resulting directly or indirectly from Operator's interpretation or application of rules,
26 rulings, regulations or orders of the Department of Energy or predecessor or successor agencies to the extent such interpretation or ap-
27 plication was made in good faith. Each Non-Operator further agrees to reimburse Operator for any amounts applicable to such Non-
28 Operator's share of production that Operator may be required to refund, rebate or pay as a result of such an incorrect interpretation or
29 application, together with interest and penalties thereon owing by Operator as a result of such incorrect interpretation or application.
30

31   Non-Operators authorize Operator to prepare and submit such documents as may be required to be submitted to the purchaser
32 of any crude oil sold hereunder or to any other person or entity pursuant to the requirements of the "Crude Oil Windfall Profit Tax Act
33 of 1980", as same may be amended from time to time ("Act"), and any valid regulations or rules which may be issued by the Treasury
34 Department from time to time pursuant to said Act. Each party hereto agrees to furnish any and all certifications or other information
35 which is required to be furnished by said Act in a timely manner and in sufficient detail to permit compliance with said Act.

Figure 9.4 — *Continued*

36
37   ARTICLE XV.
38   OTHER PROVISIONS
39
40
41
42
43
44
45
46
47
48
49
50

1   ARTICLE XVI.
2   MISCELLANEOUS
3
4   This agreement shall be binding upon and shall inure to the benefit of the parties hereto and to their respective heirs, devisees,
5   legal representatives, successors and assigns.
6
7   This instrument may be executed in any number of counterparts, each of which shall be considered an original for all purposes.
8
9   IN WITNESS WHEREOF, this agreement shall be effective as of _____ day of _____, 19_____ .
10
11
12   O P E R A T O R
13
14
15
16
17   _____   _____
18
19
20
21
22   N O N - O P E R A T O R S
23
24
25
26
27
28   _____   _____
29
30
31
32
33   _____   _____
34

Pooling, Unitization, and Release

Oil and gas leases normally include a clause empowering the lessee to pool or unitize leased tracts in order to comply with state well spacing regulations and to conduct operations more efficiently. *Pooling* is the term usually applied to combining small tracts into a unit large enough to satisfy spacing requirements. The immediate aim of pooling is the formation of a drilling unit. Although sometimes used in reference to the formation of a drilling unit, the term *unitization* generally refers to field-wide or reservoir-wide operations that are planned and carried out as if all the tracts in a field were held under a single lease. Since geologic structures know nothing of property lines, and since some technologies for reservoir exploration and stimulation are essentially large-scale, unitization can be crucial to long-term success. The final aim of both pooling and unitization is successful, efficient pro-

duction. Operators hope to extract oil and gas with a minimum of waste and in amounts that will earn steady profits. Overproduction can be dangerous to oil prices and destabilizing to the world market, as can underproduction. The aim is a rough match between supply and demand, with a care for the conservation of irreplaceable resources.

Royalty owners, as well as lessees, can benefit from pooling and unitization. Either arrangement will, however, affect the terms of the leases involved and change some of the rights of the parties. In particular, the rights of working interest owners and (often) of royalty owners to production will be changed, as will the obligations of lessees. Whether unitized operations are planned for a single well or for an entire field, such operations require agreements that set out the relationships and rights of all the parties affected.

POOLING

Voluntary Pooling

Pooling is a result of state conservation laws passed during the 1930s and 1940s. Unrestrained drilling, before the days of

effective regulations for well spacing and density, sometimes led to situations like that in the East Texas field where wells were drilled so close together that their derrick legs overlapped. Restraints were imposed not only on drilling practices but also on the amount of oil actually produced. By the mid-1930s, for example, overproduction threatened to swamp the market and had driven the price of oil down to 10 cents a barrel. Two kinds of statutes were passed in a number of states to help conserve resources and to match supply with demand. *Prorationing* limited the amount of oil that a well was allowed to produce, and spacing rules established the amount of acreage that could be efficiently drained by a single well. Statutes like these were encouraged by Interstate Oil Compact, a coordinating body formed by the oil-producing states in 1935.

Prorationing, along with well spacing and density rules, created the concept of the *drilling and spacing unit,* or *DSU* (also known as a proration unit). A typical size requirement for an oil proration unit was, and is, 40 acres. But a leased tract is not always of the size desired to form a proration unit. Sometimes a DSU has to be made up by combining tracts, or pooling. When tracts owned by different lessors, and perhaps leased by different lessees, are pooled by mutual agreement, the result is voluntary pooling.

Pooling arrangements are usually made by landmen, and the timing of these arrangements vary with the particular situation. Companies usually prefer to pool after they have done most of the developmental drilling in a field where they hold leases. That is, they hope to form enough proration units without pooling to gain an accurate idea of where their productive and nonproductive acreage lies. With that knowledge, they can pool where necessary to achieve the most efficient use of their leases. This goal is not always attainable, however. To give only one example, it might be necessary to pool before drilling if a company held a lease without a pooling clause. (Older fields in which leases were acquired a number of years ago can present this

problem.) In such a case, the company might prefer to pool first on the supposition that the drill site owners will be reluctant to pool (and share royalties) after a well has demonstrated its productiveness.

In addition to the timing, the instruments used in creating a pooled unit vary with the situation. In a simple case, one lessee will hold leases with pooling clauses on several neighboring tracts. To pool these tracts, the lessee need only comply with the formalities set out in the pooling clauses and secure ratification (if he hasn't already done so) from any nonparticipating, that is, nonexecutive, royalty owners. The formalities may include filing a declaration of intent to pool with the state regulatory agency and taking care to follow the state's unit size and spacing rules. What a unit so formed is *called* depends upon the state. In Texas, for example, a pooled unit formed in this way is called a *designated unit.*

In a somewhat more complicated situation, the exercise of a pooling authority by a lessee might involve other working interest owners and *their* royalty owners in the formation of a drilling unit. If they—and any unleased owners affected—consent to the proposed pooling, they can sign an instrument to that effect. (The name of the instrument will, again, vary from place to place. It is commonly acknowledged and recorded, whatever it is called.)

Where no pooling authority exists, as in the hypothetical older oil field, securing signatures from the affected owners (on what is often called a pooling agreement) will allow a pooled unit to be formed. The agreement is usually recorded. Finally, whenever more than one working interest owner is party to a pooling arrangement, a joint operating agreement and an AFE will be needed if drilling is to proceed. The details of pooling vary, but the crucial point is simply this: whether or not a lease grants the authority to pool, pooled units can be formed once the affected owners—of land, royalties, working interests, and retained interests—have consented to the terms.

Though pooling can benefit lessors as well as lessees, everyone concerned should be aware of the changes that pooling can bring. For example, unless leases contain Pugh clauses or Freestone riders, all the lands covered by the leases will be held by the pooled unit—including lands outside the pooled area as well as lands inside it. Royalties will be shared among the interest owners, usually on the basis of acreage contributed to the pool. Finally, a well drilled anywhere on the pooled lands will hold all the leases without further payment of delay rentals—unless the leases provide for some other arrangement.

Involuntary Pooling

Most of the chief producing states have some kind of statutory, or forced, pooling laws to meet those situations in which lessees cannot reach an agreement to form a drilling unit by pooling. (These states include Alaska, California, New Mexico, Colorado, Florida, Kansas, Oklahoma, Louisiana, Texas, Wyoming, North Dakota, Mississippi, and Montana.) How often such laws are invoked depends upon local conditions, the qualifications that must be met, and so on. In some states—Oklahoma and Louisiana, for instance—forced pooling is fairly common. In others, state regulatory boards are more reluctant to compel owners to join in a pooling arrangement. In Texas, for example, the relevant statute does not really permit recalcitrant owners to be pooled forcibly. Rather, the statute provides an opportunity for a lessee who wishes to pool to make holdouts a fair and reasonable offer that will then *prevent* nonjoiners from forcing their way into the unit once it has proved productive.

However mandatory pooling works, certain features of the process are much the same from state to state. Formal application (by qualified parties) must be made to the state regulatory agency. A hearing is usually held to decide on the merits of the request. Parties who are subsequently force-pooled are sometimes given lease bonuses (if they are landowners). Working interest owners may participate in, and pay their share of, the drilling—with commensurate rewards if the well produces.

UNITIZATION

Private Lands

Unitization is usually a much larger undertaking than is pooling. The land involved is far more extensive and the number of interest owners correspondingly greater. Unitizing a field can have advantages that match this increased scale, however. These include the elimination of wasteful practices, the maintenance of reservoir pressure to facilitate maximum production, and the conduct of secondary recovery operations. In considering that primary production may extract only 15–25 percent of the oil in place and that improved recovery methods like water flooding or gas injection may bring that figure up to 80 percent, such methods seem a boon to the industry. They are extremely costly, though, and hardly feasible except on a field- or reservoir-wide scale. Unitization for the purpose of conducting such operations is usually suggested by the largest owner in a field—and only after careful study of the possible benefits and probable expenses. Achieving a unitized field depends upon persuading large numbers of people that unitization will serve their interests. At each stage of the planning, those who propose a unitization will want to be sure that they have sound arguments and convincing evidence.

After the proposing company's geologists and engineers have finished their studies, and a firm decision to proceed has been made, the next step is often a preliminary meeting with other working interest owners. Here the proposal to unitize can be explained and the economics of the situation outlined for the group. If the group agrees that unitization is feasible and desirable, committees can be formed to work on the many details that will need attention. A land committee, for example, might be selected to start getting in touch with the royalty owners (usually numerous and far-flung). Another committee might be put in charge of drafting the unit agreement and the unit operating agreement. A third would collect information to help decide on the basis for participation in the unit, and so on.

As noted, two agreements may be used to cover the provisions of a unitization. The *unit agreement* pools the interests of the parties and acts as a grant by the royalty owners to the working interest owners to develop the field as a unit. The *unit operating agreement* is signed by the working interest owners only. It establishes a committee, with a voting procedure, to oversee unit operations and decide on the sharing of costs. There is some inevitable overlap between these two instruments, but there are advantages to using both of them. Royalty owners have a shorter instrument to sign and one that clearly does *not* involve them in any of the working interest

owner's obligations. The American Petroleum Institute can supply model forms for both a unit agreement and a unit operating agreement. (These can be obtained in two versions—one for voluntary and one for statutory units.) The model forms caution that their provisions will need adapting to particular situations and to the laws of the individual states.

Once the agreements have been drafted, the landmen working on the unit's land committee can secure signatures from royalty owners. Many of these can usually be obtained by mail. In other instances—with local owners, civic groups, local school boards, and the like—meetings can be helpful. A unit representative meeting face-to-face with royalty owners will do best, of course, if he has prepared his presentation carefully, is ready to answer questions, and can explain how the proposed unit will affect the interests of the people he is dealing with. Sometimes the royalty owners will form their own association or committee, complete with an attorney and technical advisor. Negotiating with such a group can require tact and care, but at the end of the process, a significant number of signatures can usually be obtained.

Finally, the unit will generally need approval from the state regulatory agency. In the case of voluntary unitization, agency approval may be optional. It is normally obtained anyway, to avoid the possibility of violating antitrust laws. When the unit is *not* formed voluntarily, agency approval and an agency order will be needed. These usually involve notice, a hearing, expert testimony, an offer of fair and reasonable terms, and the agreement of some specified percentage of the lessees and the royalty owners. When a number of owners still contest the unitization, a common result is a modified plan. In those states that have a statute authorizing compulsory unitization, an agency order completes the formal process—unless enough protesting owners veto.

Federal and State Lands

The United States government encourages unitization on federal lands, both for purposes of exploration and for improved recovery. Applications for unitization were, for a number of years, made to the USGS. Special procedures and special forms of unit and unit operating agreements were necessary. The procedures and regulations will not be reviewed here, for they are in process of being revised at the time of this writing. On June 10, 1982, the Minerals Management Service (recently created to handle a number of tasks pertaining to federal leases) published in the *Federal Register* a proposed amended rulemaking for onshore federal and Indian oil and gas units. Comments were invited and received for 45 days after the publishing of the new regulations. In December of 1982, however, the secretary of the interior transferred all onshore minerals management tasks (except the management of royalties) to the Bureau of Land Management. The secretary's order was then amended to include Indian lands in this transfer.

Accordingly, the Bureau of Land Management is now in charge of the final rulemaking for unitization on federal and Indian lands. Response to comments from the industry can be read in the *Federal Register* of June 10, 1983. A final version of the regulations will appear in 1984. The regulations will (as a consequence of the administrative change described) be deleted from Chapter II, Title 30 of the Code of Federal Regulations and reappear in Title 43 (which relates to the BLM) at some future date. At present, offshore leasing of federal lands—and their unitization—is still handled by the Minerals Management Service.

It is fairly common for a federal unit to include not only federal leases but also state and private leases. The proposed unitization must, in such a case, satisfy all the interest owners—private landowners, other working interest owners, the BLM, and the concerned state. Each state will have its own provisions and its own forms for consent and ratification (obtainable from the state land board or land office). State officials must approve the agreement before it goes to the BLM for final consideration there. When copies of the executed agreement are sent to the BLM for its final approval, additional copies go to the relevant state authority.

RELEASE

Eventually the time comes when leased property, no matter how productive it once was, no longer repays the efforts of the working interest owner. At that point, a company may decide to sell the property, to farm it out, or to abandon it. Whichever course the company takes, the landman in charge of the termination phase will handle the arrangements and notify all the parties concerned.

Abandonment, usually covered in the delay rental and habendum clauses of the lease, means essentially that salvable equipment is salvaged and the lease is allowed to expire. The landman will close the files on the lease and notify the parties. Many leases contain a surrender clause that requires the lessee to notify the lessor of intent to surrender the lease. This precaution arose from landowners' concern that an expired lease without proof of the lessee's intention to let it go would put a cloud on the title and make re-leasing the property to a new lessee difficult. A few landowners also worried about who would pay for the costs of plugging abandoned wells (thereby meeting state regulations) if lessees simply walked away from a lease without giving notice. These days, however, responsible companies take care to terminate their leases in an orderly way.

When not deliberately terminated, a lease can still be lost or forfeited, of course, by failure to comply with delay rental or habendum clauses. This possibility also applies to leases acquired from states or the federal government. A lessor wishing to surrender (rather than simply forfeit) a state or federal lease must comply with state or BLM regulations. It is always prudent to check with the appropriate state land board or the nearest BLM land office when plans are being made to terminate a state or federal lease. Regulations change with some frequency, and ignorance of the law can lead at best to frustration. At worst, it may lead to penalties and unexpected changes of plan. When oil and gas leases are concerned, the most recent information obtainable is worth its weight in gold. Or at the very least, in oil.

APPENDIX A
LEASING IN CANADA

Canada became self-governing in 1867, and the written portion of its constitution—known as the British North America Act—placed ownership of natural resources like oil and gas in the provinces where those resources are located. With some exceptions, most subsurface minerals are still owned and managed by the provinces. (There are ten of these, in addition to the Northern Territories: Newfoundland, Nova Scotia, New Brunswick, Prince Edward Island, Quebec, Ontario, Manitoba, Saskatchewan, Alberta, and British Columbia.) Provincial legislatures have considerable autonomy in handling provincial concerns—that is, those matters constitutionally defined as falling within their jurisdiction. Consequently, Canada has a separate set of statutes and regulations for the oil and gas in each province.

Some subsurface minerals are privately owned. In the four western provinces—Manitoba, Saskatchewan, Alberta, and British Columbia—a number of companies received land with attached mineral rights in return for their work in building railroads and thus opening the provinces up for settlement. The settlers themselves, until 1887, were granted homestead land with the mineral rights; but after that date, the federal government excepted such rights from homestead grants. Some minerals are also owned and managed by the federal government. These include the oil and gas of the offshore lands and the Northern Territories. Finally, there are mineral properties owned by Canada's Indians; Indian property has its own separate regulations.

Three lease forms are included in this Appendix, all of them used in Alberta and similar to those used by the various other oil-producing provinces—a right-of-way agreement (fig. A.1), a surface lease (fig. A.2), and a petroleum and natural gas lease (fig. A.3). In addition, a summary of regulations for oil and gas leasing is included (fig. A.4).

Like their counterparts to the south, the Canadian provinces enact new oil and gas legislation from time to time, and anyone interested in leasing mineral rights in Canada must keep abreast of this legislation. The laws are administered by government agencies that can supply information on mineral development and leasing practices. To learn more, one may write or telephone:

Department of Energy,
  Mines and Resources
Sir William Logan Building
580 Booth Street
Ottawa, Ont. K1A 0E4
Ph: 613-995-9351
Telex: 053-3117 EMAR OTT
(National agency).

The chief provincial agencies are:

Alberta Department of Energy and
  Natural Resources
Deputy Minister Office
10th Floor, Petroleum Plaza South
9915 108th Street
Edmonton, Alta. T5K 2B6
Ph: 403-427-7727
Telex: 037-3676

Government of British Columbia
Ministry of Energy,
  Mines and Petroleum Resources
Petroleum Resources Branch
Parliament Building
Victoria, B.C. V8V 1X4
Ph: 604-387-5993

Manitoba Department of
  Energy and Mines
Mineral Resources Division
Petroleum Branch
989 Century Street
Winnipeg, Man. R3H 0W4
Ph: 204-633-9543

New Brunswick Department of
  Natural Resources
Mineral Resources
Box 6000
Fredericton, N.B. E3B 5H1
Ph: 506-453-2206
Telex: 014-46230

Newfoundland and Labrador
  Petroleum Directorate
Box 4750
St. John's, Newfoundland A1C 5T7
Ph: 307-737-2323
Telex: 016-4034

Nova Scotia Industrial Benefits Office
Nova Scotia Petroleum
  Information Centre
Box 519
Halifax, Nova Scotia B3J 2R7
Ph: 902-424-4682
Telex: 019-22548

Ministry of Natural Resources
Petroleum Resources Section
1106 Dearness Drive
London, Ont. N6E 1N9
Ph: 519-681-5350

Prince Edward Island
  Department of Tourism,
  Industry and Energy
Box 2000
Charlottetown, P.E.I. C1A 7N8
Ph: 902-894-4821

Quebec Department of
  Energy and Resources
1305 Chemin Ste-Foy
Quebec City, Que. G1S 4N5

Saskatchewan Department of
  Mineral Resources
1914 Hamilton Street
Regina, Sask. S4P 4V4
Ph: 306-565-2526
Telex: 071-2786

Figure A.1. Alberta right-of-way agreement
(Courtesy of Canadian Association of Petroleum Landmen)

ALBERTA RIGHT-OF-WAY AGREEMENT

CAPL
FAO
UNIFARM
1979

I (WE). . . . .
of . . . . (hereinafter called
"the Grantor") being the registered owner or entitled to become the registered owner of an estate in fee simple, subject however to such encumbrances, liens and interests as may be notified on existing Certificate of Title and situate in the Province of Alberta, namely:

excepting thereout all MINES and MINERALS in all of that certain tract of land (hereinafter called "the said lands"). In consideration of the sum of . . . .
($)Dollars (receipt of which is hereby acknowledged) paid to the Grantor by . . . .
. . . .
(hereinafter called "the Grantee")

and in consideration of the covenants hereinafter contained I DO HEREBY GRANT, CONVEY, TRANSFER AND SET OVER, to and unto the Grantee, its successors and assigns a right-of-way across, over, under, on or through the said lands to construct, operate and maintain a pipeline or pipelines including accessories and appurtenances and for any other purpose preparatory or incidental thereto.

The Grantor and the Grantee hereby covenant and agree to the following terms and conditions:

1. FILING PLAN OF SURVEY

The Grantee agrees that on or before one year after the date of this agreement it will file at the appropriate Land Titles Office a Plan of Survey of the right-of-way. . . . .
(   ) metres in width across the said lands in the approximate location as shown on a sketch plan initialed by the parties and delivered to the Grantor upon his signing of this agreement. If the Grantee has not either filed a Plan of Survey within the one-year period, or should the Grantee not forward to the Grantor a Plan of Survey showing the location of the right-of-way to be substantially in the location shown on the sketch plan, on or before one year from the date hereof, this agreement will be null and void and the Grantee shall thereupon execute and register such documents as may be necessary to remove the registration of this agreement from the title to the lands.

2. PARTIAL WITHDRAWAL AND DISCHARGE OF RIGHT OF WAY

Upon filing the Plan of Survey at the appropriate Land Titles Office, the Grantee shall cause to be registered such documents as shall restrict this agreement and the rights herein granted to the right-of-way shown upon the Plan of Survey.

Figure A.1 – *Continued*

3. ADDITIONAL PAYMENT

Upon the filing of the Plan of Survey at the Land Titles Office or prior to commencing any construction on the lands, whichever occurs first, the Grantee shall pay an additional consideration to the Grantor calculated at the rate of. . . . .($) Dollars per acre of right-of-way shown on the Plan of Survey which has been or will be filed. If the additional consideration is not paid to the Grantor within one year after the date of this agreement, the agreement will be null and void and the Grantee shall thereupon execute and register such documents as may be necessary to remove the registration of this agreement from the title to the lands.

4. PROTECTION OF RIGHT-OF-WAY

The Grantor shall have the right to use and enjoy the right-of-way for any purpose except that which might interfere with the rights granted herein to the Grantee. The Grantor, his successors or assigns, shall not without the prior written consent of the Grantee (which consent shall not be unreasonably withheld) enter on, over, under or through the right-of-way for any purpose which may incur a liability to the Grantee for damages resulting from that entry.

The Grantee shall be responsible for and compensate the Grantor for reasonable additional costs incurred by the Grantor which may be caused by the existence of the said pipeline, pipelines, and right-of-way, in connection with the excavation, drilling, installation, erection, repair, or construction for any permitted operation for agricultural or related purposes across, over or under, on or through the said right-of-way.

5. REMOVAL OF PROPERTY

Notwithstanding any rule of law or equity, the pipeline or pipelines shall at all times remain the property of the Grantee, notwithstanding that the same may be annexed or affixed to the said lands and shall at any time and from time to time be removable in whole or in part by the Grantee.

6. DAMAGES

The Grantee shall pay compensation for any and all damage where such damage occurs as a result of the operations of the Grantee; its servants, agents or contractors.

7. LIABILITY

The Grantee covenants and agrees to indemnify and save harmless the Grantor from any and all liabilities, damages, costs, claims, suits or actions caused by or resulting from the construction, operation, maintenance and/or repairs of the said pipeline or pipelines and/or any related fixtures and appurtenances affixed to the right-of-way other than through willful damage or gross negligence by the Grantor.

8. TOPSOIL

The Grantee shall, upon request by the Grantor, insofar as it may be practicable to do so, strip the topsoil from the ditch line prior to construction and replace it as near as possible to its original condition following construction.

9. TAXES

The Grantee shall pay all rates and taxes that may be assessed and levied from time to time against its interest in the said lands and installation, or in connection with its operations thereon.

Figure A.1 – *Continued*

10. ABOVE GROUND INSTALLATION

The Grantee shall, so far as may be practicable, locate any above ground installation in such a fashion as to provide a minimum of inconvenience to the Grantor. The Grantee agrees to compensate the Grantor for such above ground installation by separate agreement and failing such agreement within sixty (60) days from the date of such installation, the matter of compensation shall be submitted to arbitration as hereinafter provided.

11. DISCONTINUANCE AND ABANDONMENT

Upon the discontinuance of the use of the said right-of-way and of the exercise of the right hereby granted, the Grantee shall restore the said lands to the same condition, so far as may be practicable to do so, as the lands were prior to the entry thereon and the use thereof by the Grantee:

PROVIDED HOWEVER, that the Grantee may, at its option, leave and abandon the said pipeline or pipelines in place. The Grantee agrees to withdraw and discharge any encumbrance registered in the Land Titles Office pertaining to this agreement upon abandonment of the said right-of-way.

12. DISCHARGE OF ENCUMBRANCES

The Grantee shall have the right at its option, to pay or discharge any balance owing under any agreement of sale or mortgage or any tax charge, lien or encumbrances of any kind or nature whatsoever, which may exist prior to the registration of this agreement, upon or against or in any way affecting the said lands, in which event the Grantee shall be subrogated to the rights of the holder or holders thereof and may, in addition to exercising and enforcing such rights, at its option, apply and credit the amount so paid by it, to the consideration as set forth above in this agreement.

13. ARBITRATION

If the amount for compensation for damages, and/or above ground structures payable cannot be agreed upon by the Grantor and the Grantee, the matter at issue shall be determined by three disinterested arbitrators, and the decision of any two of such three arbitrators shall be final and conclusive; PROVIDED THAT in all other respects the provision of the arbitration legislation then in force in the Province of Alberta shall apply to each submission. In any event, the responsibility for the arbitration costs shall be determined by the appointed arbitrators.

14. ADDITIONAL PIPELINES

In the event the Grantee separately constructs an additional pipeline and/or pipelines within the said right-of-way, the Grantee shall pay to the Grantor for that portion of the right-of-way utilized for the construction of the additional pipeline or pipelines, a sum equal to the greater of fifty ($50.00) dollars per acre or the appraised difference, if any, by which the lands contained in the right-of-way have increased in value over the amount paid at the time of construction of the immediately preceding pipeline or pipelines; PROVIDED ALWAYS that the Grantee may, at the Grantee's sole discretion, lay more than one pipeline in the same construction operation; and that construction shall not be delayed by the provisions of this clause.

15. FORCE MAJEURE

Neither party shall be considered in default in performance of its obligations under this agreement, to the extent that the performance of such obligations or any of them, is delayed by circumstances, existing or future, which are beyond the control of the Grantor or the Grantee: PROVIDED, however, the Grantee shall not be in default in the performance of any of its covenants or obligations under this agreement until the Grantor has notified the Grantee of such default and the Grantee has failed to commence timely action to remedy the same upon receipt of such notice.

Figure A.1 – *Continued*

16. ADDITIONAL TERMS

Any additional terms, expressed or implied, shall be of no force or effect unless made in writing and agreed to by the Grantor and the Grantee.

17. ASSIGNMENT

All the covenants and conditions herein contained, shall extend to, be binding upon, and enure to the benefit of, the executors, administrators, successors, and assigns of the Grantor and the Grantee respectively.

18. QUIET ENJOYMENT

The Grantee performing and observing the covenants and conditions on its part to be performed and observed shall and may peacably hold and enjoy the rights, liberties and easements hereby granted without hindrance, molestation or interruption on the part of the Grantor or any person claiming by, through, under or in trust for the Grantor for so long thereafter as the Grantee, his successors and assigns continues to use the right-of-way for the purposes herein set forth.

19. NOTICES

All notices to be given hereunder may be given by registered letter addressed to the Grantee at . . . .
. . . .
and to the Grantor at . . . .
or such other addresses as the Grantor and the Grantee may respectively from time to time designate in writing, and any such notice shall be deemed to have been given to and received by the addressee fourteen (14) days after the mailing thereof, postage prepaid and registered.

    IN WITNESS WHEREOF the Grantor and the Grantee have hereunto set their hand and seal this . . . .
day of . . . . A.D. 19

SIGNED, SEALED AND DELIVERED   )
)
in the presence of:)
)
. . . .)· . . . .
)
. . . .)· . . . .
)
)

CONSENT OF SPOUSE

I, ... being married to the above named
. . . . (the Grantor) do hereby give my
consent to the disposition of our homestead, made in this instrument, and I have executed his document for the purpose of giving up my life estate and other dower rights in the said property given to me by the Dower Act, to the extent necessary to give effect to the said disposition.

———————————————————
                          Spouse of Grantor

Figure A.1—*Continued*

CERTIFICATE OF ACKNOWLEDGEMENT BY SPOUSE

1. This document was acknowledged before me by . . . . apart from her husband (or his wife).

2. . . . . acknowledged to me that she (or he),
   (a) is aware of the nature of the disposition.
   (b) is aware that the Dower Act, gives her (or him) a life estate in the homestead and the right to prevent disposition of the homestead by withholding consent.
   (c) consents to the disposition for the purposes of giving up the life estate and other dower rights in the homestead given to her (or him) by the Dower Act, to the extent necessary to give effect to the said disposition.
   (d) is executing the document freely and voluntarily without any compulsion on the part of her husband (or his wife).

   Dated at . . . . .in the Province of Alberta, this . . . . day of. . . . . .A.D. 19

   _____
   A Commissioner for Oaths in and for
   the Province of Alberta

AFFIDAVIT

I, ...of . . . . in the Province of Alberta . . . ., make oath and say:
(Occupation)

1. That I am the Grantor named in the within instrument.
2. That I am not married

                                    OR

3. That neither myself nor my spouse have resided on the within mentioned land at any time since our marriage.

SWORN before me at. . . . .)
)
in the Province of Alberta   ). . . . .
)
this. . . . . day of. . . . . .A.D. 19   )

   _____
   A Commissioner for Oaths in and for the Province of Alberta

Figure A.1—*Continued*

AFFIDAVIT OF EXECUTION

CANADA   I, ... of the . . . .

PROVINCE OF ALBERTA   of . . . . in the Province of Alberta,

TO WIT: . . . . , make oath and say:

1. That I was personally present and did see. . . . .
    named in the within instrument, who is personally known to me to be the person named therein, duly sign and execute
    the same for the purpose named therein.

2. That the same was executed at. . . . . .in the Province of
    Alberta, and that I am the subscribing witness thereto.

3. That I know the said . . . . and he is in my belief
    of the full age of eighteen years.

)
SWORN before me at. . . . .)
)
in the Province of Alberta   ). . . . .
)
this. . . . . .day of. . . . .)
)
A.D. 19   )
)

                              _____
                              A Commissioner for Oaths in and for
                                  the Province of Alberta

CONSENT BY OCCUPANT, VENDOR, MORTGAGEE OR OTHER INTERESTED PARTY:

I, (WE) . . . .

of. . . . . in the Province of . . . .

having an interest in the within lands by virtue of an Agreement or Instrument dated the . . . .

day of. . . . . A.D. 19   DO HEREBY AGREE that all my (our) rights, interests and estate which are,
or may be, affected by the above Alberta Right-of-Way Agreement shall be fully bound by all the terms and conditions
thereof both now and henceforth.

Dated at . . . . .in the Province of . . . .

this. . . . . day of . . . . A.D. 19

                              . . . .

. . . .
(Witness)

Figure A.2. Alberta surface lease agreement
(Courtesy of Canadian Association of Petroleum Landmen)

C.A.P.L.-1974

ALBERTA SURFACE LEASE

This Indenture of Lease made the _____ day of _____ A.D. 19____

BETWEEN: _____

of _____ , in the Province of Alberta, _____

(hereinafter called "the Lessor")

- and -

(hereinafter called "the Lessee")

WHEREAS the Lessor is the registered owner (or entitled to become the registered owner under an agreement for sale or unregistered transfer or otherwise) of an estate in fee simple, subject, however, to the exceptions, conditions, encumbrances, liens and interests contained in or noted upon the existing Certificate of Title of and in that certain parcel or tract of land situate, lying and being in the Province of Alberta and described as follows:

(hereinafter referred to as "the said lands"); and

WHEREAS the Lessor has agreed to lease and grant a certain portion of the said lands to the Lessee for the purposes and upon the terms and conditions hereinafter set forth:

NOW THEREFORE THIS INDENTURE WITNESSETH:

THE LESSOR, at the rental hereinafter set forth, HEREBY LEASES to the Lessee all and singular those parts or portions of the said lands shown outlined in red on the sketch or plan hereto attached (hereinafter called "the demised premises"), to be held by the Lessee as tenant for the term of Twenty-five (25) years from the date hereof for any and all purposes and uses as may be necessary or useful in connection with all its operations.

YIELDING AND PAYING UNTO THE LESSOR:

(a) for the first year the sum of _____
(_____) dollars, (the receipt of which sum is hereby acknowledged), which sum includes compensation in full for rental, severance, inconvenience, and damage done to the demised premises as follows:

(i) rental _____ (_____) (dollars)

(ii) compensation for severance, inconvenience, and damage to the demised premises _____
_____ (_____) (dollars)

(b) for each subsequent year the sum of _____ (_____) (dollars)
payable annually in advance of the anniversary of the date hereof in each year during the currency hereof.

Figure A.2—*Continued*

THE LESSOR HEREBY COVENANTS AND AGREES TO AND WITH THE LESSEE:

1. Taxes Paid by Lessor:

That the Lessor will promptly pay and satisfy all taxes, rates and assessments that may be assessed or levied against the said lands during the continuance of this Lease save where such are to be paid by the Lessee.

2. Quiet Enjoyment:

That the Lessor has good title to the said lands as hereinbefore set forth, has good right and full power to grant and Lease the said lands, rights and privileges in manner aforesaid, and that the Lessee, upon observing and performing the covenants and conditions on the Lessee's part herein contained, shall and may peaceably possess and enjoy the demised premises and the rights and privileges hereby granted during the said term and any extension thereof without any interruption or disturbance from or by the Lessor or any other person claiming by, through or under the Lessor.

3. Renewal:

That if the Lessee be not in default in respect of any of the covenants and conditions contained in this Lease at the date of expiration of the term of Twenty-five (25) years hereinbefore mentioned then this Lease shall be renewed automatically and the term extended for a further period of Twenty-five (25) years at an annual rental calculated from time to time as hereinafter provided for that portion of the term subsequent to the first year thereof. Such extended term shall be subject to all the provisions hereof including this provision for renewal.

THE LESSEE HEREBY COVENANTS AND AGREES TO AND WITH THE LESSOR:

4. Fencing:

During the continuance of this Lease, to erect and put upon the boundaries of the sites and roadways constructed or placed by the Lessee on the demised premises a good substantial fence if so requested by the Lessor, or if required by the Lessee, and to replace all fences which the Lessee may have removed for its purposes and repair all fences which it may have damaged, and if and when so required by the Lessor, to provide a proper livestock guard at any point of entry upon the said lands used by it and, upon the use thereof, to close all gates.

5. Taxes Payable by Lessee:

To pay all taxes, rates and assessments that may be assessed or levied in respect of any and all machinery, equipment, structures and works placed by the Lessee, in, on, over or under the said lands.

6. Compensation for Damages:

To pay compensation for damage done by its servants, agents or assigns which without restricting the generality thereof shall include growing crops, fences, buildings or other improvements of the Lessor upon the said lands other than the demised premises.

THE LESSOR AND THE LESSEE DO HEREBY MUTUALLY COVENANT AND AGREE EACH WITH THE OTHER AS FOLLOWS:

7. Review of Rental:

Notwithstanding anything contained in this Lease, upon the request of either party to this Lease, the amount of rent payable in respect to the demised premises shall be subject to review at the end of five years from the date hereof and at the end of each succeeding five year period. Such request shall be in writing and given to the other party at least ninety (90) days prior to the commencement of the period in respect of which the review of rent is sought. In case of any disagreement as to the amount of rent to be payable or any other matter in connection therewith, the same shall be determined by the arbitration legislation in force.

8. Surrender:

The Lessee shall have the right at any time and from time to time to surrender and terminate this Lease by written notice to the Lessor, provided however that there shall be no refund to the Lessee of any rental which may have been paid in advance.

9. Reduction of Acreage:

Notwithstanding anything in the immediately preceding clause hereof contained, the Lessee may from time to time and at any time surrender any part or portion of the demised premises by giving the Lessor a revised plan of the portion or portions thereof retained, and provided that the rental shall be no less than hereinbefore provided.

Figure A.2 – *Continued*

10. Removal of Equipment:

The Lessee may at all times during the continuance of this lease remove or cause to be removed from the demised premises all buildings, structures, fixtures, casing in wells, pipelines, material and equipment of whatsoever nature or kind which it may have placed on or in the demised premises or in any area to be surrendered.

11. Discharge of Encumbrances:

The Lessee may at its option pay or discharge all or part of any balance owing under any Agreement for Sale or Mortgage, or of any tax, charge, lien or encumbrance of any kind or nature whatsoever which may now or hereafter exist on or against or in any way affect the said lands, in which event the Lessee shall be subrogated to the rights of the holder or holders thereof, and may in addition thereto, at its option, reimburse itself by applying on account of repayment of the amount so paid by it the rentals or other sums accruing to the Lessor under the terms of this Lease.

12. Assignment by Lessee:

The Lessee may delegate, assign or convey to other persons or corporations, all or any of the powers, rights, and interests obtained by or conferred upon the Lessee hereunder, and may enter into all agreements, contracts, and writings and do all necessary acts and things to give effect to the provisions of this clause.

13. Default:

Notwithstanding anything herein contained to the contrary, the Lessee shall not be in default in the performance of any of its covenants or obligations under this Lease, including the payment of rental unless and until the Lessor has notified the Lessee of such default and the Lessee has failed to commence action to remedy the same, within thirty (30) days of the receipt of such notice.

14. Notices:

All notices to be given hereunder may be given personally or by registered letter addressed to the party to whom the notice is to be given, and when mailed, any such notice shall be deemed to be given to, and received by, the addressee Seven (7) days after the mailing thereof, postage prepaid.

15. Addresses:

Unless changed by written notice the addresses of the parties hereto shall be:

Lessee _____

Lessor _____

These presents and everything herein contained shall inure to the benefit of and be binding upon the Lessor, his heirs, executors, administrators, successors and assigns and upon the Lessee, its successors and assigns.

IN WITNESS WHEREOF the Lessor has hereunto set his hand and seal and the Lessee has caused its corporate seal to be hereunto affixed attested by the hands of its proper officers duly authorized in that behalf, the day and year first above written.

SIGNED, SEALED AND DELIVERED

By the above named Lessor in   _____

the presence of:

_____

                                                _____

                                                _____

Figure A.2 – *Continued*

DOWER CONSENT OF SPOUSE

I, _____ being married to the within named
_____ do hereby give my consent to the disposition of our
homestead, made in this instrument, and I have executed this document for the purpose of giving up my life
estate and other dower rights in the said property given to me by the Dower Act, 1970, to the extent
necessary to give effect to the said disposition.

_____

CERTIFICATE OF ACKNOWLEDGMENT BY SPOUSE

1.   This document was acknowledged before me by _____, apart
from her husband/his wife.

2.   _____ acknowledged to me that she/he:

    (a) Is aware of the nature of the disposition;
    (b) Is aware that The Dower Act, 1970, gives her/him a life estate in the homestead and the right to
    prevent disposition of the homestead by withholding consent;
    (c) Consent to the disposition for the purpose of giving up the life estate and other dower rights in the
    homestead given to her/him by the Dower Act, 1970, to the extent necessary to give effect to the
    said disposition.
    (d) Is executing the document freely and voluntarily without any compulsion on the part of her husband/
    his wife.

DATED at _____, in the Province of _____ this _____
day of _____, A.D. 19_____.

_____
A Commissioner for Oaths, a Notary Public
in and for the Province of Alberta.

CANADA
PROVINCE OF ALBERTA   **DOWER AFFIDAVIT**
TO WIT:

I, _____ of _____
in the Province of Alberta, _____, make oath and say:
          (occupation)

THAT I am the Lessor named in the within instrument.
THAT I am not married.

                    OR

THAT neither myself nor my spouse have resided on the within mentioned land at any time since our
marriage.

SWORN before me at _____
in the Province of Alberta, this _____
day of _____ A.D. 19_____. _____

_____
A Commissioner for Oaths, a Notary Public
in and for the Province of Alberta.

Figure A.2—*Continued*

CANADA
PROVINCE OF ALBERTA   **AFFIDAVIT OF EXECUTION**
TO WIT:

I, _____ , of _____
in the Province of Alberta _____ , make oath and say:

    1. THAT I was personally present and did see _____
named in the within instrument, who is personally known to me to be the person named therein duly sign, seal and execute the same for the purposes named therein.

    2. THAT the same was executed at _____ , in the Province of Alberta, and that I am the subscribing witness thereto.

    3. THAT I know the said _____
and he (or she) is, in my belief, of the full age of eighteen years.

SWORN before me at _____

in the Province of Alberta, this _____

day of _____ A.D. 19_____.   _____

_____
A Commissioner for Oaths, a Notary Public
in and for the Province of Alberta.

CONSENT BY OCCUPANT, VENDOR, MORTGAGEE OR OTHER INTERESTED PARTY:

I, (we) _____
of _____ in the Province of _____ having an
interest in the within lands by virtue of an Agreement or Instrument dated the_____
day of _____ A.D. 19_____ DO HEREBY AGREE that all my (our) rights, interests and estate which are, or may be, affected by the above Surface Lease shall be fully bound by all the terms and conditions thereof both now and henceforth.

DATED at _____ in the Province of _____ this _____

day of _____ A.D. 19_____.

_____

_____
Witness

CANADA
PROVINCE OF ALBERTA   **AFFIDAVIT OF EXECUTION**
TO WIT:

I, _____ , of _____
in the Province of Alberta _____ , make oath and say:

    1. THAT I was personally present and did see _____
named in the within instrument, who is (are) personally known to me to be the person(s) named therein, duly sign, seal and execute the same for the purposes named therein.

Figure A.2—*Continued*

2. THAT the same was executed at _____, in the Province of Alberta, and that I am the subscribing witness thereto.

3. THAT I know the said _____
and he (or she) is (or they are each), in my belief, of the full age of eighteen years.

SWORN before me at _____

in the Province of Alberta, this _____

day of _____ A.D. 19_____.   _____

_____
A Commissioner for Oaths, a Notary Public
in and for the Province of Alberta.

CANADA
PROVINCE OF ALBERTA   **AFFIDAVIT OF EXECUTION**
        TO WIT:

I, _____, of _____
in the Province of Alberta _____, make oath and say:

1. THAT I was personally present and did see _____
named in the within instrument, who is personally known to me to be the person named therein duly sign, seal and execute the same for the purposes named therein.

2. THAT the same was executed at _____, in the Province of Alberta, and that I am the subscribing witness thereto.

3. THAT I know the said _____
and he (or she) is, in my belief, of the full age of eighteen years.

SWORN before me at _____

in the Province of Alberta, this _____

day of _____ A.D. 19_____.   _____

_____
A Commissioner for Oaths, a Notary Public
in and for the Province of Alberta.

Figure A.3. Alberta petroleum and natural gas lease agreement, form 160-C
(Courtesy of Director of Energy and Natural Resources, Province of Alberta)

ENERGY AND
NATURAL RESOURCES
Minerals Disposition Division

PETROLEUM AND NATURAL GAS LEASE
No.

This Lease is made between the Parties:

HER MAJESTY THE QUEEN in right of Alberta, represented herein by the Minister of Energy and Natural Resources of the Province of Alberta, hereinafter called the "Minister",

OF THE FIRST PART

AND

hereinafter called the "lessee",

OF THE SECOND PART

The Minister is empowered to dispose of petroleum and natural gas rights that are the property of the Crown in right of Alberta in accordance with the provisions of Part 5 of The Mines and Minerals Act, as amended, and in accordance with other provisions of the said Act as they are applicable to dispositions of petroleum and natural gas rights.

Figure A.3 — *Continued*

Therefore, in consideration of the rents and royalties payable, and subject to the terms and conditions expressed in this Lease, the Minister grants to the lessee the exclusive right to explore for, work, win and recover petroleum and natural gas within and under the lands described in the attached Appendix, excepting from the lands described any petroleum or natural gas rights not granted under this Lease.

The lessee is entitled to hold this Lease for a term of five years; the term to commence on the date set out in the Appendix to this Lease and, subject to the Act, the lessee shall hold this Lease after the expiry date of the term for so long as this Lease is permitted to continue pursuant to the Act.

The lessee shall pay to the Minister

(a)   in advance of each year of the term or the continuation of the term the annual rent of Two dollars and fifty cents ($2.50) in Canadian funds for each hectare in the location:

(b)   a royalty on all petroleum and natural gas won, worked, recovered or obtained from the location, and on all products obtained from petroleum and natural gas, at the rate or rates as are now or may from time to time be prescribed by the Lieutenant Governor in Council, the royalty to be free and clear of any deductions.

The Lessee and the Minister agree with each other as follows:

1.   The lessee shall comply with the provisions of The Mines and Minerals Act, as amended, and any Act passed in substitution therefor, and with any regulations now made or that at any time may be made under the authority of the said Acts, and all the provisions and regulations that prescribe, relate to or affect the rights and obligations of lessees of petroleum and natural gas rights that are the property of the Crown in right of Alberta. The provisions of any other Act of the Province of Alberta that prescribes, relates to or affects the lessees of the said petroleum and natural gas rights, shall be deemed to be incorporated into this Lease and shall bind the lessee from the date it comes into force. In the event of conflict between any regulation made after the execution of this Lease and any regulation previously made, the regulation last made shall prevail.

2.   The lessee agrees, and it is an express condition upon which this Lease is granted, that natural gas produced from the location shall be used within Alberta, unless the consent of the Lieutenant Governor in Council to its use elsewhere is previously obtained.

Figure A.3 — *Continued*

3. The lessee agrees to keep the Minister indemnified against all actions, claims and demands that may be brought or made against the Minister by reason of anything done by the lessee, his servants, workmen, agents or licensees, in the exercise or purported exercise of the rights and powers granted under this Lease.

4. If default is made by the lessee in the performance or observance of any of the terms and conditions provided in this Lease for a period of 30 days from the date of the sending by mail of a notice to the lessee advising of such default, the Minister may cancel this Lease.

5. This Lease shall inure to the benefit of the lessee and those of his executors, administrators, successors or assigns as are entitled or may be permitted to benefit pursuant to The Mines and Minerals Act, as amended.

6. In this Lease, the expression "Minister" means the Minister of Energy and Natural Resources and includes a Deputy Minister for the Department of Energy and Natural Resources.

The Parties have executed this Lease in duplicate and under seal as of the Date of Issue.

SIGNED, SEALED AND DELIVERED
in the presence of

....
Minister of Energy and Natural Resources.

And by the lessee in the presence of

....
Witness as to Lessee.   Lessee.

Figure A.4. Summary of regulations concerning petroleum and natural gas leases, Alberta
(Courtesy of Seaton-Jordan & Associates Ltd.)

REGULATIONS

These notes are prepared by **SEATON-JORDAN & ASSOCIATES LTD.** and detailed information regarding lease, licence and reservation requirements may be obtained by reference to their **HANDBOOK** for **LANDMEN** series.

PETROLEUM AND NATURAL GAS LEASES - ALBERTA

There are three different types of petroleum and natural gas leases issued by the Province of Alberta that are still in active use. They are referred to as 21 year, 10 year, or 5 year leases. The terms and conditions to which these leases are subject are set out in the Mines and Minerals Act (M & M Act) and the Petroleum and Natural Gas Lease Regulations (P & NG Lse Regs). These leases do not include the right to oil sands following an amendment to section 110 of the Act that became effective July 1, 1978.

DRILLING REQUIREMENTS:

1. **Ten Year Leases**

    Drilling operations must be commenced -

    :   on or before July 1, 1977 where the lease reaches end of 9th year before then,

    :   on or before December 31, 1977 where lease reaches end of 9th year between July 1 and December 31, 1977 or where lease reaches end of 8th year during 1977.

    :   on or before the 1978 anniversary date where lease reaches end of 7th or 8th year of term during 1978,

    :   on or before the 1979 anniversary date where lease reaches end of 6th and 7th year of term during 1979,

    :   before start of 7th year where lease reaches end of 6th year during 1980 or any year thereafter,

    (Section 2, P & NG Lse Regs)

2. **Twenty-one Year Leases**

    The lessee must commence drilling operations within one year of receiving a drilling notice from the Minister which may be given anytime after lease reaches end of the 10th year.

    (Section 3, P & NG Lse Regs)

Figure A.4—*Continued*

3. **Leases Excepted from Drilling Requirement**

   : those leases the Minister considers capable of production of oil or gas in paying quantity.

   : those leases subject to unit operations,

   : thoses leases that have already been grouped and validated by drilling,

   : thoses leases from which the minister has waived the drilling requirement.

   (Section 5, P & NG Lse Regs)

ALTERNATIVES TO DRILLING ON 10 OR 21 YEAR LEASES:

1. **Drilling Penalties**

   The time for commencement of wells on both 10 and 21 year leases may be extended for a maximum of 4 years by paying penalties of:

   a) $2.50/hectare for 1st year,
   b) $7.50/hectare for 2nd year,
   c) $12.50/hectare for 3rd year,
   d) $22.50/hectare for 4th year.

   (Section 4, P & NG Lse Regs)

2. **Grouping**

   Leases may be grouped and then one well drilled on group which will satisfy drilling requirement for all leases in group.

   A. **10 Year Leases**

   (i) Leases to be included in group must all be within same area, i.e., Plains, Northern or Foothills.

   (ii) The 10 year lease group may be formed before, during, or within 60 days of completion of drilling.

   (iii) The number of sections that can be included in group is set out in Schedule B of the P & NG Lse Regs and is a factor of the location and depth of the well.

   (iv) The validating well must not be within 3.2 kilometres of a producing well* except with special consent of the Minister.

   (Section 6 & 7, P & NG Lse Regs)

Figure A.4 — *Continued*

B. **21 Year Leases**

(i)   Leases need not be in same area of Province or within proximity of one another.

(ii) The group must be formed prior to commencement of well.

(iii) The group may comprise ·

  : 6 sections for well to 900 metres
  : 8 sections for well between 900 · 1800 metres,
  : 12 sections for well deeper than 1800 metres, plus two sections for each 300 metres below 2400 metres.

(iv) The validating well must not be within 3.2 kilometres of a producing well, except with special consent of the Minister.

(Section 8, P & NG Lse Regs)

CONTINUATION BEYOND PRIMARY TERM:

1. **By Production or Deemed Production**

   All leases; 5, 10 and 21 year; expire upon the termination of the primary term, but all/or portions of the leases may continue indefinitely under certain circumstances.

   Leases may continue as to ·

   : those portions of the lease that are part of the spacing units for producing wells*,

   : those portions of the leases that are subject to unit operations,

   : those portions of leases for which compensatory royalty is being paid in lieu of drilling an offset well,

   : those portions of leases deemed by the Minister as capable of production in paying quantity.

   (Section 99, M & M Act)

2. **Drilling Operations Being Conducted at Expiration of Term**

   Where a well is being drilled on a lease at the expiration of its term or the expiration of its continuation then the lease continues as to that part of the section that is subject to the lease in which the well is being drilled.

   (Section 100, M & M Act)

Figure A.4 — *Continued*

3. **Unproven Acreage**

The Minister may allow all or any part of a lease to continue, notwithstanding that he is of the opinion that the lease comprises "unproven area". Where an application to continue a lease under clause (d) subsection (1) of section 99 is not approved in its entirety, the Minister may allow the lease to continue for an additional year upon submittal of security in the amount of $25.00 for each unproven hectare.

The unproven area may be continued under lease for two additional years if a well is being drilled to evaluate the unproven acreage at the expiration of the one-year period and the lease is located in the Northern or Foothills area subject to such conditions as the Minister may prescribe.

(Section 102, M & M Act)

REVERSION OF DEEPER RIGHTS:

The petroleum and natural gas rights below the base of the deepest zone capable of producing oil or gas in paying quantity are to be deleted from petroleum and natural gas leases and returned to the Government on certain dates which are:

a) the expiration of the initial term for five year leases,

b) the expiration of the initial term or January 1, 1983, whichever is later, for 10 year and 21 year leases.

The Minister can extend the deeper rights reversion date when it is in the public interest.

(Section 103, M & M Act)

NATURAL GAS LEASES:

The term of a natural gas lease is 21 years and they may be continued, upon expiration of primary term, under the same conditions as are provided for petroleum and natural gas leases.

(Section 110, M & M Act)

* "Producing Well" - means a well that is, in the opinion of the Minister, capable of production of petroleum or natural gas in paying quantity.

(Section 90 (d), M & M Act)

Figure A.4 – *Continued*

PETROLEUM AND NATURAL GAS LICENCES

The only petroleum and natural gas exploratory agreement that can be acquired now from the Province of Alberta is a Petroleum and Natural Gas Licence. The terms and conditions to which these licences are subject are set out in the Petroleum and Natural Gas Licence Regulations (P & NG Lic Regs).

ACQUISTION: Licences may be acquired only at the sales held in Calgary every second Wednesday.

(Section 4, P & NG Lic Regs)

RENTAL: Two dollars and fifty cents a hectare per year.

(Section 5, P & NG Lic Regs)

TERM: Plains Area - 2 years   Where the Minister determines that two years is
Northern Area - 4 years   not sufficient for drilling a well, he may extend
Foothills Area - 5 years   the term of the licence for a period of one year.

(Section 6, P & NG Lic Regs)

MAXIMUM SIZE: Plains Area - 29 sections
Northern Area - 32 sections
Foothills - 36 sections

(Section 7, P & NG Lic Regs)

WORK REQUIREMENT: In order to earn leases at least one "lease-earning well"* must be drilled on a licence or group of licences.

(Section 13, P & NG Lic Regs)

GROUPING: Only two licences may be grouped.
Licences must be within 3.2 Kilometres of one another.
Grouped licences need not be in same area.
Grouped licences need not be in same name.
Licences are grouped for each well.

(Section 12, P & NG Lic Regs)

LEASE SELECTION: The number of sections a licensee is entitled to for each "lease-earning well"* is determined by the depth of the well and the area of the Province in which it is located and is set out in Schedule B of the regulations. By drilling deeply enough or by drilling a sufficient number of wells 100% of the licence area can be acquired under petroleum and natural gas lease (5 year lease)

(Section 13, P & NG Lic Regs)

RENTAL
REDUCTION: Where a well is commenced on licenced lands no rental is payable on the licence for the subsequent licence years for that portion of the licence earned under lease by drilling of the well.

(Section 16, P & NG Lic Regs)

* "lease-earning well" -   means, with respect to any licence, any well drilled on the location of the licence or any other well drilled by the licensee that is considered by the Minister to be a lease-earning well whether or not the well is drilled on the location of the licence.

(Section 1 (b) P & NG Lic Regs)

NATURAL GAS LICENCES

Natural Gas Licences may still be acquired in Alberta where the presence of natural gas is determined when drilling on a petroleum and natural gas reservation. A natural gas licence application can comprise the natural gas in the zone in which the presence of gas has been determined and affords an opportunity to acquire all the natural gas rights in a reservation. The terms and conditions to which these natural gas licences are subject are set out in the Natural Gas Licence Regulations (Nat Gas Lic Regs).

RENTAL: Twelve cents per hectare for each six months.

(Section 4, Nat Gas Lic Regs)

MAXIMUM
SIZE: Thirty-six sections.

(Section 6, Nat Gas Lic Regs)

TERM: Maximum of three years.

(Section 9, Nat Gas Lic Regs)

WORK
REQUIREMENT: Well must be commenced within three months of issue of licence and subsequent wells must be commenced within three months of completion or abandonment of previous well. Minister may extend time for commencement of any well up to a maximum of six months.

(Section 10 & 15, Nat Gas Lic Regs)

Figure A.4—*Continued*

ADDING
ZONES: Where gas is discovered in commercial quantities in zones not granted by
                      the licence, these zones may be added to the licence.

                                                              (Section 11, Nat Gas Lic Regs)

LEASE
SELECTION: Natural Gas Leases may be selected only where wells are completed as com-
                      mercial gas wells. The number of sections granted under lease is determined
                      by the depth of the productive zone. By drilling enough gas wells the whole
                      of licenced area may be acquired under lease, (21 year natural gas lease).

                                                              (Section 17, Nat Gas Lic Regs)

OIL
DISCOVERY: Where oil is discovered in a licenced zone, a **petroleum and natural gas lease**
                      can be acquired comprising the discovery quarter section where three quarter
                      sections in the immediate vicinity of the discovery are surrendered from the
                      licence.

                                                              (Section 21, Nat Gas Lic Regs)

SURRENDER: Upon surrender of a licence in its entirety the natural gas may be returned to
                      the petroleum and natural gas agreements from which it came.

                                                              (Section 22, Nat Gas Lic Regs)

OIL SANDS PROSPECTING PERMITS

Oil Sands Prospecting Permits are governed by the Oil Sands Regulations, 1978.

ACQUISITION: Prospecting Permits may be acquired when oil sands have been determined
                      by drilling on petroleum and natural gas reservations or leases. Does not
                      apply to some leases issued after June 30, 1978.

RENTAL: Twelve cents a hectare 1st year.
                      Twenty-five cents a hectare 2nd and 3rd year.

                                                              (Sections 4 and 11, Oil Sands Regs)

TERM: One year.

                                                              (Section 11, Oil and Sands Regs)

RENEWAL: 2 one year renewals.

                                                              (Section 11, Oil Sands Regs)

Figure A.4 – *Continued*

MAXIMUM SIZE: 20,000 hectares.

(Section 6, Oil Sands Regs)

WORK
REQUIREMENT: Exploration program approved by the Minister must be conducted each year.

(Section 7, 11 and 12, Oil Sands Regs)

DEPOSIT: $50,000 deposit, required to guarantee performance of work requirement.

(Section 4, Oil Sands Regs)

LEASES: Can convert to Oil Sands Lease when oil sands deposit delimited.

(Section 21, Oil Sands Regs)

OIL SANDS LEASES

Oil Sands Leases are governed by the Oil Sands Regulation, 1978.

ACQUISITION: Leases may be acquired following a satisfactory exploration program on an oil sands prospecting permit, or by direct application.

(Section 21 and 31, Oil Sands Regs)

RENTAL: $2.50 a hectare.

(Section 26, Oil Sands Regs)

TERM: Twenty-one years.   (Section 24, Oil Sands Regs)

RENEWAL: (a) One term of twenty-one years, and
(b) Twenty-one year terms as long as plant or other works are in operation.

(Section 24, Oil Sands Regs)

Figure A.4—*Continued*

MAXIMUM SIZE: 20,000 hectares.

                                                    (Maximum size of Prospecting Permit)

WORK
REQUIREMENT: (a) Continuing 5 year work programs with expenditures of at least $5.00 per
                              hectare each year.
                      (b) Commence to construct plant or other works within one year of receiving
                              notice from Minister, minimum size or capacity is set out in lease.

                                                              (Section 30, Oil Sands Regs)

DEPOSIT: $12.50 per hectare, minimum $10,000,
                          maximum $50,000. Deposit returned when
                          lease is in production or when surrendered.

                                                              (Section 27, Oil Sands Regs)

APPENDIX B
LEASING IN ALASKA

In nearly every instance a company that wishes to acquire Alaskan oil or gas must lease from the federal government, the state of Alaska, or both. Private landowners come far behind the federal and state governments in the size and known producing potential of their holdings. Private ownership is increasing (for reasons we shall review in a moment), but much privately owned land is still an unknown factor in the estimates of Alaskan oil and gas reserves. Its development will depend, in many cases, on federal action, especially on the construction of transport facilities on nearby federal lands.

The massive federal presence in Alaska is partly due to the fact that the territory—purchased from Russia in 1867—did not become a state until 1959. At that time, Alaska was granted 103 million acres from its approximate total of 370 million to support the expenses of statehood and to create an economy for its citizens. Alaska is still choosing acreage for patent to itself. Once all this land-grant acreage is conveyed, Alaska will still own less land with oil and gas potential than does the federal government. When the federal share is seen to include the National Petroleum Reserve-Alaska (a large area in the northern part of the state, formerly known as Naval Petroleum Reserve #4) and the Arctic Wildlife Range, it will come as no surprise to realize that the federal government will continue to own about two-thirds of all potential onshore oil and gas land in the state.

The federal presence is also partly due to the strategic importance of Alaska during and after World War II. Until the discovery of large oil reserves on the North Slope at Prudhoe Bay in 1968, U.S. military forces provided Alaska's single greatest source of income and employment. With the Prudhoe Bay lease sale in 1969, the basis of Alaska's economy changed drastically. Military Alaska, though much less important today, left its legacy, however, and the federal government still provides a critical number of jobs for Alaska residents.

A year or two before the Prudhoe Bay discovery was announced, a series of events that was to extend private land ownership to 44 million acres of federal land took place. In 1966, the Alaska natives (Indians, Eskimos, and Aleuts) combined eight of their regional associations into a statewide organization called the Alaska Federation of Natives. By 1967, this group had filed land claims based on aboriginal use and occupancy to most of Alaska. Secretary of the Interior Stewart Udall stopped all disposal of public lands in Alaska until these aboriginal claims could be settled. In the late 1960s, settlement became an urgent matter when the construction of the Alaskan pipeline was seen to be at stake. Congress passed the Alaska Native Claims Settlement Act in 1971, granting the natives title to 44 million acres—plus a cash bonus of nearly a billion dollars.

Transfer of both the land and the money required the creation of special institutions known as Native Corporations. The details of the transfer are extremely complex and will take time to implement, but the Native Corporations are now the largest *private* owners of land in the state. Their goals include, where feasible and not destructive of hunting, fishing, and other valuable resources, the development of such mineral reserves as may be discovered on Native Corporation property.

Completion of the trans-Alaska pipeline and passage of the Alaska National Interest Lands Conservation Act in 1980 are two factors presently encouraging the exploration of both state and federal lands. The Act of 1980 authorized establishment of a leasing program for non-North Slope federal land, and the state had, by 1982, outlined its own 5-year leasing program. Both federal and state procedures are complex and require detailed information gathering, public hearings, impact studies, and other preliminary steps before a lease sale is finally held.

It should be noted that, despite similarities in procedure, the state and the federal governments have come into conflict from time to time over the leasing of oil and gas lands. Proposed leasing in the Beaufort Sea, for example, has led to lawsuits and jurisdictional disputes. Private groups also call attention to conflicting goals among Alaska's citizens. The protection of the environment, for instance, is peculiarly complex, given the state's climatic conditions and the abundance of its wildlife. Despite the bounty to be tapped, then, and the encouragement given to petroleum companies, exploration and development in Alaska is unlikely to occur in a precipitous fashion. Federal, state, and private interests continue to exercise powerful influences upon one another and to pull, now together, now in opposition, as the state's resources are examined and prepared for leasing.

Included in this Appendix is the lease form most commonly used in Alaska, a federal lease form for submerged lands under the Outer Continental Shelf Act (fig. B.1). It has been slightly changed; note the pertinent text from the *Federal Register* that is appended (fig. B.2).

To learn more about mineral development and federal and state leasing practices in Alaska, write or telephone:

Alaska Department of Commerce
 and Economic Development
Pouch D
Juneau, AK 99811
907/465-2500

Alaska
Department of Natural Resources
Division of Mineral and
 Energy Management
Pouch 7-034
Anchorage, AK 99510
907/276-2653

Alaska Oil and Gas
 Conservation Commission
3001 Porcupine Drive
Anchorage, AK 99501
907/279-1433

National Petroleum Reserve in Alaska
NPRA District Operations Office
2525 C Street, Suite 400
Anchorage, AK 99503
907/276-7422

U.S. Department of Interior
Bureau of Land Management
Alaska State Office
Box 13
701 C Street
Anchorage, AK 99513
907/271-5960

U.S. Department of Interior
Bureau of Land Management
Fairbanks Land Office
Box 1150
Fairbanks, AK 99701
907/356-2025

U.S. Department of Interior
Minerals Management Service
Alaska OCS Region
Leasing and Environment
Box 101159
Anchorage, AK 99510
907/261-2414

Figure B.1. Federal lease form for submerged lands
(Courtesy of U. S. Department of the Interior)

Form MMS-2005 (August 1982) (formerly Form 3300-1)	Office	Serial number
UNITED STATES DEPARTMENT OF THE INTERIOR MINERALS MANAGEMENT SERVICE	Cash bonus	Rental rate per acre, hectare or fraction thereof
OIL AND GAS LEASE OF SUBMERGED LANDS UNDER THE OUTER CONTINENTAL SHELF LANDS ACT	Minimum royalty rate per acre, hectare or fraction thereof	Royalty rate
This form does not constitute an information collection as defined by 44 U.S.C. 3502 and therefore does not require approval by the Office of Management and Budget.	Work commitment	Profit share rate

This lease is effective as of   (hereinafter called the "Effective Date") and shall continue for an
initial period of   years (hereinafter called the "Initial Period") by and between the United States of America (hereinafter
called the "Lessor"), by the
Minerals Management Service, its authorized officer, and

(hereinafter called the "Lessee"). In consideration of any cash payment heretofore made by the Lessee to the Lessor and in consideration of the
promises, terms, conditions, and covenants contained herein, including the Stipulation(s) numbered
attached hereto, the Lessee and Lessor agree as follows:

Sec. 1. Statutes and Regulations. This lease is issued pursuant to the Outer Continental Shelf Lands Act of August 7, 1953,
67 Stat. 462; 43 U. S.C. 1331 et seq., as amended (92 Stat. 629), (hereinafter called the "Act"). The lease is issued subject to the Act; all regulations
issued pursuant to the statute and in existence upon the Effective Date of this lease; all regulations issued pursuant to the statute in the future which
provide for the prevention of waste and the conservation of the natural resources of the Outer Continental Shelf, and the protection of correlative
rights therein; and all other applicable statutes and regulations.

Sec. 2. Rights of Lessee. The Lessor hereby grants and leases to the Lessee the exclusive right and privilege to drill for, develop, and produce oil and gas resources, except helium gas, in the submerged lands of the Outer Continental Shelf containing approximately
                      acres or   hectares (hereinafter referred to as the "leased area"), described as follows:

Figure B.1 – *Continued*

These rights include:

(a) the nonexclusive right to conduct within the leased area geological and geophysical explorations in accordance with applicable regulations;

(b) the nonexclusive right to drill water wells within the leased area, unless the water is part of geopressured-geothermal and associated resources, and to use the water produced therefrom for operations pursuant to the Act free of cost, on the condition that the drilling is conducted in accordance with procedures approved by the Director of the Minerals Management Service or the Director's delegate (hereinafter called the "Director"); and

(c) the right to construct or erect and to maintain within the leased area artificial islands, installations, and other devices permanently or temporarily attached to the seabed and other works and structures necessary to the full enjoyment of the lease, subject to compliance with applicable laws and regulations.

Sec. 3. Term. This lease shall continue from the Effective Date of the lease for the Initial Period and so long thereafter as oil or gas is produced from the leased area in paying quantities, or drilling or well reworking operations, as approved by the Lessor, are conducted thereon.

Sec. 4. Rentals. The Lessee shall pay the Lessor, on or before the first day of each lease year which commences prior to a discovery in paying quantities of oil or gas on the leased area, a rental as shown on the face hereof.

Sec. 5. Minimum Royalty. The Lessee shall pay the Lessor at the expiration of each lease year which commences after a discovery of oil and gas in paying quantities, a minimum royalty as shown on the face hereof or, if there is production, the difference between the actual royalty required to be paid with respect to such lease year and the prescribed minimum royalty, if the actual royalty paid is less than the minimum royalty.

Sec. 6. Royalty on Production. (a) The Lessee shall pay a fixed royalty as shown on the face hereof in amount or value of production saved, removed, or sold from the leased area. Gas of all kinds (except helium) is subject to royalty. The Lessor shall determine whether production royalty shall be paid in amount or value.

(b) The value of production for purposes of computing royalty on production from this lease shall never be less than the fair market value of the production. The value of production shall be the estimated reasonable value of the production as determined by the Lessor, due consideration being given to the highest price paid for a part or for a majority of production of like quality in the same field or area, to the price received by the Lessee, to posted prices, to regulated prices, and to other relevant matters. Except when the Lessor, in its discretion, determines not to consider special pricing relief from otherwise applicable Federal regulatory requirements, the value of production for the purposes of computing royalty shall not be deemed to be less than the gross proceeds accruing to the Lessee from the sale thereof. In the absence of good reason to the contrary, value computed on the basis of the highest price paid or offered at the time of production in a fair and open market for the major portion of like-quality products produced and sold from the field or area where the leased area is situated, will be considered to be a reasonable value.

(c) When paid in value, royalties on production shall be due and payable monthly on the last day of the month next following the month in which the production is obtained, unless the Lessor designates a later time. When paid in amount, such royalties shall be delivered at

pipeline connections or in tanks provided by the Lessee. Such deliveries shall be made at reasonable times and intervals and, at the Lessor's option, shall be effected either (i) on or immediately adjacent to the leased area, without cost to the Lessor, or (ii) at a more convenient point closer to shore or on shore, in which event the Lessee shall be entitled to reimbursement for the reasonable cost of transporting the royalty substance to such delivery point. The Lessee shall not be required to provide storage for royalty paid in amount in excess of tankage required when royalty is paid in value. When royalties are paid in amount, the Lessee shall not be held liable for the loss or destruction of royalty oil or other liquid products in storage from causes over which the Lessee has no control.

Sec. 7. Payments. The Lessee shall make all payments to the Lessor by check, bank draft, or money order unless otherwise provided by regulations or by direction of the Lessor. Rentals, royalties, and any other payments required by this lease shall be made payable to the Minerals Management Service and tendered to the Director.

Sec. 8. Bonds. The Lessee shall maintain at all times the bond(s) required by regulation prior to the issuance of the lease and shall furnish such additional security as may be required by the Lessor if, after operations have begun, the Lessor deems such additional security to be necessary.

Sec. 9. Plans. The Lessee shall conduct all operations on the leased area in accordance with approved exploration plans, and approved development and production plans as are required by regulations. The Lessee may depart from an approved plan only as provided by applicable regulations.

Sec. 10. Performance. The Lessee shall comply with all regulations and orders relating to exploration, development, and production. After due notice in writing, the Lessee shall drill such wells and produce at such rates as the Lessor may require in order that the leased area or any part thereof may be properly and timely developed and produced in accordance with sound operating principles.

Sec. 11. Directional Drilling. A directional well drilled under the leased area from a surface location on nearby land not covered by this lease shall be deemed to have the same effect for all purposes of the lease as a well drilled from a surface location on the leased area. In those circumstances, drilling shall be considered to have been commenced on the leased area when drilling is commenced on the nearby land for the purpose of directionally drilling under the leased area, and production of oil or gas from the leased area through any directional well surfaced on nearby land or drilling or reworking of any such directional well shall be considered production or drilling or reworking operations on the leased area for all purposes of the lease. Nothing contained in this Section shall be construed as granting to the Lessee any interest, license, easement, or other right in any nearby land.

Sec. 12. Safety Requirements. The Lessee shall (a) maintain all places of employment within the leased area in compliance with occupational safety and health standards and, in addition, free from recognized hazards to employees of the Lessee or of any contractor or subcontractor operating within the leased area;

(b) maintain all operations within the leased area in compliance with regulations intended to protect persons, property, and the environment on the Outer Continental Shelf; and

(c) allow prompt access, at the site of any operation subject to safety regulations, to any authorized Federal inspector and shall provide any documents and records which are pertinent to occupational or public health, safety, or environmental protection as may be requested.

Figure B.1 – *Continued*

Sec. 13. Suspension and Cancellation. (a) The Lessor may suspend or cancel this lease pursuant to Section 5 of the Act and compensation shall be paid when provided by the Act.

(b) The Lessor may, upon recommendation of the Secretary of Defense, during a state of war or national emergency declared by Congress or the President of the United States, suspend operations under the lease, as provided in Section 12(c) of the Act, and just compensation shall be paid to the Lessee for such suspension.

Sec. 14. Indemnification. The Lessee shall indemnify the Lessor for, and hold it harmless from, any claim, including claims for loss or damage to property or injury to persons caused by or resulting from any operation on the leased area conducted by or on behalf of the Lessee. However, the Lessee shall not be held responsible to the Lessor under this section for any loss, damage, or injury caused by or resulting from:

(a) negligence of the Lessor other than the commission or omission of a discretionary function or duty on the part of a Federal agency whether or not the discretion involved is abused; or

(b) the Lessee's compliance with an order or directive of the Lessor against which an administrative appeal by the Lessee is filed before the cause of action for the claim arises and is pursued diligently thereafter.

Sec. 15. Disposition of Production. (a) As provided in Section 27(a)(2) of the Act, the Lessor shall have the right to purchase not more than 16-2/3 percent by volume of the oil and gas produced pursuant to the lease at the regulated price, or if no regulated price applies, at the fair market value at the wellhead of the oil and gas saved, removed, or sold, except that any oil or gas obtained by the Lessor as royalty or net profit share shall be credited against the amount that may be purchased under this subsection.

(b) As provided in Section 27(d) of the Act, the Lessee shall take any Federal oil or gas for which no acceptable bids are received, as determined by the Lessor, and which is not transferred to a Federal agency pursuant to Section 27(a)(3) of the Act, and shall pay to the Lessor a cash amount equal to the regulated price, or if no regulated price applies, the fair market value of the oil or gas so obtained.

(c) As provided in Section 8(b)(7) of the Act, the Lessee shall offer 20 percent of the crude oil, condensate, and natural gas liquids produced on the lease, at the market value and point of delivery as provided by regulations applicable to Federal royalty oil, to small or independent refiners as defined in the Emergency Petroleum Allocation Act of 1973.

(d) In time of war, or when the President of the United States shall so prescribe, the Lessor shall have the right of first refusal to purchase at the market price all or any portion of the oil or gas produced from the leased area, as provided in Section 12(b) of the Act.

Sec. 16. Unitization, Pooling, and Drilling Agreements. Within such time as the Lessor may prescribe, the Lessee shall subscribe to and operate under a unit, pooling, or drilling agreement embracing all or part of the lands subject to this lease as the Lessor may determine to be appropriate or necessary. Where any provision of a unit, pooling, or drilling agreement, approved by the Lessor, is inconsistent with a provision of this lease, the provision of the agreement shall govern.

Sec. 17. Equal Opportunity Clause. During the performance of this lease, the Lessee shall fully comply with paragraphs (1) through (7) of Section 202 of Executive Order 11246, as amended (reprinted in 41 CFR 60–1.4(a)), and the implementing regulations, which are for the purpose of preventing employment discrimination against persons on the basis of race, color, religion, sex, or national origin. Paragraphs (1) through (7) of Section 202 of Executive Order 11246, as amended, are incorporated in this lease by reference.

Sec. 18. Certification of Nonsegregated Facilities. By entering into this lease, the Lessee certifies, as specified in 41 CFR 60–1.8, that it does not and will not maintain or provide for its employees any segregated facilities at any of its establishments, and that it does not and will not permit its employees to perform their services at any location under its control where segregated facilities are maintained. As used in this certification, the term "segregated facilities" means, but is not limited to, any waiting rooms, work areas, restrooms and washrooms, restaurants and other eating areas, timeclocks, locker rooms and other storage or dressing areas, parking lots, drinking fountains, recreation or entertainment areas, transportation, and housing facilities provided for employees which are segregated by explicit directive or are in fact segregated on the basis of race, color, religion, or national origin, because of habit, local custom, or otherwise. The Lessee further agrees that it will obtain identical certifications from proposed contractors and subcontractors prior to award of contracts or subcontracts unless they are exempt under 41 CFR 60–1.5.

Sec. 19. Reservations to Lessor. All rights in the leased area not expressly granted to the Lessee by the Act, the regulations, or this lease are hereby reserved to the Lessor. Without limiting the generality of the foregoing, reserved rights include:

(a) the right to authorize geological and geophysical exploration in the leased area which does not unreasonably interfere with or endanger actual operations under the lease, and the right to grant such easements or rights-of-way upon, through, or in the leased area as may be necessary or appropriate to the working of other lands or to the treatment and shipment of products thereof by or under authority of the Lessor;

(b) the right to grant leases for any minerals other than oil and gas within the leased area, except that operations under such leases shall not unreasonably interfere with or endanger operations under this lease;

(c) the right, as provided in Section 12(d) of the Act, to restrict operations in the leased area or any part thereof which may be designated by the Secretary of Defense, with approval of the President, as being within an area needed for national defense, and so long as such designation remains in effect no operations may be conducted on the surface of the leased area or the part thereof included within the designation except with the concurrence of the Secretary of Defense. If operations or production under this lease within any designated area are suspended pursuant to this paragraph, any payments of rentals and royalty prescribed by this lease likewise shall be suspended during such period of suspension of operations and production, and the term of this lease shall be extended by adding thereto any such suspension period, and the Lessor shall be liable to the Lessee for such compensation as is required to be paid under the Constitution of the United States.

Sec. 20. Transfer of Lease. The Lessee shall file for approval with the appropriate field office of the Minerals Management Service any instrument of assignment or other transfer of this lease, or any interest therein, in accordance with applicable regulations.

Figure B.1 – *Continued*

Sec. 21. Surrender of Lease. The Lessee may surrender this entire lease or any officially designated subdivision of the leased area by filing with the appropriate field office of the Minerals Management Service a written relinquishment, in triplicate, which shall be effective as of the date of filing. No surrender of this lease or of any portion of the leased area shall relieve the Lessee or its surety of the obligation to pay all accrued rentals, royalties, and other financial obligations or to abandon all wells on the area to be surrendered in a manner satisfactory to the Director.

Sec. 22. Removal of Property on Termination of Lease. Within a period of one year after termination of this lease in whole or in part, the Lessee shall remove all devices, works, and structures from the premises no longer subject to the lease in accordance with applicable regulations and orders of the Director. However, the Lessee may, with the approval of the Director, continue to maintain devices, works, and structures on the leased area for drilling or producing on other leases.

Sec. 23. Remedies in Case of Default. (a) Whenever the Lessee fails to comply with any of the provisions of the Act, the regulations issued pursuant to the Act, or the terms of this lease, the lease shall be subject to cancellation in accordance with the provisions of Section 5(c) and (d) of the Act and the Lessor may exercise any other remedies which the Lessor may have, including the penalty provisions of Section 24 of the Act. Furthermore, pursuant to Section 8(o) of the Act, the Lessor may cancel the lease if it is obtained by fraud or misrepresentation.

(b) Nonenforcement by the Lessor of a remedy for any particular violation of the provisions of the Act, the regulations issued pursuant to the Act, or the terms of this lease shall not prevent the cancellation of this lease or the exercise of any other remedies under paragraph (a) of this section for any other violation or for the same violation occurring at any other time.

Sec. 24. Unlawful Interest. No member of, or Delegate to, Congress, or Resident Commissioner, after election or appointment, or either before or after they have qualified, and during their continuance in office, and no officer, agent, or employee of the Department of the Interior, except as provided in 43 CFR Part 7, shall be admitted to any share or part in this lease or derive any benefit that may arise therefrom. The provisions of Section 3741 of the Revised Statutes, as amended, 41 U.S.C. 22, and the Act of June 25, 1948, 62 Stat. 702, as amended, 18 U.S.C. 431–433, relating to contracts made or entered into, or accepted by or on behalf of the United States, form a part of this lease insofar as they may be applicable.

THE UNITED STATES OF AMERICA, Lessor

_____
(Lessee)

_____
(Signature of Authorized Officer)

_____
(Name of Signatory)

_____
(Title)

_____
(Date)

_____
(Address of Lessee)

_____
(Signature of Authorized Officer)

_____
(Name of Signatory)

_____
(Title)

_____
(Date)

Figure B.1 – *Continued*

_____   _____
(Lessee)   (Lessee)

_____   _____
(Signature of Authorized Officer)   (Signature of Authorized Officer)

_____   _____
(Name of Signatory)   (Name of Signatory)

_____   _____
(Title)   (Title)

_____   _____
(Date)   (Date)

_____   _____
(Address of Lessee)   (Address of Leesee)

_____   _____
(Lessee)   (Lessee)

_____   _____
(Signature of Authorized Officer)   (Signature of Authorized Officer)

_____   _____
(Name of Signatory)   (Name of Signatory)

_____   _____
(Title)   (Title)

_____   _____
(Date)   (Date)

_____   _____
(Address of Lessee)   (Address of Lessee)

If this lease is executed by a corporation, it must bear the corporate seal.

Figure B.2. Notice of revised lease form
(*Federal Register,* Nov. 22, 1983)

Oil and Gas Operations on the Outer Continental Shelf; Revised Lease Form

AGENCY: Minerals Management Service, Interior.

ACTION: Notice of revised lease form.

SUMMARY: This Notice informs the public of revisions to the lease form for oil and gas operations on the Outer Continental Shelf. The Minerals Management Service (MMS) is making these changes to clarify and otherwise improve the form.

EFFECTIVE DATE: The effective date of the revised form will be announced in the notices of lease offering for particular oil and gas lease offerings.

FOR FURTHER INFORMATION CONTACT: Mr. David A. Shuenke, telephone (703) 850-7916, (FTS) 928-7916.

SUPPLEMENTARY INFORMATION: The MMS has revised the lease form for oil and gas operations offshore. The revisions are intended to remove confusing and unnecessary information, clarify the language of the lease form, and otherwise improve the lease form. The following changes have been made to the lease form:

1. In Section 1, *Statutes and Regulations*, the phrase "which provides for the prevention of waste and the conservation of the natural resources of the Outer Continental Shelf, and the protection of correlative rights therein," has been deleted. The revisions are intended to clarify for the benefit of the lessee and the lessor the existing policy that leases are subject to all relevant regulations, including those to be issued in the future, and not only those in effect at the time the lease is executed. The deleted portion has been interpreted to include all regulations but has been known to cause confusion as to whether some future regulations are not covered in the three categories listed.

2. In Section 3, *Term*, the phrase "or as otherwise provided by regulation" is added to the end of the last sentence. The added phrase alerts the lessee that there may be methods for extending a lease term, other than production and drilling or well reworking, such as suspensions of production or other operations as may be appropriate under certain circumstances and as authorized by the regulations.

3. In part (a) of Section 6, *Royalty on Production*, "Gas of all kinds (except helium)" is replaced by "Gas (except helium) and oil of all kinds" and the sentence "Any Lessee is liable for royalty payments on oil or gas lost or wasted from a lease site when such loss or waste is due to negligence on the part of the operator of the lease, or due to the

failure to comply with any rule or regulation, order, or citation issued under the Federal Oil and Gas Royalty Management Act of 1982 or any mineral leasing law." is added between the second and third sentences. These additions are made to implement section 308 of the Federal Oil and Gas Royalty Management Act of 1982.

4. In the third sentence of part (c) of Section 6, *Royalty on Production*, the phrase "in which event the Lessee shall be entitled to" is replaced by "in which event the Lessee may be entitled to" and "as part of the royalty value determination" is added to the end of the sentence. The change is intended to clarify that the lessee is not automatically entitled to reimbursement for the reasonable cost of transporting the royalty substance but may be entitled under certain circumstances.

5. In Section 7, *Payments*, the new sentence "Determinations made by the Lessor as to the amount of payment due shall be presumed to be correct and paid as due." is added as the last sentence in the section. This addition is intended to clarify that the lessee is obligated to pay the amount due as determined by MMS and requires payment of the amount determined by MMS while any dispute is being settled.

6. In Section 10, *Performance*, the phrase "relating to exploration, development, and production" is deleted from the first sentence. This modification is intended to clarify the existing policy that the lessee must comply with all regulations and Orders.

7. In part (b) of Section 12, *Safety Requirements*, the phrase "compliance with regulations" is replaced with the phrase "compliance with regulations or orders." This addition is a clarification of existing policy and specifically alerts the lessee that operations must comply with the more detailed requirements of orders as well as the regulations.

8. In part (b) of Section 15, *Disposition of Production*, the sentence "Pursuant to section 27 (b) and (c) of the Act, the Lessor may offer and sell certain oil and gas obtained or purchased pursuant to a lease." is added as the first sentence. This addition is intended to clarify the provisions of part (b) of Section 15.

The following lease form will be used by MMS for all lease sales after the effective date given in the preamble.

Dated: November 9, 1983.

David C. Russell,

Acting Director, Minerals Management Service.

Form MMS-2005

(October 1983)

United States Department of the Interior Minerals Management Service.	Office	Serial number
Oil and Gas Lease of Submerged Lands Under the Outer Continental Shelf Lands Act.	Cash bonus	Rental rate per acre, hectare or fraction thereof
This form does not constitute an information collection as defined by 44 U.S.C. 3502 and therefore does not require approval by the Office of Management and Budget.	Minimum royalty rate per acre, hectare or fraction thereof	Royalty rate
		Profit share rate.

This lease is effective as of —————— (hereinafter called the "Effective Date") and shall continue for an initial period of —————— years (hereinafter called the "Initial Period") by and between the United States of America (hereinafter called the "Lessor"), by the —————— Minerals Management Service, its authorized officer, and

——————————————

(hereinafter called the "Lessee"). In consideration of any cash payment heretofore made by the Lessee to the Lessor and in consideration of the promises, terms, conditions, and covenants contained herein, including the Stipulation(s) numbered—————— attached hereto, the Lessee and Lessor agree as follows:

Sec. 1. *Statutes and Regulations.* This lease is issued pursuant to the Outer Continental Shelf Lands Act of August 7, 1953, 67 Stat. 462; 43 U.S.C. 1331 et seq., as amended (92 Stat. 629) (hereinafter called the "Act"). The lease is issued subject to the Act; all regulations issued pursuant to the Act and in existence upon the Effective Date of this lease; all regulations issued pursuant to the Act in the future; and all other applicable statutes and regulations.

Sec. 2. *Rights of Lessee.* The Lessor hereby grants and leases to the Lessee the exclusive right and privilege to drill for, develop, and produce oil and gas resources, except helium gas, in the submerged lands of the Outer Continental Shelf containing approximately—————— acres or—————— hectares (hereinafter referred to as the "leased area"), described as follows:

——————————————

The rights include:

(a) the nonexclusive right to conduct within the leased area geological and geophysical explorations in accordance with applicable regulations;

(b) the nonexclusive right to drill water wells within the leased area, unless the water is part of geopressured-geothermal and associated resources, and to use the water produced therefrom for operations pursuant to the Act free of cost, on the condition that the drilling is conducted in accordance with procedures approved by the Director of the Minerals Management Service or the Director's delegate (hereinafter called the "Director"); and

(c) the right to construct or erect and to maintain within the leased area artificial islands, installations, and other devices permanently or temporarily attached to the seabed and other works and structures necessary to the full enjoyment of the lease, subject to compliance with applicable laws and regulations.

Sec. 3. *Term.* This lease shall continue from the Effectie Date of the lease for the Initial Period and so long thereafter as oil or gas is produced from the leased area in paying quantities, or drilling or well reworking operations, as approved by the Lessor, are conducted thereon or as otherwise provided by regulation.

Sec. 4. *Rentals.* The lessee shall pay the Lessor, on or before the first day of each lease year which commences prior to a discovery in paying quantities of oil or gas on the leased area, a rental as shown on the face hereof.

Sec. 5. *Minimum Royalty.* The Lessee shall pay the Lessor, at the expiration of each lease year which commences after a discovery of oil and gas in paying quantities, a minimum royalty as shown on the face hereof or, if there is production, the difference between the actual royalty required to be paid with respect to such lease year and the prescribed minimum royalty if the actual royalty paid is less than the minimum royalty.

Sec. 6. *Royalty of Production.* (a) The Lessee shall pay a fixed royalty as shown on the face hereof in amount or amount or value of production saved, removed, or sold from the leased area. Gas (except helium) and oil of all kinds are subject to royalty. Any Lessee is liable for royalty payments on oil or gas lost or wasted from a lease site when such loss or waste is due to negligence on the part of the operator of the lease, or due to the failure to comply with any rule or regulation, order, or citation issued under the Federal Oil and Gas Royalty Management Act of 1982 or any mineral leasing law. The Lessor shall determine whether production royalty shall be paid in amount or value.

(b) The value of production for purposes of computing royalty on

production from this lease shall never be less than the fair market value of the production. The value of production shall be the estimated reasonable value of the production as determined by the Lessor, due consideration being given to the highest price paid for a part or for a majority of production of like quality in the same field or area, to the price received by the Lessee, to posted prices, to regulated prices, and to other relevant matters. Except when the Lessor, in its discretion, determines not to consider special pricing relief from otherwise applicable Federal regulatory requirements, the value of production for the purposes of computing royalty shall not be deemed to be less than the gross proceeds accruing to the Lessee from the sale thereof. In the absence of good reason to the contrary, value computed on the basis of the highest price paid or offered at the time of production in a fair and open market for the major portion of like-quality products produced and sold from the field or area where the leased area is situated will be considered to be a reasonable value.

(c) When paid in value, royalties on production shall be due and payable monthly on the last day of the month next following the month in which the production is obtained, unless the Lessor designates a later time. When paid in amount, such royalties shall be delivered at pipeline connections or in tanks provided by the Lessee. Such deliveries shall be made at reasonable times and intervals and, at the Lessor's option, shall be effected either (i) on or immediately adjacent to the leased area, without cost to the Lessor, or (ii) at a more convenient point closer to shore or on shore, in which event the Lessee may be entitled to reimbursement for the reasonable cost of transporting the royalty substance to such delivery point as part of the royalty value determination. The Lessee shall not be required to provide storage for royalty paid in amount in excess of tankage required when royalty is paid in value. When royalties are paid in amount, the Lessee shall not be held liable for the loss or destruction or royalty oil or other liquid products in storage from causes over which the Lessee has no control.

Sec. 7. *Payments.* The Lessee shall make all payments to the Lessor by check, bank draft, or money order unless otherwise provided by regulations or by direction of the Lessor. Rentals, royalties, and any other payments required by this lease shall be made payable to the Minerals Management Service and tendered to the Director. Determinations made by the Lessor as

to the amount of payment due shall be presumed to be correct and paid as due.

Sec. 8. *Bonds.* The Lessee shall maintain at all times the bond(s) required by regulation prior to the issuance of the lease and shall furnish such additional security as may be required by the Lessor if, after operations have begun, the Lessor deems such additional security to be necessary.

Sec. 9. *Plans.* The Lessee shall conduct all operations on the leased area in accordance with approved exploration plans and approved development and production plans as are required by regulations. The Lessee may depart from an approved plan only as provided by applicable regulations.

Sec. 10. *Performance.* The Lessee shall comply with all Regulations and Orders. After due notice in writing, the Lessee shall drill such wells and produce at such rates as the Lessor may require in order that the leased area or any part thereof may be properly and timely developed and produced in accordance with sound operating principles.

Sec. 11. *Directional Drilling.* A directional well drilled under the leased area from a surface location on nearby land not covered by this lease shall be deemed to have the same effect for all purposes of the lease as a well drilled from a surface location on the leased area. In those circumstances, drilling shall be considered to have been commenced on the leased area when drilling is commenced on the nearby land for the purpose of directionally drilling under the leased area, and production of oil or gas from the leased area through any directional well surfaced on nearby land or drilling or reworking of any such directional well shall be considered production or drilling or reworking operations on the leased area for all purposes of the lease. Nothing contained in this Section shall be construed as granting to the Lessee any interest, license, easement, or other right in any nearby land.

Sec. 12. *Safety Requirements.* The Lessee shall: (a) maintain all places of employment within the leased area in compliance with occupational safety and health standards and, in addition, free from recognized hazards to employees of the Lessee or of any contractor or subcontractor operating within the leased area;

(b) maintain all operations within the leased area in compliance with regulations or orders intended to protect persons, property, and the environment on the Outer Continental Shelf; and

(c) allow prompt access, at the site of any operation subject to safety

Figure B.2 – *Continued*

regulation, to any authorized Federal inspector and shall provide any documents and records which are pertinent to occupational or public health, safety, or environmental protection as may be requested.

Sec. 13. *Suspension and Cancellation.* (a) The Lessor may suspend or cancel this lease pursuant to section 5 of the Act, and compensation shall be paid when provided by the Act.

(b) The Lessor may, upon recommendation of the Secretary of Defense, during a state or war or national emergency declared by Congress or the President of the United States, suspend operations under the lease, as provided in section 12(c) of the Act, and just compensation shall be paid to the Lessee for such suspension.

Sec. 14. *Indemnification.* The Lessee shall indemnify the Lessor for, and hold it harmless from, any claim, including claims for loss or damage to property or injury to persons caused by or resulting from any operation on the leased area conducted by or on behalf of the Lessee. However, the Lessee shall not be held responsible to the Lessor under this section for any loss, damage, or injury caused by or resulting from:

(a) negligence of the Lessor other than the commission or omission of a discretionary function or duty on the part of a Federal Agency whether or not the discretion involved is abused; or

(b) the Lessee's compliance with an order or directive of the Lessor against which an administrative appeal by the Lessee is filed before the cause of action for the claim arises and is pursued diligently thereafter.

Sec. 15. *Disposition of Production.* (a) As provided in section 27(a)(2) of the Act, the Lessor shall have the right to purchase not more than 16⅔ percent by volume of the oil and gas produced pursuant to the lease at the regulated price, or if no regulated price applies, at the fair market value at the wellhead of the oil and gas saved, removed, or sold, except that any oil or gas obtained by the Lessor as royalty or net profit share shall be credited against the amount that may be purchased under this subsection.

(b) Pursuant to section 27 (b) and (c) of the Act, the Lessor may offer and sell certain oil and gas obtained or purchased pursuant to a lease. As provided in section 27(d) of the Act, the Lessee shall take any Federal oil or gas for which no acceptable bids are received, as determined by the Lessor, and which is not transferred to a Federal Agency pursuant to section 27(a)(3) of the Act, and shall pay to the Lessor a cash amount equal to the regulated price, or if no regulated price

applies, the fair market value of the oil or gas so obtained.

(c) As provided in section 8(b)(7) of the Act, the Lessee shall offer 20 percent of the crude oil, condensate, and natural gas liquids produced on the lease, at the market value and point of delivery as provided by regulations applicable to Federal royalty oil, to small or independent refiners as defined in the Emergency Petroleum Allocation Act of 1973.

(d) In time of war, or when the President of the United States shall so prescribe, the Lessor shall have the right of first refusal to purchase at the market price all or any portion of the oil or gas produced from the leased area, as provided in section 12(b) of the Act.

Sec. 16. *Unitization, Pooling, and Drilling Agreements.* Within such time as the Lessor may prescribe, the Lessee shall subscribe to and operate under a unit, pooling, or drilling agreement embracing all or part of the lands subject to this lease as the Lessor may determine to be appropriate or necessary. Where any provision of a unit, pooling, or drilling agreement, approved by the Lessor, is inconsistent with a provision of this lease, the provision of the agreement shall govern.

Sec. 17. *Equal Opportunity Clause.* During the performance of this lease, the Lessee shall fully comply with paragraphs (1) through (7) of section 202 of Executive Order 11246, as amended (reprinted in 41 CFR 60–1.4(a)), and the implementing regulations which are for the purpose preventing employment discrimination against persons on the basis of race, color, religion, sex, or national origin. Paragraphs (1) through (7) of section 202 of Executive Order 11246, as amended, are incorporated in this lease by reference.

Sec. 18. *Certification of Non-segregated Facilities.* By entering into this lease, the Lessee certifies, as specified in 41 CFR 60–1.8, that it does not and will not maintain or provide for its employees any segregated facilities at any of its establishments and that it does not and will not permit its employees to perform their services at any location under its control where segregated facilities are maintained. As used in this certification, the term "segregated facilities" means, but is not limited to, any waiting rooms, work areas, restrooms and washrooms, restaurants and other eating areas, timeclocks, locker rooms and other storage or dressing areas, parking lots, drinking fountains, recreation or entertainment areas, transportation, and housing facilities provided for employees which are segregated by explicit directive or are in fact

segregated on the basis of race, color, religion, or national origin, because of habit, local custom, or otherwise. The Lessee further agrees that it will obtain identical certifications from proposed contractors and subcontractors prior to award of contracts or subcontracts unless they are exempt under 41 CFR 60–1.5.

Sec. 19. *Reservations to Lessor.* All rights in the leased area not expressly granted to the Lessee by the Act, the regulations, or this lease are hereby reserved to the Lessor. Without limiting the generality of the foregoing, reserved rights include:

(a) the right to authorize geological and geophysical exploration in the leased area which does not unreasonably interfere with or endanger actual operations under the lease, and the right to grant such easements or rights-of-way upon, through, or in the leased area as may be necessary or appropriate to the working of other lands or to the treatment and shipment of products thereof by or under authority of the Lessor;

(b) the right to grant leases for any minerals other than oil and gas within the leased area, except that operations under such leases shall not unreasonably interfere with or endanger operations under this lease;

(c) the right, as provided in section 12(d) of the Act, to restrict operations in the leased area or any part thereof which may be designated by the Secretary of Defense, with approval of the President, as being within an area needed for national defense, and so long as such designation remains in effect, no operations may be conducted on the surface of the leased area or the part thereof included within the designation except with the concurrence of the Secretary of Defense. If operations or production under this lease within any designated area are suspended pursuant to this paragraph, any payments of rentals and royalty prescribed by this lease likewise shall be suspended during such period of suspension of operations and production, the term of this lease shall be extended by adding thereto any such suspension period, and the Lessor shall be liable to the Lessee for such compensation as is required to be paid under the Constitution of the United States.

Sec. 20. *Transfer of Lease.* The Lessee shall file for approval with the appropriate field office of the Minerals Management Service any instrument of assignment or other transfer of this lease, or any interest therein, in accordance with applicable regulations.

Figure B.2 — Continued

Sec. 21. *Surrender of Lease*. The Lessee may surrender this entire lease or any officially designated subdivision of the leased area by filing with the appropriate field office of the Minerals Management Service a written relinquishment, in triplicate, which shall be effective as of the date of filing. No surrender of this lease or of any portion of the leased area shall relieve the Lessee or its surety of the obligation to pay all accrued rentals, royalties, and other financial obligations or to abandon all wells on the area to be surrendered in a manner satisfactory to the Director.

Sec. 22. *Removal of Property on Termination of Lease*. Within a period of 1 year after termination of this lease in whole or in part, the Lessee shall remove all devices, works, and structures from the premises no longer subject to the lease in accordance with applicable regulations and Orders of the Director. However, the Lessee may, with the approval of the Director, continue to maintain devices, works, and structures on the leased area for drilling or producing on other leases.

Sec. 23. *Remedies in Case of Default*. (a) Whenever the Lessee fails to comply with any of the provisions of the Act, the regulations issued pursuant to the Act, or the terms of this lease, the lease shall be subject to cancellation in accordance with the provisions of section 5 (c) and (d) of the Act and the Lessor may exercise any other remedies which the Lessor may have, including the penalty provisions of section 24 of the Act. Furthermore, pursuant to section 8(o) of the Act, the Lessor may cancel the lease if it is obtained by fraud or misrepresentation.

(b) Nonenforcement by the Lessor of a remedy for any particular violation of the provisions of the Act, the regulations issued pursuant to the Act, or the terms of this lease shall not prevent the cancellation of this lease or the exercise of any other remedies under paragraph (a) of this section for any other violation or for the same violation occurring at any other time.

Sec. 24. *Unlawful Interest*. No member of, or Delegate to, Congress or Resident Commissioner, after election or appointment, or either before or after they have qualified, and during their continuance in office, and no officer, agent, or employee of the Department of the Interior, except as provided in 43 CFR Part 20, shall be admitted to any share or part in this lease or derive any benefit that may arise therefrom. The provisions of Section 3741 of the Revised Statutes, as amended, 41 U.S.C. 22, and the Act of June 25, 1948, 62 Stat. 702, as amended, 18 U.S.C. 431–433,

relating to contracts made or entered into, or accepted by or on behalf of the United States, form a part of this lease insofar as they may applicable.

(Lessee) —————
(Signature of Authorized Officer) ——

(Name of Signatory) ————
(Title) ————
(Date) ————
(Address of Lessee) ————
The United States of America, Lessor
(Signature of Authorized Officer) ——

(Name of Signatory) ————
(Title) ————
(Date) ————
(Lessee) ————
(Signature of Authorized Officer) ·——

(Name of Signatory) ————
(Title) ————
(Date) ————
(Address of Lessee) ————
(Lessee) ————
(Signature of Authorized Officer) ——

(Name of Signatory) ————
(Title) ————
(Date) ————
(Address of Lessee) ————
(Lessee) ————
(Signature of Authorized Officer) ——

(Name of Signatory) ————
(Title) ————
(Date) ————
(Address of Lessee) ————
(Lessee) ————
(Signature of Authorized Officer) ——

(Name of Signatory) ————
(Title) ————
(Date) ————
(Address of Lessee) ————
(Lessee) ————
(Signature of Authorized Officer) ——

(Name of Signatory) ————
(Title) ————
(Date) ————
(Address of Lessee) ————
(Lessee) ————
(Signature of Authorized Officer) ——

(Name of Signatory) ————
(Title) ————
(Date) ————
(Address of Lessee) ————
(Lessee) ————
(Signature of Authorized Officer) ——

(Name of Signatory) ————
(Title) ————
(Date) ————
(Address of Lessee) ————

If this lease is executed by a corporation, it must bear the corporate seal.

[FR Doc. 83–31270 Filed 11–21–83; 8:45 am]
BILLING CODE 4310–MR–M

Oil and Gas and Sulphur Operations in the Outer Continental Shelf; ODECO Oil and Gas Co.

AGENCY: Minerals Service, Interior.

ACTION: Notice of the receipt of a proposed development and production plan.

SUMMARY: Notice is hereby given that ODECO Oil and Gas Company has submitted a Development and Production Plan describing the activities it proposes to conduct on Lease OCS–G 3164, Block 135, Ship Shoal Area, offshore Louisiana.

The purpose of this Notice is to inform the public, pursuant to Section 25 of the OCS Lands Act Amendments of 1978, that the Minerals Management Service is considering approval of the Plan and that it is available for public review at the Office of the Regional Manager, Gulf of Mexico Region, Minerals Management Service, 3301 North Causeway Blvd., Room 147, Metairie, Louisiana 70002.

FOR FURTHER INFORMATION CONTACT: Minerals Management Service, Public Records, Room 147, open weekdays 9 a.m. to 3:30 p.m., 3301 North Causeway Blvd., Metairie, Louisiana 70002, Phone (504) 838–0519.

SUPPLEMENTARY INFORMATION: Revised rules governing practices and procedures under which the Minerals Management Service makes information contained in Development and Production Plans available to affected States, executives of affected local governments, and other interested parties became effective December 13, 1979 (44 FR 53685). Those practices and procedures are set out in a revised § 250.34 of Title 30 of the Code of Federal Regulations.

Dated: November 14, 1983.

John L. Rankin,
Regional Manager, Gulf of Mexico Region.
[FR Doc. 83–31304 Filed 11–21–83; 8:45 am]
BILLING CODE 4310–MR–M

National Park Service

National Register of Historic Places; Notification of Pending Nominations

Nominations for the following properties being considered for listing in the National Register were received by the National Park Service before November 12, 1983. Pursuant to § 60.13 of 36 CFR Part 60 written comments concerning the significance of these properties under the National Register criteria for evaluation may be forwarded to the National Register, National Park

APPENDIX C
LEASING IN CALIFORNIA

Leasing in California differs from leasing in other states in two important ways. The first involves the routine purchase of title insurance for drill sites and the correspondingly larger role played by title companies in checking and reporting on tract titles. The second involves the lease forms, which are considerably longer and more detailed than forms in other states—so long and detailed, in fact, as to encourage the use of additional short forms to lower recording costs and protect confidentiality.

Title insurance that covers the tracts making up a drill site is purchased by the lessee from a title company. (Insuring *all* the tracts in an acquired block of leases usually costs more in time and money than lessees are willing to pay.) The lessee's landman or lease broker has already made a preliminary check of all the tracts in a block in order to locate and contact the mineral owners. This preliminary title check often requires going no further than the records of the title company, though the county records are also available to be examined. Such a check by a landman will often be adequate for all tracts except those in the drill site. The drill site tracts will be insured, and for those the lessee needs a more thorough investigation.

Obtaining an Oil Leasehold Report from the title company will give the lessee a list of any clouds, liens, or other problems with the titles he is most concerned about. The lessee can then arrange to have these defects cured. Curing the titles should remove any impediments to the issuing of a leasehold policy of title insurance. The lessee will specify how much insurance he wants. On less important leases, the amount may be only a few thousand dollars. For such an amount, the title company does not always check the chain of title back to the original patent. Larger amounts in the neighborhood of $100,000 or more guarantee a thorough title check, often reviewed by the title company's home office. An insurance policy that protects the lessee against unforeseen title defects or encumbrances can then be issued.

In California, the surface of the land is often so valuable that landowners require lease forms with very detailed provisions for drilling, equipment placement, and other uses of the surface. Some leases forbid drilling on the leased surface; some specify particular sites to which drilling must be confined and for which a surface rental must be paid. So carefully are the terms laid out that implied covenants are few; many lease forms contain a clause that prevents implied covenants from being read into the lease. The resulting long lease forms are rarely recorded. Instead, petroleum companies often use short forms that give the essentials—names, dates, land descriptions, and a sentence or two identifying the short forms with their longer counterparts. A short form thus stands for a particular long form. Recording these short forms is relatively inexpensive and avoids making the particulars, like royalty figures, available for public inspection. A final difference between California and most other producing states may be found in the fact that production does not routinely lead to the execution of division orders. Division orders tend to be used only in doubtful cases where an estate may present special problems, where fractional interests may be open to question, and so forth.

Examples of a California Oil Leasehold Report (fig. C.1), a California lease form

Figure C.1. California oil leasehold report
(Courtesy of AAPL)

OIL LEASEHOLD REPORT*

(Not to be used for subleases, Royalties, Production Payments and Like Interests)
Issued for the sole use of: Order No. _____
_____   Lease No. _____
_____
_____
Attn: _____
This report on the title to the leasehold estate hereinafter described is issued as an accommodation, and is made without liability and without obligation to issue a policy.
Dated as of_____at 7:30 a.m._____
                                                                    Title Officer

(1) The "leasehold," title to which is covered by this report, consists of those rights and interests in the land described in paragraph (4) herein, which are set forth in and are demised, granted, or otherwise conveyed to the lessee by the terms of that certain

(2) The title to said land, at the time of the recording of said lease, was vested in

(3) The title of the leasehold described in paragraph (1), at the date hereof, is vested in

(4) The land, subject to said lease, and which is referred to in this report as "said land," is described as:

(5) The title to the land described in paragraph (4) herein is subject to the following defects, liens and encumbrances existing at the date of the recordation of said lease and still existing at the date of this report:

    1. Unpatented mining claims.
    2.
    3.
    4.
    5.
    6.   To be completed by Title Officer
    7.
    8.
    9.
    10.

(6) The title to the leasehold described in paragraph (1) herein is subject to the following defects, liens and encumbrances, in addition to those set forth in paragraph (5) herein:

    1.
    2.   To be completed by Title Officer
    3.

NOTE NO. 1: Item No. 1 under paragraph (5) above will appear in Part One of Schedule B of the policy when written.
NOTE NO. . . . .: The following under paragraph (6) above will appear in part One of Schedule B of the policy when written.
Item:
NOTE NO. . . . .: In addition to any exception shown herein, and not cleared, the policy if issued will contain stipulations and also exceptions as to matters outside its coverage which are required by the particular form.

*Leslie Moses, *The AAPL Guide for Landmen,* Tulsa: Kraftbilt, 1980, 98.

(fig. C.2), its corresponding short form (fig. C.3), and a special form, sometimes known as a Wilmington form (fig. C.4), appear below. The Wilmington form is used to provide for directional drilling from a location other than the surface of the leased land in order to satisfy environmental or other considerations.

Figure C.2. California oil and gas lease
(Courtesy of Exxon)

FORM 53A

OIL AND GAS LEASE

THIS AGREEMENT, made this................................day of.., 19........, by and between

...., hereinafter styled "Lessor," and

...., hereinafter styled "Lessee."

WITNESSETH: That Lessor, for and in consideration of One Dollar ($1.00), in hand paid, the receipt of which is hereby acknowledged, and of the covenants and agreements hereinafter contained on the part of Lessee to be paid, kept and performed, has granted, demised, leased and let and by these presents does grant, demise, lease and let unto said Lessee exclusively, for the purpose of exploring, mining and operating for oil, gas and casinghead gas, and other hydrocarbon substances, and taking, storing, removing and disposing of same, and manufacturing gasoline and other products therefrom, with the right for such purposes to the free use of oil, gas or water from said land, but not from Lessor's water wells or ponds, and granting the right to build tanks, power houses, stations, houses for employees and such other structures (excepting refinery) as may be necessary or convenient in its operations, together with rights of way, easements and servitudes for pipe lines, power lines, telephone and telegraph lines, with the right of removing, either during or after the term hereof, any and all improvements placed or erected on the premises by Lessee,

including the right to pull all casing, all that certain tract of land situated in the County of...,

State of.., described as follows, to wit:

and containing..acres, more or less, hereinafter referred to as "said land."

TO HAVE AND TO HOLD the same for a term of ten (10) years from and after the date hereof, and so long thereafter as oil or gas or casinghead gas or other hydrocarbon substances, or either or any of them, is produced from said land or from acreage pooled therewith in quantities deemed paying by Lessee, and/or so long thereafter as Lessee in good faith shall conduct drilling, redrilling, deepening or remedial operations on said land or on acreage pooled therewith, and/or so long thereafter as Lessee's drilling, producing or remedial obligations hereunder are suspended, all as herein provided.

In consideration of the premises it is hereby mutually agreed as follows:

1. Lessor's crude oil royalty shall be the equal one-eighth ($\frac{1}{8}$) part of all the oil produced and saved from said land. At the option of Lessor, Lessee either shall purchase Lessor's royalty oil at the market value in the same field for oil of similar gravity and quality, or shall yield and deliver to Lessor on said land Lessor's one-eighth ($\frac{1}{8}$) part of said oil. On thirty days' written notice to Lessee, but not oftener than once in any calendar year, Lessor may change the said option, but if no such notice is given by Lessor, it shall be deemed that Lessee shall purchase Lessor's royalty oil. If Lessor elects to receive royalty oil in kind, Lessee will provide, free of cost, storage tanks for not more than ten days' accumulation of Lessor's royalty oil and will yield and deliver to Lessor at tank outlets in accordance with usual and customary pipe line and shipping practices.

2. Lessee shall pay Lessor as royalty one-eighth ($\frac{1}{8}$) of the net proceeds derived from the sale of gas from each well on said land while same is being sold or used off the premises, but nothing in this agreement contained shall require Lessee to save or market gas from said land, unless there shall be a surplus above lease requirements and a market at the well for same.

3. Lessee shall pay to Lessor one-eighth ($\frac{1}{8}$) of 40% of casinghead gasoline if extracted or manufactured from the natural gas produced on said land. This royalty shall be payable each month in cash and based on the market value thereof at the point of its production. No charge shall be made for the manufacturing or extraction of the gasoline, but the gas used as fuel in the process shall not be subject to payments of royalty. If the remaining dry gas is sold or consumed by Lessee (in excess of the amount herein allowed to be used by Lessee free of royalty) Lessee will pay Lessor, as royalty, one-eighth ($\frac{1}{8}$) of the market value thereof as that term is herein defined. Lessee shall have the right to commingle gas produced from said land with gas produced from other properties.

4. Lessee shall not be required to account to Lessor for or pay royalty on oil, gas or water used by Lessee in its operations hereunder, including gas lost or consumed in the processing of any gas produced hereunder, and Lessee may use such oil, gas and/or water free of charge.

Figure C.2—*Continued*

5. Lessee agrees to commence drilling operations on said land within...(..........) years from the date hereof (unless Lessee has sooner commenced the drilling of an offset well on said land as herein provided) and to prosecute the same with reasonable diligence until oil or gas is found in paying quantities, or to a depth at which further drilling would, in the judgment of Lessee, be unprofitable; or it may at any time without commencing drilling operations terminate this lease and surrender said land as hereinafter provided. No implied covenant shall be read into this lease requiring Lessee to drill or to continue drilling on said land, or fixing the measure of diligence therefor.

6. Commencing...if Lessee has not theretofore commenced drilling operations on said land or terminated this lease, Lessee shall pay to Lessor...in advance, as rental, the sum of...per acre for so much of said land as may be held under this lease at the time of such payment, until drilling operations are commenced or this lease terminated. The consideration paid for this lease covers all rentals for the first...(..........) years of the term hereof.

7. If Lessee shall elect to drill on said land, as aforesaid, and oil or gas shall not be obtained in paying quantities in the first well drilled, Lessee shall, except as in this paragraph otherwise provided, within six (6) months after the completion or abandonment of the first well, either terminate this lease and surrender said land or commence on said land drilling operations for a second well, and shall prosecute the same with reasonable diligence until oil or gas is found in paying quantities or until the well is drilled to a depth at which further drilling would, in the judgment of Lessee, be unprofitable; and Lessee shall in like manner continue its operations until oil or gas in paying quantities is found, but subject always to the right of Lessee to terminate this lease and surrender said land and to the other terms and conditions hereof, and to the rights and privileges to Lessee herein given; provided, however, that if Lessee shall elect to drill on said land, as aforesaid, and oil or gas shall not be obtained in paying quantities in any well so drilled, Lessee shall have the right, at its option, prior to the discovery of oil or gas in paying quantities on said land, to defer drilling on said land and to continue this lease without additional drilling, except for any offset wells required hereunder, for any period for which rental has been paid, pursuant to Paragraph 6 hereof, and for additional rental periods provided under Paragraphs 5 and 6 hereof, by commencing or resuming on or before six (6) months after the completion or abandonment of the last preceding well, or on or before the expiration of any period for which rental has been paid, whichever is later, the payment of rental at the rate specified in Paragraph 6 hereof, pro-rated on a monthly basis, if necessary, for each month or major fraction thereof then remaining before the next rental payment date under this lease. Upon commencement or resumption of the payment of rental as herein provided this lease shall continue in force as though there had been no interruption in rental payments.

8. If oil is found in paying quantities, whether alone or in conjunction with gas, in any well so drilled by Lessee on said land, Lessee, subject to the provisions hereof and the suspension privileges hereinafter set forth, shall continue to drill additional wells on said land as rapidly as one string of tools working with reasonable diligence can complete the same, until there shall have been completed on said land an average, no matter where drilled, of one (1) well to each forty (40) acres, or major portion thereof, then held under this lease, whereupon Lessee shall hold all of said land free of further drilling obligations; provided, that Lessee may defer the commencement of drilling operations for the second or any subsequent well for a period not to exceed four (4) months from the date of completion of the well last preceding it. Lessee shall, however, be entitled to drill as many additional wells on said land as it desires. Except as herein otherwise provided, it is agreed that Lessee shall drill such wells and operate each completed oil well with reasonable diligence and in accordance with good oil field practice so long as such wells shall produce oil in paying quantities while this lease is in force as to the portion of said land on which such well or wells are situated.

9. If prior to the discovery of oil, Lessee shall complete a well or wells capable of producing gas in excess of one million cubic feet per day, Lessee shall, after the use of such gas necessary for lease and/or repressuring requirements, sell so much of remaining available gas at the well as it may be able to find a market for. Thereafter Lessee shall have no further obligation to conduct the drilling of oil wells on said land, except the drilling of offset wells for oil as in this lease provided, and shall not be required to drill further gas wells until in its judgment the drilling of additional gas wells is warranted in view of existing market requirements; provided that Lessee shall never be required to drill more than one (1) gas well to each six hundred forty (640) acres, or major portion thereof, including offset wells, said number to be an average regardless of where drilled, subject to the orders and regulations of the Petroleum Administrator for War or other federal agency purporting to act under authority and issuing orders or regulations as to the drilling and spacing of wells and the manner and rate of producing gas therefrom. During such times that a market at the well for such remaining available gas does not exist, Lessee may suspend the operation of any such gas well or wells, provided, however, that if at the expiration of any calendar year Lessor shall not have received as royalty from the proceeds of the sale of any such remaining available gas an amount equal to or in excess of $1.00 per acre for the total acreage then held subject to this lease, Lessee shall, on or before the 20th day of January next succeeding, pay to Lessor an amount equal to the difference between the total amount of all such royalties paid to Lessor during such calendar year from the proceeds of the sale of such remaining available gas and the said amount of $1.00 per acre for such total acreage so held; provided that any and all sums so paid by Lessee to Lessor in excess of the actual amount of royalties paid from Lessee to Lessor from the proceeds of such remaining available gas shall be considered as advance royalties to be repaid to Lessee from any proceeds from the sale of gas to which Lessor is thereafter entitled, and Lessee is authorized to deduct the same from gas royalties thereafter due and payable. If oil is subsequently discovered on said land, then the drilling obligations provided in this lease for Lessee to perform with respect to oil wells shall again come into effect.

10. If at any time it should appear that Lessor owns a less interest in said land than the whole undivided fee in the oil, gas, and other hydrocarbon substances in, under, or which may be recovered from said land, then the royalties and rentals herein provided for shall be paid Lessor only in the proportion which his interest in said oil, gas and other hydrocarbon substances bears to the whole undivided fee therein. If Lessor hereafter acquires any additional interest or title in said land, then this lease shall cover such additional after-acquired interest or title.

11. If Lessor shall sell or transfer any part or parts of said land or any interest in the oil and/or gas under any part or parts thereof Lessee's drilling obligations shall not thereby be altered, increased or enlarged, but Lessee may continue to operate said land and pay and settle rents and royalties as an entirety.

12. In the event a well is drilled on adjoining property within three hundred thirty feet (330') of the exterior limits of any land at the time embraced in this lease and oil or gas is produced therefrom in paying quantities and the drilling requirements as specified in paragraph 8 hereof are not fully complied with, and the owner of such well shall operate the same and market the oil or gas produced therefrom, then Lessee agrees to offset such well by the commencement of drilling operations on said land within ninety (90) days after it is ascertained that the production of oil or gas from such well is in paying quantities and that the operator thereof is then producing and marketing oil or gas therefrom. For the purpose of satisfying obligations hereunder such offset well or wells shall be considered as other wells required to be drilled hereunder.

13. The obligations of Lessee hereunder shall be suspended while Lessee is prevented from complying therewith, in whole or in part, by strikes, lockouts, action of the elements, accidents, laws, rules and regulations of any federal, state, municipal or other

Figure C.2 – *Continued*

governmental agency, acts or requests of any governmental officer or agent purporting to act under authority, exhaustion or unavailability or delays in delivery of necessary materials and equipment, or other matters or conditions beyond the control of Lessee, whether or not similar to the matters or conditions herein specifically enumerated. It is expressly understood and agreed, notwithstanding any other provision of this lease inconsistent herewith, that all of Lessee's operations under this lease, including (but without limiting the generality hereof) the drilling and spacing of wells and the manner and rate of producing oil and/or gas therefrom, shall be conducted in accordance with any applicable law, whether now or hereafter enacted, of the United States and/or of the state in which said land is situated, and/or of any county or municipality or other governmental authority, and in accordance with regulations prescribed and/or orders issued under any such law, and, in the absence of any such law, may be conducted in conformity with any recommendation or request made in writing or published by any governmental authority or agency, or in accordance with any plan or program of conservation or curtailment voluntarily followed by producers of crude oil in said state generally. Drilling and producing operations hereunder may also be suspended while the price offered generally to producers in the same vicinity for oil of the quality produced from said land is seventy-five cents or less per barrel at the well, or when there is no available market for the same at the well.

14. Lessee shall pay all taxes on its improvements and all taxes on its oil stored on said land. Lessor agrees to pay all taxes and assessments levied against the land as such and against Lessor's improvements thereon, except that Lessee shall pay seven-eighths (⅞) of the increase of taxes on such portion of said lands as remain subject to this lease, when such increase is caused by the discovery of oil or gas thereon, whether assessed upon said land as increased valuation or as petroleum mineral rights, or otherwise, and whether assessed against Lessee or Lessor, and Lessor agrees to pay the remaining portion of such increased assessment. In the event the United States, the state, county, municipality or other governmental authority or agency levies a license, severance, production or other tax on the oil or gas produced hereunder, or on Lessee's right to operate on said land, then and in that event Lessee agrees to pay seven-eighths (⅞) of said tax and Lessor agrees to pay one-eighth (⅛) of said tax.

15. Lessee agrees not to drill any well on said land within one hundred fifty feet (150') of the now existing buildings thereon without the written consent of Lessor. Lessee agrees to pay all damages to crops, trees (including injuries suffered through prevention of cultivation, irrigation and maintenance thereof by usual methods), fences, pipe lines, canals, buildings and other improvements upon said land caused by Lessee's operations hereunder. Whenever required by Lessor in writing Lessee shall fence all sump holes or other openings to safeguard livestock on said land.

16. Lessor may at all reasonable times examine said land, the work done and in progress thereon, and the production therefrom, and may inspect the books kept by Lessee in relation to the production from said land, to ascertain the production and the amount saved and sold therefrom. Lessee agrees, on written request, to furnish to Lessor a copy of the driller's log of all wells drilled by Lessee on said land.

17. All labor to be performed and materials to be furnished in the operations of Lessee hereunder shall be at the cost and expense of Lessee, and Lessor shall not be chargeable with, or liable for, any part thereof; and Lessee shall protect said land against liens of every character arising from its operations thereon.

18. Lessor shall have the right to occupy or to lease the surface of said land for residential, business, agricultural, horticultural or grazing purposes to such an extent as will not interfere with the proper operation of the lease for oil or gas. Lessee agrees to conduct its operations so as to interfere with the use of said land for residential, business, agricultural, horticultural or grazing purposes as little as is consistent with the economical operation of the property for oil or gas.

19. On the expiration of this lease, or if sooner terminated, Lessee shall quietly and peacefully surrender possession of said land to Lessor and deliver to Lessor a good and sufficient quitclaim deed for said land and, so far as practicable, shall cover all sump holes and excavations made by it and clear the land of all debris placed thereon by Lessee and restore the surface of the land as nearly as practicable to the condition in which it was received. In the event of abandonment of any well by Lessee, Lessor may, if he so desires, retain such abandoned well as a water well by notifying Lessee to that effect prior to the abandonment of such well, and thereupon Lessee shall leave the surface casing in the well and Lessor shall pay to Lessee fifty per cent (50%) of the original cost of such casing on the ground.

20. All oil containing more than 3% of water and basic sediment, at Lessee's option, shall be dehydrated, and the cost of dehydration shall be paid by Lessor in proportion to his royalty interest therein at the actual cost thereof, or, if Lessee dehydrates the oil, the cost shall be 5¢ per barrel. No correction for gravity shall be made for the water and basic sediment content, when the said content does not exceed 3%.

21. All sampling, testing, gauging, measuring and the taking of gravities which may be required to be done by Lessee in order to determine the gravities and non-petroleum substances contained in the oils referred to herein, shall, at the option of Lessee, be taken, done, and performed by any method or process generally regarded in the industry where the work is to be done as reliable and in accordance with good practice.

22. Upon the violation of any of the terms or conditions of this lease by Lessee and the failure to begin to remedy the same within sixty (60) days after written notice from Lessor so to do and thereafter diligently and in good faith to prosecute the remedying of such default, then, at the option of Lessor, this lease shall forthwith cease and terminate and all rights of Lessee in and to said land shall be at an end, saving and excepting as to any and all wells producing or being drilled and in respect to which Lessee shall not be in default, together with an area surrounding each such well which shall, at the time of such default, be equivalent to the number of acres by which the minimum number of wells to be drilled under this lease is determined pursuant to the provisions of paragraph 8 hereof as to oil wells, but not less than forty (40) acres as to oil wells, and paragraph 9 hereof as to gas wells, but not less than six hundred forty (640) acres as to gas wells, and saving and excepting rights of way necessary for Lessee's operations, provided, however, that Lessee may at any time after such default, and upon payment of the sum of Ten Dollars ($10.00) to Lessor as and for fixed and liquidated damages quitclaim to Lessor all of the right, title and interest of Lessee in and to the leased lands in respect to which it has made default, and thereupon all rights and obligations of the parties hereto one to the other shall cease and terminate as to the premises quitclaimed, except the obligation to pay rents or royalties theretofore accrued, and the obligations of paragraphs 15 and 19 hereof as applied to the area so quitclaimed.

23. All royalties and rents payable in money hereunder may be paid to Lessor by mailing or delivering a check therefor to

....at..;
its successors and assigns, herein designated by Lessor as depository, Lessor hereby granting to said depository full power and authority on behalf of Lessor, his heirs, executors, administrators, successors and assigns, to collect and receipt for all sums of money due and payable from Lessee to Lessor hereunder. No change in the ownership of the land or minerals covered by this lease, and no assignment of rents or royalties shall be binding on Lessee or said depository until it has been furnished with satisfactory written evidence thereof.

Figure C.2—Continued

24. Lessor agrees that he will promptly examine each and all statements and remittances forwarded by Lessee to him hereunder and promptly advise Lessee of any objection thereto, and it is further agreed that upon the failure of Lessor to so object to such statements and remittances within six (6) months of the receipt thereof by Lessor such statements and payments shall thereupon become conclusive and binding upon both parties.

25. Lessor hereby agrees that Lessee, at its option, may pay and discharge any taxes, mortgages, trust deeds, realty sales contracts, or other liens existing, levied or assessed on or against said land; and, in the event it exercises such option, it shall be subrogated to the rights of any holder or holders thereof and may reimburse itself by applying to the discharge of any such mortgage, trust deed, realty sales contract, tax, or other lien, any royalty or rentals accruing hereunder.

26. The words "drilling operations" as used herein shall be held to mean any work or actual operations undertaken or commenced in good faith for the purpose of carrying out any of the rights, privileges or duties of Lessee under this lease, followed diligently and in due course by the construction of a derrick and other necessary structures for the drilling of an oil or gas well, and by the actual operation of drilling in the ground.

27. The term "market value" as used in this lease shall be applied to the particular product at its point of production and shall be deemed to be the actual sales price when sold to third parties or the current available posted or published price in the field (as posted or published by Lessee or other responsible purchasing companies for products of like quality and quantity) when purchased by Lessee.

28. Lessee may at any time quitclaim this lease in its entirety or as to part of the acreage covered thereby and thereupon Lessee shall be released from all further obligations and duties as to the area so quitclaimed, and all rentals and drilling requirements shall be reduced pro rata. All lands quitclaimed shall remain subject to the easements and rights of way hereinabove provided for. Except as so provided, full right to the land so quitclaimed shall revest in Lessor, free and clear of all claims of Lessee, except that Lessor, his successors or assigns, shall not drill any well on the land quitclaimed, or on land in respect to which this lease shall otherwise terminate, within three hundred thirty feet (330') of any producing or drilling well retained by Lessee.

29. If this lease shall be assigned as to a particular part or as to particular parts of said land, such division or severance of the lease shall constitute and create separate and distinct holdings under the lease of and according to the several portions of said land as thus divided, and the holder or owner of each such portion of said land shall be required to comply with and perform Lessee's obligations under this lease for, and only to the extent of, his portion of said land, provided that nothing herein shall be construed to enlarge or multiply the drilling or rental obligations, and provided further that the commencement of the drilling operations and the prosecution thereof, either by Lessee or any assignee hereunder, shall protect the lease as a whole.

30. Any notice from Lessor to Lessee must be given by sending the same by registered mail addressed to Lessee at...................... ...., and any notice from Lessee to Lessor must be given by sending the same by registered mail, addressed to .... For the purpose of this section, either party may change its address by written notice to the other. Any quitclaim and surrender from Lessee to Lessor of this lease in its entirety or as to part of the acreage covered thereby may be made to Lessor, his successors and assigns in the ownership of the land quitclaimed, as they may be entitled thereto, and shall be completely effective for all purposes when deposited by Lessee in the United States post office as registered mail, with postage thereon fully prepaid, and addressed to Lessor at the address provided for in this paragraph. Such mailing of such quitclaim and surrender shall be deemed complete delivery thereof to Lessor, his successors and assigns. If this lease is recorded Lessee shall also cause a duplicate original of such quitclaim and surrender to be recorded in the office of the county recorder of the county in which said land is located with instructions to the county recorder to return the same to Lessee after it has been recorded.

31. Any payment due from Lessee to Lessor may be made by good and valid check or draft payable to Lessor or depository herein named. Payment of royalties shall be made on or before the 25th day of each calendar month for the preceding month.

32. Lessor hereby grants to Lessee or to Lessee's nominee, for Lessee's benefit, permission to conduct geophysical surveys on said land provided that Lessee or Lessee's nominee shall pay Lessor for any damage to person or property, including damage to water wells located on said land, resulting from the making of such surveys; provided further, that claim therefor is made by Lessor within ninety (90) days from the date such survey or surveys are completed.

33. Lessee is hereby given the right at its sole option to combine or pool this lease, including Lessor's interest herein, and all the oil and gas rights in the land hereby leased, or any portion thereof, with any other lease or leases and the oil, gas and royalty rights in and under any other tract or tracts of land, or parts thereof, regardless of ownership thereof, situated in the section in which the above described lands are located or in any other contiguous or adjacent section or projected section if there be no government survey, so as to create by such combining or pooling one or more operating units for the production of oil, gas or other hydrocarbon substances. Such right may be exercised from time to time at any time prior to sixty (60) days after completion of a well for the production of oil or gas on the particular area to be pooled. No operating unit so created shall exceed 40 acres in area for oil development and operating purposes, or 660 acres in area for gas development and operating purposes. Such an operating unit shall be created hereunder and shall become effective upon the execution by Lessee in writing of a "Declaration of Pooling" which shall identify and describe the pooled acreage. Written notice of such declaration shall be given to Lessor. In the event production of oil, gas or other hydrocarbon substances is obtained from any such operating unit or units created hereunder there shall be allocated to land hereby leased and included in such operating unit, regardless of whether or not such production is from any part of the lands hereby leased, that portion of the production from such unit that the number of acres, validly leased hereby and included in such operating unit, bears to the total number of acres included in any such unit, and the royalties and payments (other than delay rentals under paragraph 6 hereof) herein provided for shall be calculated on the portion of such production so allocated to lands hereby leased, and shall be paid in the same manner and subject to the same terms and conditions as other royalties and payments herein provided for, and such portion of said royalties and payments shall be in lieu of any other royalties and payments which would accrue to Lessor hereunder on account of production of oil, gas or other hydrocarbon substances from any part or parts of the lands hereby leased which are included in any such operating unit created pursuant hereto, and in lieu of the taxes provided to be paid by Lessor under paragraph 14 hereof (other than taxes on the land as such) Lessor shall bear and pay one-eighth (⅛) of his proportionate share of such taxes on such operating unit and the production therefrom in the same proportion as production is allocated to Lessor's land in such unit. Upon the pooling of less than all of the land hereby leased, as above provided, this lease shall be severed and shall be considered as separate and distinct leases on separately pooled acreage and on unpooled acreage, as the case may be, and the term of this lease and all the rights and obligations of Lessee under this lease shall apply separately to separately pooled acreage and to unpooled acreage under this lease. Any act or obligation required by this lease to be performed or fulfilled by Lessee with respect to the acreage included in any such operating unit shall be deemed fully performed, fulfilled and effective by the performance or fulfillment of such

Figure C.2 — *Continued*

act or obligation upon or with respect to any part of such operating unit. Any part of the lands hereby leased not pooled into an operating unit shall be and remain subject to the terms and conditions of this lease unaffected by the pooling of any other part or parts of said land, or by operations on any such operating unit. Lessee may at any time quitclaim to the persons entitled thereto all or any part of the land in an operating unit and thereupon Lessee shall be released from all further obligations and duties as to the area of such operating unit so quitclaimed and all drilling requirements thereon shall be reduced pro rata, and no further quitclaim shall be required among owners of land in the operating unit to terminate leases on quitclaimed land in so far as the interest of such owners in such operating unit is concerned; provided, however, that the initial portion of production from an operating unit so allocated to lands hereby leased shall remain unchanged notwithstanding the surrender by Lessee of less than all of the land pooled into such unit, except:

(1) that after the surrender by Lessee of less than all of the land included in an operating unit, if the owner of such surrendered land shall commence or cause to be commenced the drilling of a well for oil or gas on such surrendered land, or any part thereof, thereupon and forever thereafter such surrendered land shall cease to participate in production from that part of such operating unit retained by Lessee;

(2) that land lost or quitclaimed by Lessee because of loss or failure of title for any cause beyond Lessee's control shall be removed from the operating unit and shall not thereafter participate in production;

(3) whenever quitclaimed land, or land on which title is lost, within an operating unit shall cease to participate in production as above provided, production from that portion of the operating unit retained by Lessee shall thereafter be allocated, on the basis hereinabove provided, only to the remaining land in the operating unit entitled to participate in production.

Lessee shall not be liable to any party for reduction of the acreage content of any operating unit resulting from loss of title for any cause beyond its control and in such event Lessee shall have the right to cancel any such unit. Lessee shall not be obligated to make any retroactive apportionment of royalties or payments in the event of any reduction in participation in production or in acreage content of an operating unit as above provided. In case any action is brought at law or in equity by persons claiming title to any land in an operating unit in hostility to the Lessors from whom Lessee holds a lease on such land, then during the pendency of said action, until the final decision thereof, Lessee may discontinue operations upon the land in controversy, or if it operates wells thereon, may impound royalties accruing from production thereon until the ownership thereof is finally determined. Lessee shall not be required to drill any offset well on that part of the land hereby leased pooled into an operating unit to offset any other well drilled on the acreage pooled into such unit.

34. This lease may be executed in any number of counterparts, by any person having an interest in said land, with the same effect as if all Lessors herein were named as Lessor in one document and had all signed the same document. All counterparts shall be construed together and shall constitute one lease. The failure of any person owning an interest in said land to execute a counterpart hereof, or the failure of any person named as Lessor in any counterpart to execute the same, shall not affect the binding force of this lease as to those who have executed or shall execute a counterpart hereof.

35. This lease and all its terms, conditions and stipulations shall extend to and be binding upon the heirs, executors, administrators, grantees, successors and assigns of the parties hereto.

IN WITNESS WHEREOF, the parties hereto have caused this agreement to be duly executed as of the date first hereinabove written.

LESSOR   LESSEE

....

....

....

....

                                                         ....

STATE OF CALIFORNIA
                                    } ss.
COUNTY OF LOS ANGELES

On this................day of................................, 19........., before me, the undersigned, a Notary Public in and for said

County and State, personally appeared.., known to me to be the

....,
the corporation that executed the within instrument, known to me to be the person who executed the within instrument on behalf of said corporation, and acknowledged to me that said corporation executed the within instrument pursuant to its by-laws or resolution of its board of directors.

WITNESS my hand and official seal.

                              ....
                              Notary Public in and for said County and State
                              (Print, Type or Stamp Name)

Figure C.2—*Continued*

STATE OF CALIFORNIA

) ss.

COUNTY OF..)

    On this................day of..................................., A.D., 19........, before me, ...,
a Notary Public in and for said County and State, personally appeared..
...., known to me to be the person......whose name.................................
subscribed to the within instrument, and acknowledged to me that.................................executed the same.

    IN WITNESS WHEREOF, I have hereunto set my hand and affixed my official seal the day and year first above written.

....

Notary Public in and for said County and State.
(Print, Type or Stamp Name)

STATE OF CALIFORNIA

) ss.

COUNTY OF..)

    On this................day of..................................., A.D., 19........, before me, the undersigned, a Notary Public in and for **said**
County and State, personally appeared...,
known to me to be the person whose name is subscribed to the within Instrument as subscribing witness thereto, who, being duly
sworn, deposes and says: that he resides in...;
that he was present and saw...
....personally known to him to be the same person............................
whose name..subscribed to the within and annexed Instrument, execute and deliver the same; that ......he......
acknowledged to affiant that ......he...... executed the same and requested affiant to sign as subscribing witness and thereupon affiant subscribed his name thereto as such subscribing witness.

    IN WITNESS WHEREOF, I have hereunto set my hand and affixed my official seal the day and year first above written.

....

Notary Public in and for said County and State.
(Print, Type or Stamp Name)

Figure C.3. California oil and gas lease, short form
(Courtesy of Exxon)

RECORDING REQUESTED BY

AND WHEN RECORDED MAIL TO

Name

Street
Address

City
State
Zip

———————————————————————————— SPACE ABOVE THIS LINE FOR RECORDER'S USE ——

OIL AND GAS LEASE (SHORT FORM)

THIS OIL AND GAS LEASE (SHORT FORM) made and entered into this _____ day of _____ , 19_____ ,

by and between _____

_____

hereinafter styled "Lessor",
and

_____

hereinafter styled "Lessee".

WITNESSETH:

1. That Lessor, for valuable consideration, receipt of which is hereby acknowledged, and in consideration of the covenants and agreements contained in the Oil and Gas Lease hereinafter particularly referred to, has granted, demised, leased and let and by these presents does grant, demise, lease and let unto Lessee exclusively the real property hereinafter described, for the purpose of exploring, mining and operating for oil, gas and casinghead gas and other hydrocarbon substances and taking, storing, removing and disposing of same, and uses and purposes incidental thereto, as provided in said hereinafter referred to Oil and Gas Lease. The property covered by this lease is situated in the City of _____ ,

County of _____ , State of California and is described as follows:

and containing _____ acres, more or less, hereinafter referred to as "said land".

2. This Lease shall continue for a term of _____ years from and after the date hereof, and so long thereafter as oil or gas or casinghead gas or other hydrocarbon substances or either or any of them, is produced from said land or from acreage pooled therewith in quantities deemed paying by Lessee, and/or so long thereafter as Lessee in good faith shall continue drilling, re-drilling, deepening or remedial operations on said land or on acreage pooled therewith, and/or so long thereafter as Lessee's drilling, producing or remedial obligations thereunder are suspended, all as particularly set forth in the Oil and Gas Lease hereinafter referred to, and subject to termination as therein provided.

Figure C.3—*Continued*

---

3. This Oil and Gas Lease (Short Form) is made upon the terms, covenants and conditions set forth in that certain Oil and Gas Lease bearing even date herewith by and between the said parties hereto, covering the real property above described, which Oil and Gas Lease is by this reference incorporated herein and made a part hereof in all respects as though the same were fully set forth herein.

4. This Lease and all its terms, conditions and stipulations shall extend to and be binding upon the heirs, executors, administrators, grantees, successors and assigns of the parties hereto.

IN WITNESS WHEREOF the parties hereto have caused this Agreement to be duly executed as of the date first hereinabove written.

                                                        _____

                                                        _____

                                                        _____

                                                        _____
                                                                                          LESSOR

                                                        _____

                                                        _____
                                                                                          LESSEE

STATE OF CALIFORNIA   }
                             } ss
COUNTY OF _____   }

On this _____ day of _____ , A.D., 19 _____ , before me, _____ , a Notary Public

in and for said County and State, personally appeared _____

_____ , known to me to be the person ____ whose name _____

subscribed to the within instrument, and acknowledged to me that _____ executed the same.

IN WITNESS WHEREOF, I have hereunto set my hand and affixed my official seal the day and year first above written.

                                                        _____
                                                        Notary Public in and for said County and State

STATE OF CALIFORNIA   }
                             } ss
COUNTY OF   }
_____

On _____ , before me, the undersigned, a Notary Public in and for said County and

State, personally appeared _____ known to me to be the person whose name is sub-

scribed to the within Instrument as subscribing witness thereto, who, being duly sworn, deposes and says: that he resides in _____

_____ ; that he was present and saw _____

_____ personally known to him to be the same person ____ whose name _____

_____ subscribed to the within and annexed Instrument, execute and deliver the same; that ____ he ____ acknowledged to

affiant that ____ he ____ executed the same and requested affiant to sign as subscribing witness and thereupon affiant subscribed his name thereto as such

subscribing witness.

WITNESS my hand and official seal.

                                                        _____
                                                        Notary Public in and for said County and State

Figure C.3 — *Continued*

STATE OF CALIFORNIA
COUNTY OF LOS ANGELES } ss

On this _____ day of _____ , 19 _____ , before me, the undersigned, a Notary Public in and for said County and State; personally appeared _____ , known to me to be the

_____ ,
the corporation that executed the within instrument, known to me to be the person who executed the within instrument on behalf of said corporation, and acknowledged to me that said corporation executed the within instrument pursuant to its by-laws or resolution of its board of directors.

  WITNESS my hand and official seal.

                                                   _____
                                                   Notary Public in and for said County and State

STATE OF CALIFORNIA
COUNTY OF_____ } ss

On this _____ day of _____ , A.D., 19 _____ , before me, _____ , a Notary Public in and for said County and State, personally appeared _____ , known to me to be

the _____ , and _____ , known to be the _____

Secretary of _____ , the corporation that executed the within instrument, known to me to be the persons who executed the within instrument on behalf of the corporation herein named, and acknowledged to me that such corporation executed the same pursuant to its by-laws or a resolution of its board of directors.

  IN WITNESS WHEREOF, I have hereunto set my hand and affixed my official seal the day and year in this certificate first above written.

                                                   _____
                                                   Notary Public in and for said County and State

**Figure C.4. Subsurface oil and gas lease and ratification of unit agreement
(Courtesy of Exxon)**

062-0137   **SUBSURFACE OIL AND GAS LEASE**
                                                              AND
                                       RATIFICATION OF UNIT AGREEMENT

THIS AGREEMENT, made this _____ day of _____, 19____, by and between _____

_____

_____whose address is _____

_____, hereinafter styled "Lessor," and EXXON CORPORATION, a New Jersey corporation, whose address is 1800 Avenue of the Stars, Los Angeles, California, 90067, hereinafter styled "Lessee."

Lessor, for and in consideration of One Dollar ($1.00) and other valuable consideration in hand paid, the receipt of which is hereby acknowledged, and of the covenants and agreements hereinafter contained on the part of Lessee to be paid, kept and performed, has granted, demised, leased and let and by these presents does grant, demise, lease and let unto said Lessee exclusively, for the purpose of exploring, mining and operating for oil, gas and other hydrocarbon substances, and taking, storing, treating, owning, removing and disposing of same, and manufacturing gasoline and other products therefrom, with the right of removing, either during or after the term hereof, any and all improvements placed in the premises by Lessee, including the right to pull all casing, all that certain tract of land situated in the City of Los Angeles, County of Los Angeles, State of California, described as follows, to wit:

ALL THAT PORTION OF THE LANDS LYING BELOW 500 FEET FROM THE SURFACE OF:

including all right, title and interest of Lessor in and to any adjacent parcels of land including, but without limitation, public highways, streets, alleys, railroad rights-of-way, drainage ditches, canals and waterways, hereinafter referred to as "said land".

In consideration of the premises, it is hereby mutually agreed as follows.

1. SUBSURFACE ONLY. Lessee shall have no right, without the consent of Lessor in writing being first obtained, to drill any well or wells from the surface of said land or to use the surface of said land for any purpose. It is understood and agreed, however, that Lessee may, at its option, obtain rights in respect to other lands in the vicinity of said land and may have available on such other land drillsites from which wells can be slant-drilled into or through said land. Lessee shall have the full, unrestricted and exclusive right, power and authority to produce the oil, gas and other hydrocarbon substances lying in or recoverable from said land, by means of any well or wells the surface drillsites of which are located on other lands, and which said well or wells are slant-drilled through or into said land.

2. RATIFICATION OF UNIT AGREEMENT. Lessor acknowledges that he has had made available to him for reading and examination a copy of an instrument entitled "Unit Agreement, Fault Block I Townlot Unit, Wilmington Oil Field, Los Angeles County", dated March 1, 1971. Said Unit Agreement provides that any person therein defined as a Royalty Owner may become a party to such Unit Agreement by signing the original thereof, a counterpart, or other instrument agreeing to be bound by the provisions thereof. Lessor hereby acknowledges that he is, or claims to be a Royalty Owner in one or more of the Tracts described in Exhibit "A" of said Unit Agreement and does hereby become a party to and is bound by the provisions of said Unit Agreement the same as if he had signed the original, and further agrees that the parties to the Unit Agreement are those persons who signed the original, any counterpart, or any instrument that evidences an agreement to be so bound. Where the terms "unit area" or "unitized area" are used herein they refer to the Unit Area described in said Unit Agreement. Where the provisions of this lease and that Unit Agreement are in conflict, the latter shall be controlling.

3. SECONDARY TRACT ASSIGNMENT UNDER UNIT AGREEMENT. Said land shall have a Secondary Tract Assignment and will participate in royalties during the Period of Secondary Production, as those terms are defined in the Unit Agreement ratified under paragraph 2 hereof.

4. TERM OF LEASE. Except as otherwise provided herein, this lease shall remain in force for a term of twenty (20) years from and after the date hereof, and so long thereafter as oil, gas or other hydrocarbon substances are produced from said land or the unitized area, in quantities deemed paying by Lessee, or so long thereafter as Lessee in good faith conducts primary or secondary drilling, redrilling, deepening, remedial or secondary recovery operations in said land or in the unitized area.

Figure C.4— *Continued*

5. "ROYALTY SHARE"; ROYALTY SHARE OF OIL. The expression "royalty share" when used in this lease shall mean the fraction one-sixth (1/6). Lessor's crude oil royalty shall be the royalty share of all the oil produced, saved and removed from or allocated to said land. Lessee shall purchase Lessor's royalty oil at the market value in the same field for oil of similar gravity and quality, after making correction for temperature and customary deductions for water and other foreign substances therein.

6. ROYALTY SHARE ON GAS AND LIQUEFIED PETROLEUM. In case of sale by Lessee of gas produced from or allocated to said land in the natural state as produced Lessee shall pay Lessor in cash the royalty share of the net proceeds of such sale received by Lessee. In case Lessee delivers such gas to a third party for treatment, Lessee shall pay Lessor (a) the royalty share of the market value of the net natural gasoline redelivered to Lessee and (b) the royalty share of the market value of the net liquefied petroleum gases redelivered to Lessee and utilized by Lessee (in excess of the amount herein allowed to be used by Lessee free of royalty) and (c) the royalty share of any net proceeds received by Lessee from the sale of liquefied petroleum gases redelivered to Lessee after deducting the royalty share of the cost of delivery for sale and (d) the royalty share of any net proceeds received by Lessee from the sale of residual dry gases redelivered to Lessee and (e) the royalty share of the market value of residual dry gas redelivered to Lessee and utilized by Lessee (in excess of the amount herein allowed to be used by Lessee free of royalty). Nothing in this agreement contained shall require Lessee to save or market gas from said land unless there shall be a surplus above lease requirements and a market at the well for same.

7. ROYALTY ON GASOLINE AND LIQUEFIED PETROLEUM WHERE LESSEE EXTRACTS. If Lessee shall extract in a plant owned or operated by it natural gasoline and/or liquefied petroleum gases from the gas produced from or allocated to said land, Lessee shall pay Lessor as royalty the royalty share of forty per cent (40%) of the natural gasoline so extracted and the royalty share of forty per cent (40%) of any liquefied petroleum gases so extracted and sold by Lessee or utilized by Lessee (in excess of the amount herein allowed to be used by Lessee free of royalty). Lessee shall not, however, be required to extract any of said products. This royalty shall be payable in cash and royalty on natural gasoline shall be based on the market value thereof, and the royalty on liquefied petroleum gases utilized by Lessee (in excess of the amount allowed to be used by Lessee free of royalty) shall be based on the market value thereof. Royalties on liquefied petroleum gases sold by Lessee shall be based on the net proceeds of such sales after deducting the royalty share of the cost of delivery for sale. If the residual dry gas is sold by Lessee, Lessee will pay Lessor as royalty thereon the royalty share of the net proceeds received by Lessee from the sale of such residual dry gas. If residual dry gas is utilized by Lessee (in excess of the amount herein allowed to be used by Lessee free of royalty) Lessee will pay Lessor as royalty thereon the royalty share of the market value thereof. Lessee shall have the right to deduct from Lessor's royalty on any gas produced hereunder the royalty share of the cost, if any, of transportation, delivery and compression for delivery thereof. Lessee shall have the right to commingle gas produced from or allocated to said land with other gas and thereupon the royalty shall be computed upon an appropriate fraction of the commingled gas.

8. OIL AND GAS USED IN OPERATIONS OR LOST. Lessee shall not be required to account to Lessor for, or pay royalty or other charge on oil, gas or other hydrocarbon substances or water used or lost by Lessee in its operations hereunder including, without limiting the generality thereof, operations for primary or secondary recovery, gathering, compressing and processing. In no event shall Lessee be responsible to Lessor for its failure or inability to save any of said substances, or for shrinkage or loss thereof and royalty shall not be payable in respect to any of such substances lost through evaporation, leakage, fire or otherwise, prior to its removal from Lessee's shipping facilities. In the event Lessee in its operations hereunder shall substitute other fuel or power for fuel obtained from said land, Lessee shall be entitled to deduct from the amount of the increased royalty accruing thereby to Lessor the royalty share of the cost of such other fuel or power, provided that no deduction hereunder shall in any event exceed the amount of such increased royalty.

9. COMMENCEMENT OF OPERATIONS. Lessee agrees to commence primary or secondary drilling or recovery operations in the unit area within ten (10) years from the date hereof and to prosecute the same with reasonable diligence However, no implied covenant shall be read into this lease requiring Lessee to commence or continue said operations or fixing the measure of diligence therefor.

10. DELAY RENTALS. Commencing two (2) years from the date hereof, if Lessee has not theretofore commenced primary or secondary drilling operations in said land or in the unit area or quitclaimed this lease, Lessee shall pay or tender to Lessor yearly in advance, a rental of Ten Dollars ($10.00) until said primary or secondary drilling operations are commenced, or Lessor is receiving royalties hereunder or this lease is quitclaimed or otherwise terminated; provided, however, that if Lessee shall commence such primary or secondary drilling operations in said land or in the unit area prior to the expiration of the maximum period during which Lessee is permitted to delay such primary or secondary drilling operations under paragraph 9 hereof, Lessee may, at its option, at any time and from time to time during the remainder of said period, suspend or defer such primary or secondary drilling operation, provided that whenever Lessee shall so suspend or defer operations during any period for which rental has not been paid, Lessee shall pay to Lessor rental at the rate above specified, prorated for that portion of said period during which such drilling operations shall be so suspended or deferred. Prorated rental herein provided for shall be paid or tendered to Lessor on or before the expiration date of such rental period or at the end of the period of such suspension or deferment, whichever shall first occur. All rentals hereunder shall cease upon the commencement or resumption of any primary or secondary drilling operations hereunder or when Lessor is receiving royalties hereunder or this lease is quitclaimed or otherwise terminated. The consideration paid for this lease covers rental for the first two (2) years of the term hereof.

Figure C.4 – *Continued*

---

11. PAYMENT OF RENTALS AND ROYALTIES. Lessee, at its election, may make all payments accruing to Lessor hereunder and deliver statements provided for herein by mailing or delivering the same to Lessor personally, or by mailing or delivering the same to _____ , California, or to its successors or assigns, herein designated by Lessor as depository, for the credit of Lessor, and Lessor hereby appoints said depository as the agent of Lessor to receive royalty and other payments and statements hereunder, give acquittance therefor and otherwise act for Lessor in regard to such payments and statements. Any payment or tender by Lessee to such depository shall be a full acquittance and discharge of Lessee of and from any and all liability to Lessor and any assignees or successors of Lessor for such payment. Lessor may at any time and from time to time, on thirty (30) days written notice to Lessee, designate another depository and agent in the State of California. Should said depository at any time cease to exist or refuse to act and Lessor fail to designate a successor, as herein provided, then Lessee may designate a successor. Lessor agrees to instruct said depository as to the proper distribution of royalties and other payments, and Lessee will not be responsible at any time for the disposition or disbursement by any such depository of all or any part of any moneys received by it hereunder. Lessee shall not under any circumstances be required to split royalties as between various lessors or any assignees or successors of Lessor, but such depository, notwithstanding any such assignments, shall continue authorized to receive and distribute royalty and other payments and statements hereunder. If in Lessee's opinion any dispute or uncertainty exists as to the party or parties entitled to receive any such payment, or any part thereof, Lessee may, without incurring any liability of any kind or character, withhold payment of any amount as to which such dispute or uncertainty exists, pending the determination of such dispute or uncertainty, or may interplead the claimants, and thereupon the payment into court by Lessee of any such amount or amounts shall be deemed a compliance with the provisions of this lease with respect to such payment. Notwithstanding actual or constructive knowledge or notice thereof by Lessee, no change in the ownership of said land or oil and gas or other substances covered by this lease, and no assignment of rents or royalties hereunder shall be effective as to Lessee for any purpose until the first day of the calendar month following the day on which Lessee has been furnished with either an original recordable instrument or a certified copy of a recorded original of the instrument which, in Lessee's opinion, sufficiently evidences such change of ownership.

12. NOTICES. Lessor may give any notice or deliver any document hereunder to Lessee by mailing the same addressed to Lessee at the address hereinbefore set forth in the caption hereof. Lessee may give any notice or deliver any document hereunder to Lessor by mailing the same addressed to Lessor at the address hereinbefore set forth in the caption hereof, or by delivering the same to any lessor in person. For the purposes of this paragraph either party may change its address by written notice to the other. In case of any notice or document delivered by mail the same shall be deemed delivered when deposited in the United States mails, properly addressed as herein provided, with postage fully prepaid.

13. WHERE LESSOR HAS LESS THAN FULL TITLE. At any time that Lessor owns a less interest in said land than the whole undivided fee in the oil, gas, and the aforesaid other substances in, under, or which may be recovered from said land, then the royalties and rentals shall be paid Lessor only in the proportion which his interest in said oil, gas and other hydrocarbon substances bears to the whole undivided fee therein. If Lessor hereafter acquires any additional interest or title in said land then this lease shall cover such additional after-acquired interest or title.

14. NO EFFECT WHERE TRANSFERRED BY LESSOR. If Lessor shall sell or transfer any part or parts of said land or any interest in the oil, gas or other hydrocarbon substances under any part or parts thereof, Lessee's obligations hereunder shall not thereby be altered, increased or enlarged, but Lessee may continue to operate said land, and pay and settle rents and royalties as an entirety.

15. FORCE MAJEURE; COMPLIANCE WITH LAWS; LOW MARKET PRICE. Lessee's obligations and operations hereunder shall be suspended while Lessee is prevented from complying therewith, in whole or in part, by strikes, lockouts, action of the elements, war, accidents, laws, rules and regulations of any federal, State, County, Municipal or other governmental agency, acts or requests of any governmental officer or agent purporting to act under authority, exhaustion or unavailability or delays in delivery of necessary materials and equipment, or other matters or conditions beyond the reasonable control of Lessee, whether or not similar to the matters or conditions herein specifically enumerated, and without regard to whether such cause exists at the date hereof or hereafter arises. Notwithstanding any other provision of this lease inconsistent herewith, all of Lessee's operations under this lease shall be conducted in accordance with any applicable law whether now or hereafter enacted, of the United States, County, Municipality or other governmental authority, and in accordance with regulations prescribed or orders issued under any such law and, in the absence of any such law, may be conducted in conformity with any recommendation or request made in writing or published by any governmental authority or agency or in accordance with any plan or program of conservation or curtailment voluntarily followed by producers of crude oil in said state generally. Drilling and producing operations hereunder may also be suspended while the price offered generally to producers in the same vicinity for oil of the quality produced from said land is seventy five cents or less per barrel at the well, or when there is no available market for oil or gas at the well.

16. TAXES AND ASSESSMENTS. Lessee shall pay all taxes and assessments on its property in said land. Lessor shall pay all taxes and assessments levied against the land as such and against Lessor's property thereon, except that Lessee shall pay all but the royalty share of the increase of taxes on such portion of said land as remains subject to this lease, when such increase is caused by the discovery of oil, gas or any other hydrocarbon substances therein, or in land unitized therewith, whether assessed upon said land as increased valuation or as petroleum mineral rights, or otherwise, and whether assessed against Lessee or Lessor, and Lessor agrees to pay the royalty share of such increase of taxes In the event the United States, the State, County, Municipality or other governmental authority or agency levies a license, severance, production or other tax or assessment on the oil or gas or any of the aforesaid other substances produced hereunder, or on Lessee's right to operate in said land, then and in that event Lessor agrees to pay the royalty share of said taxes and Lessee agrees to pay the remainder thereof.

Figure C.4— *Continued*

17. LABOR AND MATERIALS. All labor to be performed and materials to be furnished in the operations of Lessee hereunder shall be at the cost and expense of Lessee, and Lessor shall not be chargeable with, or liable for, any part thereof. Lessee shall protect said land against liens of every character arising from its operations therein.

18. WET OIL. All oil containing more than three per cent (3%) of water and other foreign substances may, at Lessee's option, be dehydrated and Lessor shall pay his royalty share of the actual cost thereof not to exceed five cents (5¢) per barrel.

19. SAMPLING AND TESTING. All sampling, testing, gauging, measuring and the taking of gravities which may be required to be done by Lessee in order to determine the gasoline content of gas, or the gravity of the water and other foreign substances contained in the oil, or the qualities of other substances, referred to herein, shall at the option of Lessee be taken, done and performed by any method or process generally regarded in the industry where the work is to be done as reliable and in accordance with good practice.

20. DEFAULT AND TERMINATION. Upon the violation of any of the terms or conditions of this lease by Lessee and the failure to begin to remedy the same within sixty (60) days after written notice from Lessor so to do and thereafter diligently and in good faith to prosecute the remedying of such default, then at the option of Lessor this lease shall forthwith cease and terminate and all rights of Lessee in and to said land shall be at an end, saving and excepting subsurface rights of way necessary for continuing Lessee's operation in lands retained in the unit area and including subsurface rights of way and easements to other lands as provided in paragraph 25 hereof. Forfeiture shall be the only remedy of Lessor for failure to comply with any of its obligations hereunder except such as relate to the payment of money. In respect to any breach relating to the payment of money the accrual of which Lessee in good faith disputes, Lessor, if Lessee pays the undisputed portion thereof, shall have no right to declare a forfeiture until the existence of such breach has been fully judicially determined and Lessee has not within thirty (30) days after such final judicial determination complied therewith, in which latter event Lessor may declare the absolute forfeiture of this lease and all of Lessee's rights hereunder except the right to remove Lessee's property.

21. DEFAULT OF LESSOR ON TAXES, ETC. Lessor hereby agrees that in the event Lessor fails to pay and discharge when they become due any taxes, mortgages, trust deeds, other liens, or realty sales contracts existing, levied or assessed on or against said land, other than those Lessee has herein agreed to pay, then Lessee at its option may make such payments, and in the event Lessee exercises such option it shall be subrogated to the rights of any holder or holders thereof and may reimburse itself by applying to the discharge of any such tax, mortgage, trust deed, other lien or realty sales contract, any royalty, rentals or other payments accruing hereunder.

22. "MARKET VALUE". The term "market value" as used in this lease shall be applied to the particular product at its point of production and shall be deemed to be the actual sales price when sold to third parties or the current available posted or published price in the field (as posted or published and paid by Lessee or other major producing and purchasing companies for products of like quality and quantity) when purchased or retained by Lessee, and if the prices so posted or published and paid by such companies are not uniform, then Lessee shall pay the highest of such prices.

23. TERMINATION BY LESSEE. Lessee may without commencing secondary operations as provided herein at any time and from time to time quitclaim this lease in its entirety or as to any part of said land by recording in the office of the County Recorder of Los Angeles County an appropriate quitclaim deed, and thereupon Lessee shall be released from further obligations and duties as to the land so quitclaimed and all rentals, royalties and drilling requirements shall be reduced pro rata, and such quitclaim shall become effective for all purposes when filed for record with said County Recorder. Lessee shall give Lessor notice of any such quitclaim. Quitclaims shall be made to Lessor, his successors and assigns in the ownership of the land quitclaimed, as they may be entitled thereto. All land quitclaimed shall remain subject to the easements and rights of way herein provided for. Except as so provided, full right to the land so quitclaimed shall revest in Lessor, free and clear of all claims of Lessee, except that Lessor, his heirs, successors or assigns, shall not bottom any well in the land quitclaimed or in land in respect to which this lease shall otherwise terminate, within three hundred thirty feet (330') of any portion of the producing interval of any well or drilling well retained by Lessee in said land or in the unitized area.

24. ROYALTY STATEMENT FOR LESSOR. On or before the last day of each month Lessee shall furnish Lessor a written statement of the royalties due Lessor hereunder for the preceding calendar month and make payment to Lessor of Lessor's royalty. Any payment hereunder may be made by good and valid check upon a bank doing business in California. Lessor agrees to promptly examine each and all statements and payments hereunder forwarded to him or to his depository, and to promptly satisfy himself of the accuracy of such statements and payments, as well as of all determinations, measurements and tests entering therein, and for this purpose Lessor shall have the right at all reasonable times to inspect any and all of Lessee's records relating to the production from said land, and the amount saved and removed. Lessee shall have no liability to Lessor for any alleged deficiencies in royalty statements or payments hereunder unless Lessor shall have filed with Lessee a written claim specifying with particularity any asserted defects and the amount of any asserted deficiency within six (6) months after the receipt by Lessor or by his depository of the statement or payment in which any such defect or deficiency is alleged to have occurred.

25. SUBSURFACE EASEMENTS; EASEMENTS AFTER TERMINATION. Lessor hereby grants exclusively unto Lessee and its assigns such rights of way, easements, and servitudes in and through the subsurface of the land hereby leased, at depths at least five hundred feet (500') beneath the surface, as Lessee or its assigns may from time to time desire for boring well holes from surface locations outside the land hereby leased and for casing and otherwise completing and maintaining such wells and using the same for producing from other land, whether or not unitized with the land hereby leased,

Figure C.4 — *Continued*

such rights of way, easements, and servitudes to continue for the duration of this lease and thereafter as hereinafter provided. If Lessee shall assign to any third party or parties rights granted to Lessee under this paragraph, the rights of Lessee shall not thereby be diminished, but in such event both Lessee and its assignee shall have, hold, and enjoy said rights, each independently of the other. The rights of Lessee and of each assignee of Lessee under this paragraph shall continue after the expiration, surrender, forfeiture, or other termination of this lease for a period of twenty (20) years from the date of this lease and so long thereafter as oil, gas or other hydrocarbon substances are produced by means of any such well and so long thereafter as drilling, redrilling, remedial or secondary recovery operations are being conducted with respect to any such well, whichever period is the longer. Lessee and each such assignee utilizing any such rights after the expiration, surrender, forfeiture, or other termination of this lease shall pay to Lessor a rental for each well subsequently maintained by it under the leased land at the rate of One Dollar ($1.00) per annum per foot of the horizontal projection (computed to the nearest part of a foot) of the surveyed course of the part of the well of such Lessee or assignee lying within the confines of the land hereby leased, the rental with respect to any such well to commence on the completion thereof (or, if completed before the date of the expiration, surrender, forfeiture, or other termination of this lease, then upon such last-mentioned date) and to continue until such well is abandoned in accordance with the requirements of the Division of Oil and Gas of the State of California. Lessor shall not be entitled to receive any rental under the provisions of this paragraph during such times as Lessor is entitled to receive royalty or rentals under this lease During the term of this lease, Lessor shall not grant any rights of way, easements or servitudes in and to said land in respect to the drilling for or the production of oil, gas and other hydrocarbon substances to any other person, firm or corporation without the written consent of Lessee.

26. EXECUTION. This lease may be executed in any number of counterparts, by any person having an interest in said land, with the same effect as if all lessors herein were named as Lessor in one document and had all signed the same document. All counterparts shall be construed together and shall constitute one lease. The failure of any person owning an interest in said land to execute a counterpart hereof, or the failure of any person named as Lessor in any counterpart to execute the same shall not affect the binding force of this lease as to those who have executed or shall execute a counterpart hereof.

27. POWERS. The term of this lease as hereinabove set forth shall apply to any interest leased hereunder by a party or parties whose powers in respect to leasing are not limited or restricted by law. The term of this lease in respect to any interest leased hereunder by a guardian, executor, or administrator of an estate, municipality, public corporation or other party whose right to lease is limited or restricted by law shall be limited to a period authorized by law, and any such interest shall be a part of the leased land only during such authorized term unless, during such period, the term is extended by appropriate instrument or by operation of law, in which event the interest affected by such extension shall continue to be a part of the leased land for the extended period. Any counterpart of this lease executed by any party whose right to lease is limited or restricted by law may set forth the term for which such party joins in this lease and refer to the court order or other authority authorizing his execution of this lease.

28. PARAGRAPH HEADINGS. The paragraph headings of this lease are for convenience only and are not part of this lease and do not in any way limit or amplify the terms or provisions of this lease.

29. PARTIES. This lease and all its terms, conditions and stipulations shall inure to the benefit of and shall extend to and be binding upon the heirs, executors, administrators, grantees, successors and assigns of the parties hereto.

IN WITNESS WHEREOF, the parties hereto have caused this agreement to be duly executed as of the date first hereinabove written.

SUBSCRIBING WITNESS:

_____   _____

_____   _____

_____   _____

Figure C.4 — *Continued*

_____   _____

_____   _____

                                                                            LESSOR

                                                    EXXON CORPORATION

                                                    By _____

                                                                Its Attorney in Fact

                                                                    LESSEE

APPENDIX D
LEASING IN LOUISIANA

Throughout the producing states, mineral leasing is governed by case law as modified by state statute. (The statutes allow regulatory agencies to formulate rules aimed primarily at conservation and efficient production.) The great exception to this pattern of case law plus statute law can be found in Louisiana, which has a statutory code (the Louisiana Mineral Code) enacted specifically to deal with, among other matters, the leasing of oil and gas.

Another difference between leasing in Louisiana and leasing in states like Texas, Mississippi, or West Virginia arises from the view taken of mineral ownership. In Louisiana, unextracted minerals like oil and gas cannot be owned as land can be owned. There is no such thing as a mineral estate separate from a surface estate. What can be owned are mineral rights or interests—that is, the rights to explore for, produce, and sell minerals. This distinction does not, of course, prevent people from talking about the sale or purchase of oil and gas *as if* these minerals could be owned in place.

This distinction has another effect in Louisiana. Unlike the case in most other states in which a mineral sale or reservation is perpetual, in Louisiana an assignment of mineral or royalty interests, or a reservation of mineral or royalty interests in the sale of land, terminates if the interests are not used. When the mineral or royalty rights in the land are owned by someone other than the owner of the land itself, the outstanding mineral rights are considered to be a burden or encumbrance on the full ownership of the land. A mineral or royalty interest that is not owned by the same person who owns the land itself will expire upon the passage of 10 years from the creation of the mineral or royalty right unless operations have been carried on that will interrupt the running of this period. Such operations are the drilling of a well in the case of a mineral servitude, or production in the case of a royalty right. (The mineral servitude confers the same rights as ownership of the minerals themselves in other states, including the right to grant leases and retain bonuses and delay rentals; the royalty interest is a right to production and royalty only, if any, from the land.) At the end of this 10-year period, whoever owns the land itself automatically becomes the owner of the mineral or royalty right that had been outstanding.

The practical differences that flow from Louisiana's history and legal peculiarities are numerous, but most affect the details of leasing without adding up to major *procedural* differences of the kind found in California or Alaska. (Such details would be, for example, the way to record a lease, mentioned in chapter 7, or the use of the *arpent* in land measurement, mentioned in chapter 4.) Louisiana lease forms, like those used in other states, show a number of variations. The most commonly used forms are those printed by the M.L. Bath Company of Shreveport and referred to as the "Bath forms" in the same casual way that the "Producers 88" is mentioned by landmen and attorneys in the Midcontinent. The "New South Louisiana Revised" 42 CPM forms run from the "Bath 2" through the "Bath 7." The Spec. 14-BR 1-2A-PX 10-65 form for northern Louisiana is also printed by the Bath Company, though some of its versions were drafted by independent producers. Following are examples of a southern Louisiana (fig. D.1) and a northern Louisiana (fig. D.2) form.

Figure D.1. Oil, gas, and mineral lease for southern Louisiana
(Courtesy of M. L. Bath Co.)

THE M L BATH COMPANIES
SHREVEPORT—DALLAS—LAKE CHARLES
BATH-●-GRAM
REG NO 512 391 U S PAT OFF
FORM 42 CPM—NEW SOUTH
LOUISIANA REVISED SIX (6)—POOLING

OIL, GAS AND MINERAL LEASE

THIS AGREEMENT, entered into effective as of_____, 19_____,

by and between_____

_____

_____

_____

herein called "Lessor" (whether one or more) and_____

hereinafter called "Lessee", witnesseth, that:

Lessor, in consideration of the sum of_____ ($_____),
hereby leases and lets unto Lessee, the exclusive right to enter upon and use the land hereinafter described for the exploration for, and production of oil, gas, sulphur and all other minerals, together with the use of the surface of the land for all purposes incident to the exploration for and
production, ownership, possession, storage and transportation of said minerals (either from said land or acreage pooled therewith), and the right
to dispose of salt water, with the right of ingress and egress to and from said lands at all times for such purposes, including the right to construct, maintain and use roads, pipelines and/or canals thereon for operations hereunder or in connection with similar operations on adjoining
land, and including the right to remove from the land any property placed by Lessee thereon and to draw and remove casing from wells drilled

by Lessee on said land; the land to which this lease applies and which is affected hereby being situated in_____
Parish, Louisiana, and described as follows, to-wit:

All land owned by the Lessor in the above mentioned Section or Sections or Surveys, all property acquired by prescription and all accretion
or alluvion attaching to and forming a part of said land are included herein, whether properly or specifically described or not. Whether or not
any reduction in rentals shall have previously been made, this lease, without further evidence thereof, shall immediately attach to and affect any
and all rights, titles, and interests in the above described land, including reversionary mineral rights, hereafter acquired by or inuring to Lessor
and Lessor's successors and assigns.

For the purpose of calculating the rental payments hereinafter provided for, the above described land is estimated to comprise_____
acres, whether it actually comprises more or less.

This lease shall be for a term of_____years and_____months from the date hereof (called
"primary term") and so long thereafter as oil, gas or some other mineral is being produced or drilling operations are conducted either on this
land or on acreage pooled therewith (or with any part thereof), all as hereinafter provided for; all subject to the following conditions and
agreements:

1. This lease shall terminate on_____, 19_____, unless on or before
said date the Lessee either (1) commences operations for the drilling of a well on the land, or on acreage pooled therewith (or with any part
thereof), in search of oil, gas or other minerals and thereafter continues such operations and drilling to completion or abandonment; or (2)

pays to the Lessor a rental of _____Dollars ($_____)
per acre for all or that part of the land which Lessee elects to continue to hold hereunder, which payment shall maintain Lessee's rights in effect
as to such land without drilling operations for one year from the date last above mentioned; and Lessee may continue to maintain the rights
granted without drilling operations for successive twelve months' periods (during the primary term) by paying Lessor, on or before the begin-

ning of such respective periods_____Dollars ($_____)
per acre for all or that part of the land held hereunder. Payments may be made to the Lessor or may be mailed or delivered for deposit to

Lessor's credit in the_____Bank of_____
which Bank or its successor shall continue to be the depository for such rentals as the representative of Lessor and Lessor's successors and

Figure D.1—*Continued*

assigns; and the death or incapacity of Lessor shall not terminate or affect Lessee's right to continue to deposit all payments in said depository bank or its successor. The mailing of the check or draft of Lessee or Lessee's successors to Lessor at the address set forth above or to the said Bank on or before the rental paying date shall be considered as payment of rental and operate to maintain Lessee's rights in force and effect. Should said Bank fail or liquidate, or if it should for any reason fail or refuse to accept Lessee's check or draft, the attempted payment in the manner above provided shall not be thereby rendered ineffective and Lessee shall not be in default for failure to pay said rental until thirty (30) days after Lessor shall have furnished Lessee with a recordable instrument naming a new depository; and this provision shall apply to all such new and subsequently named depositories. Wherever used in this lease, "operations for drilling", "drilling operations" and "operations" shall be deemed to have been commenced when work is commenced or materials placed on the ground at or near the well site preparatory to the drilling of a well.

2. Lessee, at its option, is hereby given the right and power without any further approval from Lessor, at any time and from time to time, to pool or combine the land or mineral interest covered by this lease, or any portion thereof, with other land, lease or leases and mineral interests in the immediate vicinity thereof, when, in Lessee's judgment, it is necessary or advisable to do so in order to properly explore or develop or operate said premises so as to promote the conservation of oil, gas or other minerals in and under and that may be produced from said premises or to prevent waste or to avoid the drilling of unnecessary wells or to comply with the spacing or unitization order of any Regulatory Body of the State of Louisiana or the United States having jurisdiction. The term "Regulatory Body" shall include any governmental officer, tribunal or group (civil or military) issuing orders governing the drilling of wells or the production of minerals. Such pooling shall be of adjacent tracts which will form a reasonably compact (but not necessarily contiguous) body of land for each unit, and the unit or units so created shall not exceed substantially forty (40) acres each for each well for oil exploration or production and substantially one hundred sixty (160) acres each for each well for gas and gas-condensate exploration or production unless a larger spacing pattern or larger drilling or production units (including a field or pool unit) shall have been fixed and established by an order of a Regulatory Body of the State of Louisiana or of the United States, in which event the unit or units shall be the same as fixed by said order. Lessee shall execute and file for record in the Conveyance Records of the Parish in which the land herein leased is situated a declaration describing the pooled acreage; and upon such filing, the unit or units shall thereby become effective, except that when a unit is created by order of a Regulatory Body the pooling shall be effective as of the effective date of such order, and no declaration shall be required in connection therewith. The royalties herein elsewhere specified, and subject to the provisions of Paragraph 10 hereof, shall be computed only on the proportionate part of the production from any pooled unit that is allocated to the land herein described; and unless otherwise allocated by order of a Regulatory Body, the amount of production to be so allocated from each pooled unit shall be that proportion of such total production that the surface area of the land affected hereby and included in the unit bears to the total surface area of all the lands included in such pooled unit. Drilling or reworking operations on or production of oil, gas or other minerals from land included in such pooled unit shall have the effect of continuing this lease in force and effect during or after the primary term as to all of the land covered hereby (including any portion of said land not included in said unit) and as to all strata underlying said land, whether or not such operations be on or such production be from land covered hereby. Any unit formed by Lessee hereunder may be created either prior to or during or after the drilling of the well which is then or thereafter becomes the unit well. Separate units may be created for oil and for gas, or for separate stratum or strata of oil or gas, even though the areas thereof overlap, and the creation of a unit as to one mineral or strata or stratum shall not exhaust the right of Lessee (even as to the same well) to create different or additional units for other minerals or for other strata or stratum of the same or other minerals. The failure of the leasehold title (in whole or in part) to any tract or interest therein included in a pooled unit shall not affect the validity of said unit as to the tracts or interests not subject to such failure, but the unit may thereafter be revised as hereinafter provided. Lessee shall have the right and power to reduce and diminish the extent of any unit created under the terms of this paragraph so as to eliminate from said unit any interest or lease to which title has failed or upon which there is or may be an adverse claim. Such revision of the unit shall be evidenced by an instrument in writing executed by Lessee, which shall describe the lands included in the unit as revised and shall be filed for record in the Conveyance Records of the Parish where the lands herein leased are situated. The revised declaration shall not be retroactive but shall be effective as of the date that it is filed for record. Any unit created by Lessee hereunder shall also be revised so as to conform with an order of a Regulatory Body issued after said unit was originally established; such revision shall be effective as of the effective date of such order without further declaration by Lessee, but such revision shall be limited to the stratum or strata covered by said order and shall not otherwise affect the unit originally created.

3. Lessee, may, at any time prior to or after the discovery and production of minerals on the land, execute and deliver to Lessor or file for record a release or releases of any portion or portions of the lands or any stratum or strata and be relieved of all requirements hereof as to the land, stratum or strata so released; and, in the event of a release of all strata under a portion of the land during the primary term, the rental shall be reduced proportionately, according to acreage. In the event of the forfeiture of this lease for any cause, Lessee shall have the right to retain around each well then producing oil, gas or other minerals or being drilled or worked on the number of acres fixed and located by or in accordance with the spacing or unit or proration allowable order of any Regulatory Body of the State of Louisiana or of the United States under which said well is being drilled or produced, or if said well has been or is being drilled on a unit pooled by Lessee as provided herein, then Lessee may retain all of the acreage comprising said pooled unit and if no spacing or proration allowable order has been issued nor any pooled unit established, then Lessee shall have the right to retain forty (40) acres surrounding each oil well then producing or being drilled or worked on, and one hundred sixty (160) acres around each gas or gas condensate well then producing, or being drilled or worked on or shut in under Paragraph 6 hereof, each of such tracts to be in as near a square form as is practicable. Lessee shall have such rights of way or servitudes affecting the acreage released or forfeited as are necessary for Lessee's operations on the land retained hereunder.

4. Prior to the time that oil, gas or some other mineral is being produced from the leased land or land pooled therewith (or with any part thereof), Lessee may maintain the rights granted during and after the primary term by carrying on operations on said lands or land pooled therewith (or with any part thereof) without the lapse of more than ninety (90) days between abandonment of work on one well and the commencement of operations for drilling or reworking another; and during the primary term such operations may be discontinued and the rights granted maintained by commencing or resuming rental payments, by paying within ninety (90) days from the discontinuance of operations (regardless of the fixed rental paying date) the proportion of the fixed yearly rental that the number of days between the end of said ninety (90) days and the next ensuing rental paying date or the expiration of the primary term bears to the twelve months' period; but, if said ninety (90) days should expire prior to the initial rental paying date or during any year for which rental or other payment has been made, no rental shall be due until the next fixed rental paying date, or, as the case may be, for the balance of the last year of the primary term.

5. If, prior to or after the discovery of oil or gas on the lands held hereunder, a well producing oil or gas in paying quantities for 30 consecutive days should be brought in on adjacent lands not owned by Lessor and not included in a pooled unit containing all or a portion of the lands herein described, Lessee shall drill such offset well to protect the land held hereunder from drainage as and within the time that a reasonable and prudent operator would drill under the same or similar circumstances; it being provided, however, that Lessee shall not be required to drill any such offset well unless the well on adjacent land is within 330 feet of any line of the lands held hereunder, nor shall such offset well be necessary when said lands are being reasonably protected by a well on the leased premises or land pooled therewith (or with any part thereof).

6. After the production of oil, gas or any other mineral in paying quantities, either on the leased premises or on lands pooled therewith (or with any part thereof), the rights granted shall be maintained in effect during and after the primary term and without the payment of the rentals hereinabove provided for so long as oil, gas, or some other mineral is being produced in paying quantities. It is provided, however, that if, after the production of oil, gas or other minerals in paying quantities, the production thereof should cease from any cause, and Lessee is not then engaged in drilling or reworking operations, this lease shall terminate unless Lessee resumes or restores such production, or commences additional drilling, reworking or mining operations within ninety (90) days thereafter and continues such operations without the lapse of more than ninety (90) days between abandonment of work on one well and commencement of reworking operations or operations for the

Figure D.1— *Continued*

drilling of another, in an effort to restore production of oil, gas or other minerals, or (if during the primary term) commences or resumes the payment of rentals in the manner hereinabove provided for in connection with the abandonment of wells drilled. Lessee shall not be required to produce more than one mineral, the production of any one mineral in paying quantities and with reasonable diligence being sufficient to maintain all of Lessee's rights. In the event that any well on the land or on property pooled therewith (or with any part thereof), is capable of producing gas or gaseous substances in paying quantities but such minerals are not being produced, then Lessee's rights may be maintained, in the absence of production or drilling operations, by commencing or resuming rental payments as hereinabove provided for in connection with the abandonment of wells drilled. Should such conditions occur or exist at the end of or after the primary term, or within ninety (90) days prior to the expiration thereof, Lessee's rights may be extended beyond and after the primary term by the commencement, resumption or continuance of such payments at the rate and in the manner herein provided for rental payments during the primary term, and for the purpose of computing and making such payments the expiration date of the primary term and each anniversary date thereof shall be considered as a fixed rental paying date; provided, however, that in no event shall Lessee's rights be so extended by rental payments and without drilling operations or production of oil, gas or some other mineral for more than five consecutive years.

7. Subject to the provisions of Paragraphs 2 and 10 hereof the royalties to be paid by Lessee are: (a) on oil (which includes condensate and other liquid hydrocarbons when separated by lease separator units), one-eighth (1/8) of that produced and saved from the land and not used for fuel in conducting operations on the property (or on acreage pooled therewith or with any part thereof), or in treating such liquids to make them marketable; (b) on gas, one-eighth (1/8) of the market value at the well of the gas used by Lessee in operations not connected with the land leased or any pooled unit containing all or a part of said land; the royalty on gas sold by Lessee to be one-eighth (1/8) of the amount realized at the well from such sales; (c) one-eighth (1/8) of the market value at the well of gas used by Lessee in manufacturing gasoline or other by-products, except that in computing such value, there shall be excluded all gas or components thereof used in lease or unit operations, or injected into subsurface strata as hereinafter provided; (d) One Dollar ($1.00) for each ton of 2240 pounds of sulphur, payable when marketed; and (e) one-eighth (1/8) of the market value at the well or mine of all other minerals produced and saved or mined and marketed. Oil royalties shall be delivered to Lessor free of expense at Lessor's option in tanks furnished by Lessor at the well or to Lessor's credit in any pipe line connected therewith. In the event Lessor does not furnish tanks for such royalty oil and no pipe line is connected with the well, Lessee may sell Lessor's such oil at the best market price obtainable and pay Lessor the price received f.o.b. the leased property, less any severance or production tax imposed thereon. Lessee shall have the right to inject gas, water, brine or other fluids into subsurface strata, and no royalties shall be due or computed on any gas or component thereof produced by Lessee and injected into subsurface stratum or strata through a well or wells located either on the land or on a pooled unit containing all or a part of the land.

8. The Lessee shall be responsible for all damages to timber and growing crops of Lessor caused by Lessee's operations.

9. All provisions hereof shall inure to the benefit of and bind the successors and assigns (in whole or in part) of Lessor and Lessee, (whether by sale, inheritance, assignment, sub-lease or otherwise), but regardless of any actual or constructive notice thereof, no change in the ownership of the land or any interest therein or change in the capacity or status of Lessor or any other owner of rights hereunder, whether resulting from sale or other transfer, inheritance, interdiction, emancipation, attainment of majority or otherwise, shall impose any additional burden on Lessee, or be binding on Lessee for making any payments hereunder unless, at least forty-five (45) days before any such payment is due, the record owner of this lease shall have been furnished with certified copy of recorded instrument or judgment evidencing such sale, transfer or inheritance, or with evidence of such change in status or capacity of Lessor or other party owning rights hereunder. The furnishing of such evidence shall not affect the validity of payments theretofore made in advance. A sublessee may, as to the Lessor, exercise the rights and discharge the obligations of the Lessee, without joinder of any sublessor. In the event of an assignment of the lease as to a segregated portion of the land, delay rentals shall be apportioned among the several leasehold owners according to the surface area of each, and default in payment by one shall not affect the rights of others. Any owner of rights under this lease may pay the entire rental payable hereunder and such payment shall be for the benefit of those holding leasehold rights hereunder. If at any time two or more persons are entitled to participate in the rental payable hereunder, Lessee may pay or tender said rental jointly to such persons or to their joint credit in the depository named herein; or, at Lessee's election, the proportionate part of said rental to which each participant is entitled may be paid or tendered to him separately or to his separate credit in said depository and payment or tender to any participant of his portion of the rentals hereunder shall maintain this lease as to such participant.

10. Lessor hereby warrants and agrees to defend the title to said land and agrees that Lessee may, at its option, discharge any tax, mortgage or other lien upon the land and be subrogated thereto and have the right to apply to the repayment of Lessee any rentals and/or royalties accruing hereunder. If Lessor owns less than the entire undivided interest in all or any portion of the lands or mineral rights relating thereto (whether such interest is herein specified or not) rentals and royalties as to the land in which an interest is outstanding in others shall be reduced proportionately to the interest of the Lessor therein, but the failure of Lessee to reduce rentals shall not affect Lessee's rights to reduce royalties; and all outstanding royalty rights shall be deducted from the royalties herein provided for. Lessee shall have the right to purchase a lease or leases from others to protect its leasehold rights and shall not thereby be held to have disputed Lessor's title; and in the event Lessor's title or an interest therein is claimed by others, Lessee shall have the right to withhold payment of royalties or to deposit such royalties in the registry of the Court until final determination of Lessor's rights.

11. In the event the Lessor at any time considers that operations are not being conducted in compliance with this lease, Lessor shall notify Lessee in writing of the facts relied upon as constituting a breach hereof, and Lessee shall have sixty (60) days after receipt of such notice in which to commence any operations that are then legally necessary to comply with the requirements hereof. The service of said notice and the lapse of sixty (60) days without Lessee meeting or commencing to meet the alleged breaches shall be a condition precedent to any action by Lessor for any cause hereunder. It is provided, however, that after production of oil, gas, sulphur, or other mineral has been obtained from the land covered hereby or land pooled therewith (or with any part thereof), this lease shall not be subject to forfeiture or loss, either in whole or in part, for failure to comply with the express or implied obligations of this contract except after final judicial ascertainment of such failure and Lessee has been given a period of sixty (60) days after such final judicial ascertainment to prevent such loss or forfeiture by complying with and discharging the obligations as to which Lessee has been judicially determined to be in default.

12. If the land herein described is owned in divided or undivided portions by more than one party, this instrument may be signed in any number of counterparts, each of which shall be binding on the party or parties so signing regardless of whether all of the owners join in the granting of this lease; and the failure of any party named herein as Lessor to sign this lease shall not affect its validity as to those whose signatures appear hereon or on a counterpart hereof.

13. The requirements hereof shall be subject to any State and/or Federal law or order regulating operations on the land. It is further agreed that should Lessee be prevented from complying with any expressed or implied covenants of this lease, from conducting drilling or reworking operations thereon, or from producing oil, gas or other mineral therefrom by reason of scarcity or inability, after effort made in good faith, to obtain equipment or material or authority to use same, or by failure of carriers to transport or furnish facilities for transportation, or by operation of force majeure, any Federal or State law, or any order, rule or regulation of governmental authority, or other cause beyond Lessee's control, then while so prevented, Lessee's obligation to comply with such covenant shall be suspended and Lessee shall not be liable for damages for failure to comply therewith; and this lease shall be extended while and so long as Lessee is prevented by any such cause from conducting drilling or reworking operations on or from producing oil, gas or other mineral from the leased premises and the time while Lessee is so prevented shall not be counted against Lessee.

The consideration paid by Lessee to Lessor is accepted as full and adequate consideration for all rights, options and privileges herein granted.

Figure D.1–*Continued*

IN WITNESS WHEREOF, this instrument is executed as of the date first above written.

WITNESSES:

_____

_____

_____

_____

_____

_____

_____

_____

_____

_____

_____

_____

_____

_____

_____

_____

_____

_____

_____

_____

_____

Figure D.1 – *Continued*

STATE OF_____ }
PARISH (OR COUNTY) OF_____ }
    On this_____day of_____, 19_____, before me personally appeared
_____,
to me known to be the person described in and who executed the foregoing instrument, and acknowledged that_____executed the
same as_____free act and deed.
                                                                    Notary Public.

STATE OF_____ }
PARISH (OR COUNTY) OF_____ }
    On this_____day of_____, 19_____, before me personally appeared
_____
to me known to be the person described in and who executed the foregoing instrument, and acknowledged that_____executed the
same as_____free act and deed.
                                                                    Notary Public.

STATE OF LOUISIANA   }
PARISH OF_____ }
    BEFORE ME, the undersigned Notary Public, on this day personally appeared_____
who, being by me duly sworn, stated under oath that_____was one of the subscribing witnesses to the foregoing instrument and
that the same was signed by_____
_____

(Lessor, as above mentioned) in_____presence and in the presence of the other subscribing witness(es).

    SWORN TO AND SUBSCRIBED before me_____, 19_____

                                       Notary Public in and for_____Parish, Louisiana.

STATE OF LOUISIANA   }
PARISH OF_____ }
    BEFORE ME, the undersigned Notary Public, on this day personally appeared_____
who, being by me duly sworn, stated under oath that_____was one of the subscribing witnesses to the foregoing instrument and
that the same was signed by_____

(Lessor, as above mentioned) in_____presence and in the presence of the other subscribing witness(es).

    SWORN TO AND SUBSCRIBED before me_____, 19_____

                                       Notary Public in and for_____Parish, Louisiana.

Figure D.1 — *Continued*

CORPORATION ACKNOWLEDGMENT

STATE OF_____ }

PARISH (OR COUNTY) OF_____ }

ON THIS_____day of_____, 19____, before me, appeared_____

to me personally known, who, being by me duly sworn, did say that he is the_____

of the_____and that said instrument was signed in behalf of said corporation by

authority of its Board of Directors and said_____acknowledged said instrument to

be the free act and deed of said corporation.

_____
Notary Public.

No._____

Oil, Gas and Mineral Lease
(LOUISIANA)

FROM_____

TO_____

Dated_____, 19____

No. of Acres_____

_____Parish, Louisiana

Term_____

This instrument was filed for record on the_____

day of_____, 19____, at_____o'clock_____M., and duly recorded in

Book_____, Page_____

_____of the records of this office.

By_____, Deputy

THE H. L. BATH COMPANIES
BATH-GRAM
FORM 42 CPM—NEW SOUTH
LOUISIANA REVISED SIX (6)—POOLING

Figure D.2. Oil, gas, and mineral lease for northern Louisiana
(Courtesy of M. L. Bath Co.)

THE M. L. BATH COMPANIES
SHREVEPORT—LOUISIANA—LAKE CHARLES
BATH-⊕-GRAM
BATH'S FORM LOUISIANA SPEC. 14-BR1-2A-PX 10-65

OIL, GAS AND MINERAL LEASE

THIS AGREEMENT made this_____day of_____, 19____, between

lessor (whether one or more), and_____
lessee, WITNESSETH:

1. Lessor in consideration of_____Dollars ($_____),
in hand paid, of the royalties herein provided, and of the agreement of Lessee herein contained, hereby grants, leases and
lets exclusively unto Lessee for the purposes of investigating, exploring, prospecting, drilling and mining for and producing
oil, gas and all other minerals, laying pipe lines, building tanks, power stations, telephone lines, and other structures thereon to produce, save, take care of, treat, transport and own said products and for dredging and maintaining canals, con-
structing roads and bridges, and building houses for its employees, and, in general, for all appliances, structures, equipment,
servitudes and privileges which may be necessary, useful or convenient to or in connection with any such operations con-

ducted by Lessee thereon, or on any adjacent lands, the following described land in_____Parish,
Louisiana, to-wit:

This lease also covers and includes battures, accretions and all other land owned by Lessor adjacent to the land
particularly described above. For the purpose of calculating the rental payments hereunder provided for, said land is esti-

mated to comprise_____acres, whether it actually comprises more or less.

2. Subject to the other provisions herein contained, this lease shall be for a period of ten years from this date
(called "primary term") and as long thereafter as (1) oil, gas, sulphur or other mineral is produced from said land hereunder or from land pooled therewith; or (2) it is maintained in force in any other manner herein provided.

(a) It is the intention of the parties that this lease shall also extend and apply to all outstanding mineral rights or
servitudes affecting the lands herein described as the same may revert to Lessor, his heirs or assigns, from time to time.

3. The royalties to be paid by Lessee are: (a) on oil, and other hydrocarbons which are produced at the well in
liquid form by ordinary production methods, one-eighth of that produced and saved from said land, same to be delivered
at the wells or to the credit of Lessor in the pipe line to which the wells may be connected; Lessor's interest in either case
to bear its proportion of any expenses for treating the oil to make it marketable as crude; Lessee may from time to time purchase any royalty oil or other liquid hydrocarbons in its possession, paying the market price therefor prevailing for the
field where produced on the date of purchase; (b) on gas, including casinghead gas, or other gaseous substance produced
from said land and sold or used off the premises or for the extraction of gasoline or other products therefrom, the market
value at the well of one-eighth of the gas so sold or used, provided that on gas sold at the wells the royalty shall be one-
eighth of the amount realized from such sale; such gas, casinghead gas, residue gas, or gas of any other nature or description whatsoever, as may be disposed of for no consideration to Lessee, either through unavoidable waste or leakage,

Figure D.2—*Continued*

---

or in order to recover oil or other liquid hydrocarbons, or returned to the ground, shall not be deemed to have been sold or used either on or off the premises within the meaning of this paragraph 3 hereof; (c) on all other minerals mined and marketed, one-eighth, either in kind or value at the well or mine, at Lessee's election, except that on sulphur the royalty shall be one dollar ($1.00) per long ton.

4. If operations for drilling or mining are not commenced on said land or on land pooled therewith on or before one year from this date, this lease shall terminate as to both parties, unless on or before one year from this date Lessee shall

pay or tender to the Lessor a rental of_____

_____DOLLARS ($_____) which shall cover the privilege of deferring commencement of such operations for a period of twelve (12) months. In like manner and upon like payments or tenders, annually, the commencement of said operations may be further deferred for successive periods of the same number of months, each during the primary term. Payment or tender may be made to the

Lessor or to the credit of Lessor in_____Bank

at_____, which bank, or any successor thereof shall continue to be agent for the Lessor, and Lessor's successors and assigns. If such bank (or any successor bank) shall fail, liquidate, or be succeeded by another bank, or for any reason fail or refuse to accept rental, Lessee shall not be held in default until thirty days after Lessor shall deliver to Lessee a recordable instrument, making provision for another method of payment, or tender, and any depository charge is a liability of the Lessor. The payment or tender of rental may be made by check or draft of Lessee, mailed or delivered to said bank or Lessor, on or before the rental paying date. The depth of the hole to which any well may be drilled hereunder in search of oil, gas or any other mineral shall be determined solely by Lessee. Lessee may at any time execute and deliver to Lessor or to the depository above named or place of record a release or releases covering any portion or portions of the above described premises and thereby surrender this lease as to such portion or portions and be relieved of all obligations as to the acreage surrendered, and thereafter the rentals payable hereunder shall be reduced in the proportion that the acreage covered hereby is reduced by said release or releases, but all lands so released shall remain subject to easements for rights of way necessary or convenient for Lessee's operations on the land retained by it.

5. If Lessee obtains production of minerals on said land or on land with which the lease premises or any portion thereof has been pooled, and if, during the life of this lease either before or after the expiration of the primary term, all such production is shut in by reason of force majeure or the lack either of a market at the well or wells or of an available pipeline outlet in the field, this lease shall not terminate but shall continue in effect during such shut-in period as though production were actually being obtained on the premises within the meaning of paragraph 2 hereof, and, during the month of January of each year immediately succeeding any year in which a shut-in period occurred when all such production was so shut in, Lessee shall pay or tender, by check or draft of Lessee, to the royalty owners or to the royalty owners' credit in any depository bank named in this lease, as royalty, one-twelfth (1/12) of the amount of the delay rental provided for in paragraph 4 hereof for each full calendar month in the preceding calendar year that this lease was continued in force solely and exclusively by reason of the foregoing provisions of this paragraph. The owners of the royalty as of the date of such payment shall be entitled thereto in proportion to their ownership of the royalty. The provisions of this paragraph shall be recurring at all times during the life of this lease. Nothing in this paragraph contained shall abridge the right of Lessee to otherwise maintain this lease in force and effect under its other provisions, and for any part of a shut-in period that this lease is otherwise being maintained in force and effect no shut-in royalty shall be due.

6. This lease will continue in full force and effect within or beyond the primary term as long as any mineral is produced from said land hereunder or from land pooled therewith. If within the primary term and prior to discovery of oil, gas, sulphur or other mineral on said land or on land pooled therewith, Lessee should drill a dry hole or holes thereon or if after discovery of oil, gas, sulphur or other mineral, the production thereof should cease from any cause, this lease shall not terminate if Lessee commences or resumes the payment or tender of rentals or commences drilling operations or reworking operations on or before the rental paying date next ensuing after the expiration of ninety days from date of completion of such dry hole or cessation of production. If at any time subsequent to ninety days prior to the beginning of the last year of the primary term Lessee should drill a dry hole thereon or on land pooled therewith, or production previously secured should cease from any cause, no rental payment or operations are necessary in order to keep the lease in force during the remainder of the primary term. If such dry hole or holes be completed or abandoned or such production cease within less than ninety days before the end of the primary term, this lease shall continue in force and effect for ninety days from such completion or abandonment or cessation of production. If at the expiration of the primary term or at the expiration of the ninety day period provided for in the preceding sentence, oil, gas, sulphur or other mineral is not being produced on said land or on land pooled therewith but Lessee is then engaged in drilling operations or reworking operations thereon, or if production previously secured should cease from any cause after the expiration of the primary term, this lease shall remain in force so long thereafter as Lessee either (a) is engaged in drilling operations or reworking operations with no cessation between operations or between such cessation of production and additional operations of more than ninety consecutive days; or (b) is producing oil, gas, sulphur or other mineral from said land hereunder or from land pooled therewith. If sulphur be encountered on said premises or on land pooled therewith this lease shall continue in force and effect so long as Lessee is engaged with due diligence in exploration for and/or erecting a plant for the production of sulphur and thereafter, subject to the foregoing provisions hereof, so long as oil, gas, sulphur or other mineral is produced from said land hereunder or from land pooled therewith.

Figure D.2 – *Continued*

---

7. Lessee is hereby granted the right as to all or any part of the land described herein, without Lessor's joinder, to combine, pool, or unitize the acreage royalty or mineral interest covered by this lease, or any portion thereof, with any other land, lease or leases, royalty or mineral interests in or under any other tract or tracts of land in the vicinity thereof, whether owned by Lessee or some other person, or corporation so as to create, by the combination of such lands and leases, one or more operating units, provided that no one operating unit shall, in the case of gas, including condensate, embrace more than six hundred forty (640) acres, and in the case of oil, including casinghead gas, embrace more than forty (40) acres; and provided further, however, that if any spacing or other rules and regulations of the State or Federal Commission, Agency, or regulatory body having or claiming jurisdiction has heretofore or shall at any time hereafter prescribe a drilling or operating unit or spacing rule in the case of gas, including condensate, greater than six hundred forty (640) acres, or in the case of oil or casinghead gas greater than forty (40) acres, then the unit or units herein contemplated may have, or may be redesigned so as to have, as the case may be, the same surface content as, but not more than, the unit or the acreage in the spacing rule so prescribed. However, it is further specifically understood and agreed, anything herein to the contrary notwithstanding, that the Lessee shall have the right to, and the benefit of an acreage tolerance of ten per cent in excess of any drilling or operating unit authorized herein. In the event such operating unit or units is/are so created by Lessee, Lessor agrees to accept and shall receive out of the production or the proceeds from the production from such operating unit or units, such portion of the one-eighth royalty specified herein as the number of acres (mineral acres) out of this lease placed in any such operating unit or units bears to the total number of acres included in such operating unit or units. The commencement of a well, or the completion of a well to production of either oil, gas, casinghead gas, condensate, or other minerals on any portion of an operating unit in which all or any part of the land described herein is embraced, or production of oil, gas, casinghead gas, condensate, or other minerals therefrom shall have the same effect under the terms of this lease as if a well were commenced, completed or producing oil, gas, casinghead gas, condensate, or other minerals in paying quantities on the land embraced by this lease. Lessee shall execute in writing and file for record in the records of the Parish in which the lands herein leased are located, an instrument identifying or describing the pooled acreage, or an instrument supplemental thereto redesignating same, as the case may be. Either prior to the securing of production from any unit created under the authority hereinabove granted, or after cessation of production therefrom Lessee shall have the right to dissolve the unit so created, without Lessor's joinder or further consent, by executing in writing and placing of record in the Parish or Parishes in which the lands making up such unit may be located, an instrument identifying and dissolving such unit. The provisions hereof shall be construed as a covenant running with the land and shall inure to the benefit of and be binding upon the parties hereto, their heirs, representatives, successors and assigns.

8. If Lessor owns a less interest in the above described land than the entire and undivided fee simple estate therein, then the royalties and rentals herein provided shall be paid to Lessor only in the proportion which Lessor's interest bears to the whole and undivided fee.

9. Lessee shall have free use of oil, gas, casinghead gas, condensate, coal and water from said land, except water from Lessor's wells, for all operations hereunder, including repressuring, pressure maintenance and recycling, and the royalty shall be computed after deducting any so used. Lessee shall have the right at any time during or after the expiration of this lease to remove all property and fixtures placed by Lessee on said land, including the right to draw and remove all casing. When required by Lessor, Lessee will bury all pipe lines below ordinary plow depth, and no well shall be drilled within two hundred feet of any residence or barn now on said land, without Lessor's consent. In the event a well or wells, producing oil, gas, casinghead gas or condensate in paying quantities should be brought in on adjacent lands not owned by the Lessor and within one hundred fifty feet of and draining the leased premises, Lessee agrees to drill such offset well or wells as a reasonably prudent operator would drill under the same or similar circumstances.

10. The rights of either party hereunder may be assigned in whole or in part and the provisions hereof shall extend to the heirs, executors, administrators, successors and assigns, but no change or division in ownership of the land, rentals, or royalties, however accomplished shall operate to enlarge the obligations or diminish the rights of Lessee. No such change or division in the ownership of the land, rentals or royalties shall be binding upon Lessee for any purpose until such person acquiring any interest has furnished Lessee, at its principal place of business, with a certified copy of the instrument or instruments, constituting his chain of title from the original Lessor. In the event of an assignment of this lease as to a segregated portion of said land, or as to an undivided interest therein, the rentals payable hereunder shall be apportioned as between the several leasehold owners ratably according to the surface area of each, or according to the undivided interest of each, and default in rental payment by one shall not affect the rights of other leasehold owners hereunder. An assignment of this lease, in whole or in part, shall, to the extent of such assignment, relieve and discharge Lessee of any obligations hereunder and, if Lessee or assignee of part or parts hereof shall fail or make default in the payment of the proportionate part of the rentals due from such Lessee, or assignee, or fail to comply with any other provisions of the lease, such default shall not affect this lease insofar as it covers a part of said lands upon which Lessee or any assignee thereof shall make payment of said rentals.

11. In case of suit, adverse claim, dispute or question as to the ownership of the rentals or royalties (or some part thereof) payable under this lease, Lessee shall not be held in default in payment of such rentals or royalties (or the part thereof in dispute), until such suit, claim, dispute or question has been finally disposed of, and Lessee shall have thirty (30) days after being furnished with a certified copy of the instrument or instruments disposing of such suit, claim, or dispute, or after being furnished with proof sufficient, in Lessee's opinion, to settle such question, within which to make payment. Should the right or interest of Lessee hereunder be disputed by Lessor, or any other person, the time covered by the pendency of such dispute shall not be counted against Lessee either as affecting the term of the lease or for any other purpose, and Lessee may suspend all payments without interest until there is a final adjudication or other determination of such dispute.

Figure D.2 — *Continued*

12. In case of cancellation or termination of this lease from any cause, Lessee shall have the right to retain, under the terms hereof, around each well producing, being worked on, or drilling hereunder, the number of acres in the form allocated to each such well under spacing and proration rules issued by the Commissioner of Conservation of the State of Louisiana, or any other State or Federal authority having control of such matters; or, in the absence of such rulings, forty (40) acres around each such well in as near a square form as practicable, and in the event Lessor considers that operations are not being conducted in compliance with this contract, Lessee shall be notified in writing of the facts relied upon as constituting a breach hereof and Lessee shall have sixty (60) days after receipt of such notice to comply with the obligations imposed by virtue of this instrument.

13. When drilling, reworking, production or other operations are delayed or interrupted by force majeure, that is, by storm, flood or other acts of God, fire, war, rebellion, insurrection, riot, strikes, differences with workmen, or failure of carriers to transport or furnish facilities for transportation, or as a result of some law, order, rule, regulation, requisition or necessity of the government, Federal or State, or as a result of any cause whatsoever beyond the control of the Lessee, the time of such delay or interruption shall not be counted against Lessee, anything in this lease to the contrary notwithstanding, but this lease shall be extended for a period of time equal to that during which Lessee is so prevented from conducting such drilling or reworking operations on, or producing oil, gas, casinghead gas, condensate or other minerals from, the premises; provided, this paragraph 13 shall not relieve Lessee from the necessity of either paying delay rentals or shut-in royalty as the case may be, during the primary term in order to continue this lease in force solely by force majeure, and during any period this lease is continued in force after its primary term solely by force majeure as herein provided, Lessee shall pay to the owners of the royalty hereunder the shut-in royalty provided in paragraph 5 hereof, and in the manner therein provided, without regard to whether or not there is a producing well shut in, located on said land or on land with which the lease premises or any part thereof has been pooled.

14. It is expressly understood and agreed that the premises leased herein shall, for all the purposes of this lease, be considered and treated as owned in indivision by the Lessor and shall be developed and operated as one lease, and there shall be no obligation on the part of Lessee to offset wells on separate tracts into which the land covered by this lease may be now or hereafter divided by sale, or otherwise, or to furnish separate measuring or receiving tanks, and all rentals, royalties and other payments accruing hereunder shall be treated as an entirety and shall be divided among and paid to Lessor in the proportion that the acreage (mineral rights) owned by each bears to the entire leased acreage. Lessee may at any time or times pay or tender all rentals or other sums accruing hereunder to the joint credit of Lessor.

15. Notwithstanding the death of any party Lessor, or his successor in interest, the payment or tender of rentals in the manner provided above shall be binding on the heirs, executors and administrators of such person.

16. Lessor hereby warrants and agrees to defend the title to the lands herein described, and agrees that the Lessee at its option shall have the right to redeem for Lessor, by payment, any mortgage, taxes or other liens on the above described lands, in the event of default of payment by Lessor, and be subrogated to the rights of the holder thereof. In case of payment of any such mortgage, taxes or other liens by Lessee, in addition to the right of subrogation herein granted, Lessee shall also have the right to retain any rentals or royalties which become due Lessor hereunder and to repay itself therefrom, and the retention of such rentals or royalties by Lessee shall have the same effect as if paid to the Lessor in whose behalf payment of any mortgage, taxes or other liens was made.

17. This lease shall be binding upon all who execute it, whether or not named in the body hereof as Lessor, and without regard to whether this same instrument, or any copy thereof, shall be executed by any other Lessor named above.

IN WITNESS WHEREOF, this instrument is executed on the date first above written.

WITNESSES:

_____ }

_____ }   _____

_____ }

_____ }   _____

_____ }

_____ }   _____

_____ }

_____ }   _____

STATE OF LOUISIANA

Parish of_____

    On this_____day of_____, 19_____, before me personally appeared

_____

_____

to me known to be the person____described in and who executed the foregoing instrument, and acknowledged that____he____executed the

same as_____free act and deed.

    In WITNESS WHEREOF I have hereunto set my official hand and seal on the date hereinabove written.

_____

Notary Public in and for_____
Parish, Louisiana.

STATE OF LOUISIANA

PARISH OF_____

    BEFORE ME, the undersigned authority, this day personally appeared_____

to me personally known to be the identical person whose name is subscribed to the foregoing instrument as an attesting witness, who being first

Figure D.2—*Continued*

duly sworn, on_____oath, says: That_____subscribed_____name to the foregoing instrument as a witness, and that_____knows_____

_____

_____

the Grantor__named in said instrument, to be the identical person__described therein, and who executed the same, and saw_____sign the same as_____voluntary act and deed, and that_____, the said_____ subscribed____name to the same at the same time as an attesting witness.

　　　　Sworn to and subscribed before me, this_____.

day of_____, 19___.

_____

Notary Public in and for_____.

_____

OIL, GAS AND MINERAL LEASE

No._____

FROM

TO

Parish of_____

THE M. L. BATH COMPANIES
BATH-GRAM

BATH'S FORM LOUISIANA SPEC. 14-BR1-2A-PX 10-65

STATE OF LOUISIANA

PARISH OF_____.

　　　　BEFORE ME, the undersigned authority, this day personally appeared_____
to me personally known to be the identical person whose name is subscribed to the foregoing instrument as an attesting witness, who being first duly sworn, on_____oath, says: That_____subscribed_____name to the foregoing instrument as a witness, and that_____knows_____

_____

_____

the Grantor__named in said instrument, to be the identical person__described therein, and who executed the same, and saw_____sign the same as_____voluntary act and deed, and that_____, the said_____ subscribed____name to the same at the same time as an attesting witness.

　　　　Sworn to and subscribed before me, this_____.

day of_____, 19___.

_____

Notary Public in and for_____.

APPENDIX E
LEASING IN THE TOP TEN
OIL-PRODUCING STATES

The following states are ranked by volume of production in November 1983. Variations in leasing practices are briefly noted, and examples of lease forms from certain states are included.

1. Texas. The Producers 88 (fig. E.1) with 40/160/640-acre pooling provision, is typical of forms used in Texas. Lease forms used in Oklahoma, Wyoming, New Mexico, Kansas, and North Dakota are similar to this form.

   In any lease agreement, the lessor may choose to specify no pooling provision. References to pooling may be manually deleted from the agreement, or a special form may be used. The nonpooling form (fig. E.2) is also a paid-up agreement. Paid-up lease forms specify that the lease continues during the entire primary term without any requirements of drilling or the payment of money other than royalties that may become due on production. Any consideration for the omitted "rentals" is included in a bonus payment made when the lease is executed. Any lease agreement may include a paid-up clause.

2. Alaska. See Appendix B.
3. Louisiana. See Appendix D.
4. California. See Appendix C.
5. Oklahoma. See Texas, Producers 88 with 40/160/640-acre pooling provision.
6. Wyoming. See Texas, Producers 88 with 40/160/640-acre pooling provision. Pooling provisions in Wyoming lease agreements are sometimes less detailed than those used in Texas, but the lease forms are otherwise similar.

   Some Wyoming leases (fig. E.3) provide a unitization clause that provides for participation in federal units, since much of the land in Wyoming belongs to the United States government and is managed by the Department of the Interior.

7. New Mexico. See Texas, Producers 88 with 40/160/640-acre pooling provision.
8. Kansas. See Texas, Producers 88 with 40/160/640-acre pooling provision.
9. North Dakota. See Texas, Producers 88 with 40/160/640-acre pooling provision.
10. Michigan. Some Michigan lease agreements include a gas-storage clause that provides for maintenance of the lease beyond the primary term either by production or by the storing of gas in the reservoir, accompanied, of course, by rental payments. An example of such an agreement is shown in figure E.4.

217

Figure E.1. Texas Producers 88 with 40/160/640-acre pooling provision
(Courtesy of Exxon)

062-0026C TEXAS
PRODUCERS 88 REV. (10 YEAR LEASE)
WITH 40/160/640 ACRE POOLING PROVISION   (TEN YEAR PAID UP LEASE)

OIL, GAS AND MINERAL LEASE

THIS AGREEMENT made this_____day of_____19_____, between

Lessor (whether one or more), whose address is:_____

and_____, Lessee, WITNESSETH:

1. Lessor in consideration of_____Dollars

($_____) in hand paid, of the royalties herein provided and of the agreements of Lessee herein contained, hereby grants, leases and lets exclusively to Lessee for the purpose of investigating, exploring, prospecting, drilling and mining for and producing oil, gas, sulphur, fissionable materials and all other minerals (whether or not similar to those mentioned), conducting exploration, geologic and geophysical tests and surveys, injecting gas, water and other fluids and air into subsurface strata, laying pipelines, establishing and utilizing facilities for the disposition of salt water, dredging and maintaining canals, building roads, bridges, tanks, telephone lines, power stations and other structures thereon, and on, over and across lands owned or claimed by Lessor adjacent and contiguous thereto necessary to Lessee in operations to produce, save, take care of, treat, transport and own said minerals, the following described land in_____County, Texas, to-wit:

This lease also covers and includes all land and interest in land owned or claimed by Lessor adjacent or contiguous to the land particularly described above, whether the same be in said survey or surveys or in adjacent surveys.

2. Without reference to the commencement, prosecution or cessation at any time of drilling or other development operations, and/or to the discovery, development or cessation at any time of production of oil, gas or other minerals, and without further payments than the royalties herein provided, and notwithstanding anything else herein contained to the contrary, this lease shall be for a term of ten years from this date (called "primary term") and as long thereafter as oil, gas or other mineral is produced from said land or land with which said land is pooled hereunder, or as long as this lease is continued in effect, as otherwise provided herein.

3. The royalties to be paid by Lessee are: (a) on oil, one-eighth of that produced and saved from said land, the same to be delivered at the wells or to the credit of Lessor into the pipeline to which the wells may be connected; Lessee may from time to time purchase any royalty oil in its possession, paying the market price therefor prevailing for the field where produced on the date of purchase, and Lessee may sell any royalty oil in its possession and pay Lessor the price received by Lessee for such oil computed at the well; (b) on gas, including casinghead gas or other gaseous substance, produced from said land and sold or used off the premises or for the extraction of gasoline or other product therefrom, the market value at the well of one-eighth of the gas so sold or used, provided that on gas sold by Lessee the market value shall not exceed the amount received by Lessee for such gas computed at the mouth of the well, and on gas sold at the well the royalty shall be one-eighth of the amount realized by Lessee from such sale; and (c) on fissionable materials and all other minerals mined and marketed, one-tenth either in kind or value at the well or mine, at Lessee's election, except that on sulphur mined or marketed, the royalty shall be Two Dollars ($2.00) per long ton. If the price of any mineral or substance upon which royalty is payable hereunder is regulated by any governmental agency, the market value or market price of such mineral or substance for the purpose of computing royalty hereunder shall not be in excess of the price which Lessee may receive and retain. Lessee shall have free from royalty or other payment the use of water, other than water from Lessor's wells or tanks, and of oil, gas and coal produced from said land in all operations which Lessee may conduct hereunder, including water injection and secondary recovery operations, and the royalty on oil, gas and coal shall be computed after deducting any so used. If Lessee drills a well on land covered by this lease or on land pooled therewith, which well is capable of producing oil or gas but such well is not being produced and this lease is not being maintained otherwise as provided herein, this lease shall not terminate, whether it be during or after the primary term, (unless released by Lessee) and it shall nevertheless be considered that oil or gas is being produced from the land covered by this lease. When the lease is continued in force in this manner, Lessee shall pay or tender (or make a bona fide attempt to pay or tender) as royalty to the parties who at the time of such payment would be entitled to

Figure E.1—*Continued*

---

receive royalty hereunder if the well were producing, or deposit to their credit in_____

Bank at_____ _____(which bank and it successors are royalty owner or owners' agent, and shall continue as depository for all such sums which Lessee may pay hereunder regardless of changes in ownership of royalties)

the sum of_____ _____Dollars ($_____) for each calendar month, or portion thereof, thereafter during which said well is situated on said land, or on land pooled therewith, and this lease is not otherwise maintained, or this lease is not released by Lessee as to the land on which or the horizon, zone or formation in which the well is completed. The first payment of such sum shall be made on or before the first day of the calendar month after expiration of ninety (90) days from the date the lease is not otherwise maintained for all accruals to such date, and thereafter on or before the first day of each third calendar month for all accruals to each such date. Lessee's failure to pay or tender or to properly or timely pay or tender any such sum as royalty shall render Lessee liable for the amount due but it shall not operate to terminate this lease. The payment or tender of royalty under this paragraph on any well which is not being produced, hereinafter referred to as "shut-in royalty", may be made by check or draft of Lessee mailed or delivered to the parties entitled thereto or to said bank on or before the date of payment.

4. The down cash payment is consideration for this lease according to its terms and shall not be allocated as rental for a period. Lessee may at any time, and from time to time, execute and deliver to Lessor, or to the depository bank, or file for record a release or releases of this lease as to any part or all of said land or of any mineral or subsurface interval or any depths thereunder and thereby be relieved of all obligations as to the released land, mineral, horizon, zone or formation. If this lease is released as to all minerals, horizons, zones and formations under a portion of said land, the shut-in royalty and other payments computed in accordance therewith shall thereupon be reduced in the proportion that the acreage released bears to the acreage which was covered by this lease immediately prior to such release.

5. Lessee, at its option, is hereby given the right and power during or after the primary term while this lease is in effect to pool or combine the land covered by this lease, or any portion thereof, as to oil, gas and other minerals, or any of them, with any other land covered by this lease, and/or any other land, lease or leases in the immediate vicinity thereof, when in Lessee's judgment it is necessary or advisable to do so in order properly to explore, or to develop and operate the leased premises in compliance with the spacing rules of the Railroad Commission of Texas, or other lawful authority, or when to do so would, in the judgment of Lessee, promote the conservation of oil, gas or other mineral in and under and that may be produced from the premises. Units pooled for oil in the interval between the surface and the top of the Glen Rose Formation shall not substantially exceed in area 40 acres each plus a tolerance of 10% thereof; units pooled for oil in formations situated below the top of the Glen Rose Formation shall not substantially exceed in area 160 acres plus a tolerance of 10% thereof; and units pooled for gas hereunder shall not substantially exceed in area 640 acres each plus a tolerance of 10% thereof, provided that should governmental authority having jurisdiction prescribe or permit the creation of units larger than those specified, units thereafter created may conform substantially in size with those prescribed or permitted by governmental regulations. Lessee may pool or combine land covered by this lease or any portion thereof, as above provided as to oil in any one or more strata and as to gas in any one or more strata. Units formed by pooling as to any stratum or strata need not conform in size or area with units as to any other stratum or strata, and oil units need not conform as to area with gas units. Pooling in one or more instances shall not exhaust the rights of Lessee to pool this lease or portions thereof into other units. Lessee shall file for record in the appropriate records of the county in which the leased premises are situated an instrument describing and designating the pooled acreage as a pooled unit; the unit shall become effective as provided in said instrument, or if said instrument makes no such provision, it shall become effective upon the date it is filed for record. Each unit shall be effective as to all parties hereto, their heirs, successors and assigns, irrespective of whether or not the unit is likewise effective as to all other owners of surface, mineral, royalty or other rights in land included in such unit. Lessee may at its election exercise its pooling option as to oil, gas and other minerals before or after commencing operations for or completing an oil or gas well or well or mine for other mineral on the leased premises, and the pooled unit may include, but is not required to include, land or leases upon which a well or mine capable of producing oil, gas or other mineral in paying quantities has theretofore been completed or upon which operations for drilling of a well or mine for oil, gas or other mineral have theretofore been commenced. Operations for drilling on, or production of, oil, gas or other mineral from any part of a pooled unit which includes all or a portion of the land covered by this lease, regardless of whether such operations for drilling were commenced or such production was secured before or after the execution of this lease or the instrument designating the pooled unit, shall be considered as operations for drilling on or production of oil, gas or other mineral from land covered by this lease whether or not the well or wells or mine be located on land covered by this lease, and the entire acreage constituting such unit or units, as to oil, gas or other minerals, or any of them, as herein provided, shall be treated for all purposes, except the payment of royalties on production from the pooled unit, as if the same were included in this lease; provided that if after creation of a pooled unit, a well or mine is drilled on the unit area, other than on the land covered hereby and included in the unit, which well is not classified as the type of well for which the unit was created (oil, gas or other mineral as the case may be), such well or mine shall be considered a dry hole for purposes of applying the additional drilling and reworking provisions of Paragraph 6 hereof. If an oil well on an oil unit, which includes all or a portion of the leased premises, is reclassified as a gas well, or if a gas well on a gas unit, which includes all or a portion of the leased premises, is reclassified as an oil well, the date of such reclassification shall be considered as the date of cessation of production for purposes of applying the additional drilling and reworking provisions of Paragraph 6 hereof as to all leases any part of which are included in the unit other than the leased premises on which the well is located. For the purpose of computing royalties to which owners of royalties and payments out of production and each of them shall be entitled on production of oil, gas or other minerals from each pooled unit, there shall be allocated to the land covered by this lease and included in said unit (or to each separate tract within the unit if this lease covers separate tracts within the unit) a pro rata portion of the oil, gas or other minerals produced from the unit after deducting that used for operations on the unit. Such allocation shall be on an acreage basis — that is, there shall be allocated to the acreage covered by this lease and included in the pooled unit (or to each separate tract within the unit if this lease covers separate tracts within the unit) that pro rata portion of the oil, gas or other minerals produced from the unit which the number of surface acres covered by this lease (or in each separate tract) and included in the unit bears to the total number of surface acres included in the unit. As used in this paragraph, the words "separate tract" mean any tract with royalty ownership differing, now or hereafter, either as to parties or amounts, from that as to any other part of the leased premises. Royalties hereunder shall be computed on the portion of such production, whether it be oil, gas or other minerals, so allocated to the land covered by this lease and included in the unit just as though such production were from such land. Production from an oil well will be considered as production from the lease or oil pooled unit from which it is producing and not as production from a gas pooled unit; and production from a gas well will be considered as production from the lease or gas pooled unit from which it is producing and not from an oil pooled unit. Any pooled unit designated by Lessee in accordance with the terms hereof may be dissolved by Lessee by instrument filed for record in the appropriate records of the county in which the leased premises are situated at any time after completion of a dry hole or cessation of production on said unit.

6. If at the expiration of the primary term, oil, gas, or other mineral is not being produced on said land, or from land pooled therewith, but Lessee is then engaged in drilling or reworking operations thereon, or shall have completed a dry hole thereon within 60 days prior to the end of the primary term, the lease shall remain in force so long as operations on said well or for drilling or reworking of any additional well are prosecuted with no cessation of more than 60 consecutive days, and if they result in the production of oil, gas, or other mineral, so long thereafter as oil, gas, or other mineral is produced from said land, or from land pooled therewith. If, after the expiration of the primary term of this lease and after oil, gas or other

Figure E.1 – *Continued*

mineral is produced from said land, or from land pooled therewith, the production thereof should cease from any cause, this lease shall not terminate if Lessee commences operations for drilling or reworking within 60 days after the cessation of such production, but shall remain in force and effect so long as Lessee continues drilling or reworking operations on said well or for drilling or reworking of any additional well with no cessation of more than 60 consecutive days, and if they result in the production of oil, gas, or other mineral, so long thereafter as oil, gas, or other mineral is produced from said land, or from land pooled therewith. In the event a well or wells producing oil or gas in paying quantities should be brought in on adjacent land and within 330 feet of and draining the leased premises, or land pooled therewith, Lessee agrees to drill such offset well or wells as a reasonably prudent operator would drill under the same or similar circumstances.

7. Lessee shall have the right at any time during or after the expiration of this lease to remove all property and fixtures placed by Lessee on said land, including the right to draw and remove all casing. When necessary for utilization of the surface for some intended use by Lessor and upon request of Lessor or when deemed necessary by Lessee for protection of the pipeline, Lessee will bury pipelines below ordinary plow depth, and no well shall be drilled within two hundred (200) feet of any residence or barn now on said land without Lessor's consent.

8. The rights of either party hereunder may be assigned in whole or in part, and the provisions hereof shall extend to their heirs, successors and assigns; but no change or division in ownership of the land or royalties, however accomplished, shall operate to enlarge the obligations or diminish the rights of Lessee, including, but not limited to, the location and drilling of wells and the measurement of production; and no change or division in such ownership shall be binding on Lessee until forty-five (45) days after Lessee shall have been furnished by registered U. S. mail at Lessee's principal place of business with a certified copy of recorded instrument or instruments evidencing same. In the event of assignment hereof in whole or in part, liability for breach of any obligation hereunder shall rest exclusively upon the owner of this lease or of a portion thereof who commits such breach. If six or more parties become entitled to royalty hereunder, Lessee may withhold payment thereof unless and until furnished with a recordable instrument executed by all such parties designating an agent to receive payment for all.

9. Breach by Lessee of any obligation hereunder shall not work a forfeiture or termination of this lease nor cause a termination or reversion of the estate created hereby nor be grounds for cancellation hereof in whole or in part. In the event Lessor considers that operations are not at any time being conducted in compliance with this lease, Lessor shall notify Lessee in writing of the facts relied upon as constituting a breach hereof, and Lessee, if in default, shall have sixty days after receipt of such notice in which to commence the compliance with the obligations imposed by virtue of this instrument. After the discovery of oil, gas or other mineral in paying quantities on said premises, Lessee shall develop the acreage retained hereunder as a reasonably prudent operator but in discharging this obligation it shall in no event be required to: (a) drill more than one well per 40 acres of the area retained hereunder and capable of producing oil in paying quantities from any formation, stratum or strata situated between the surface and the top of the Glen Rose Formation thereunder; (b) drill more than one well per 160 acres of the area retained hereunder and capable of producing oil in paying quantities from any formation, stratum or strata situated beneath the top of the Glen Rose Formation thereunder; and (c) drill more than one well per 640 acres plus an acreage tolerance not to exceed 10% of 640 acres in the area retained hereunder and capable of producing gas or other mineral in paying quantities.

10. Lessor hereby warrants and agrees to defend the title to said land and agrees that Lessee at its option may discharge any tax, mortgage or other lien upon said land, either in whole or in part, and if Lessee does so, it shall be subrogated to such lien with right to enforce same and apply royalties accruing hereunder toward satisfying same. When required by state, federal or other law, Lessee may withhold taxes with respect to royalty and other payments hereunder and remit the amounts withheld to the applicable taxing authority for the credit of Lessor. Without impairment of Lessee's rights under the warranty in event of failure of title, if Lessor owns an interest in the oil, gas or other minerals on, in or under said land less than the entire fee simple estate, whether or not this lease purports to cover the whole or a fractional interest, the royalties and shut-in royalties to be paid Lessor shall be reduced in the proportion that his interest bears to the whole and undivided fee and in accordance with the nature of the estate of which Lessor is seized. Should any one or more of the parties named above as Lessor fail to execute this lease, it shall nevertheless be binding upon the party or parties executing same.

11. Should Lessee be prevented from complying with any express or implied covenant of this lease, from conducting drilling or reworking operations thereon or on land pooled therewith or from producing oil, gas or other mineral therefrom or from land pooled therewith by reason of scarcity or of inability to obtain or to use equipment or material, or by operation of force majeure, any federal or state law or any order, rule or regulation of governmental authority, then while so prevented, Lessee's obligation to comply with such covenant shall be suspended, and Lessee shall not be liable in damages for failure to comply therewith; and this lease shall be extended while and so long as Lessee is prevented by any such cause from conducting drilling or reworking operations on or from producing oil, gas or other mineral from the leased premises or land pooled therewith, and the time while Lessee is so prevented shall not be counted against Lessee, anything in this lease to the contrary notwithstanding.

12. Each singular pronoun herein shall include the plural whenever applicable.

IN WITNESS WHEREOF, this instrument is executed on the date first above written.

_____		_____
_____		_____
LESSOR	SOCIAL SECURITY NO.	LESSOR	SOCIAL SECURITY NO.

Figure E.1—*Continued*

THE STATE OF TEXAS
COUNTY OF

    BEFORE ME, the undersigned authority, on this day personally appeared____ _____ known to me to be the person whose name is subscribed to the foregoing instrument, and acknowledged to me that he executed the same for the purposes and consideration therein expressed.

    GIVEN UNDER MY HAND AND SEAL OF OFFICE this the_____day of_____, 19_____.

Notary Public in and for_____County, Texas

THE STATE OF TEXAS
COUNTY OF

    BEFORE ME, the undersigned authority, on this day personally appeared_____ known to me to be the person whose name is subscribed to the foregoing instrument, and acknowledged to me that he executed the same for the purposes and consideration therein expressed.

    GIVEN UNDER MY HAND AND SEAL OF OFFICE this the_____day of_____, 19_____.

Notary Public in and for_____County, Texas

THE STATE OF TEXAS
COUNTY OF

    BEFORE ME, the undersigned authority, on this day personally appeared_____ and_____, known to me to be the persons whose names are subscribed to the foregoing instrument, and acknowledged to me that they executed the same for the purposes and consideration therein expressed.

    GIVEN UNDER MY HAND AND SEAL OF OFFICE this the_____day of_____, 19_____.

Notary Public in and for_____County, Texas

THE STATE OF TEXAS
COUNTY OF

    BEFORE ME, the undersigned authority, on this day personally appeared_____ and_____, known to me to be the persons whose names are subscribed to the foregoing instrument, and acknowledged to me that they executed the same for the purposes and consideration therein expressed.

    GIVEN UNDER MY HAND AND SEAL OF OFFICE this the_____day of_____, 19_____.

Notary Public in and for_____County, Texas

Figure E.1 – *Continued*

No._____

Oil, Gas and Mineral Lease

FROM

TO

_____County, Texas

Dated_____, 19_____

No. Acres_____

Term_____

This instrument was filed for record on the_____

day of_____, 19_____, at

_____o'clock_____M., and duly recorded in

Book_____, Page_____

of the_____records of this office.

_____County Clerk

By_____, Deputy

When recorded return to

Figure E.2. Texas Producers 88, nonpooling
(Courtesy of Exxon)

062-0034 (X-309)
PRODUCERS 88 REV.
(10 YEAR LEASE)

(TEN YEAR PAID UP LEASE)
OIL, GAS AND MINERAL LEASE

THIS AGREEMENT made this_____day of_____19_____, between

Lessor (whether one or more), whose address is:_____

and_____, Lessee, WITNESSETH:

1. Lessor in consideration of_____Dollars

($_____) in hand paid, of the royalties herein provided and of the agreements of Lessee herein contained, hereby grants, leases and lets exclusively to Lessee for the purpose of investigating, exploring, prospecting, drilling and mining for and producing oil, gas, sulphur, fissionable materials and all other minerals (whether or not similar to those mentioned), conducting exploration, geologic and geophysical tests and surveys, injecting gas, water and other fluids and air into subsurface strata, laying pipelines, establishing and utilizing facilities for the disposition of salt water, dredging and maintaining canals, building roads, bridges, tanks, telephone lines, power stations and other structures thereon, and on, over and across lands owned or claimed by Lessor adjacent and contiguous thereto necessary to Lessee in operations to produce, save, take care of, treat, transport and own said minerals, the following described land in

_____County, Texas, to-wit:

This lease also covers and includes all land and interest in land owned or claimed by Lessor adjacent or contiguous to the land particularly described above, whether the same be in said survey or surveys or in adjacent surveys.

2. Without reference to the commencement, prosecution or cessation at any time of drilling or other development operations, and/or to the discovery, development or cessation at any time of production of oil, gas or other minerals, and without further payments than the royalties herein provided, and notwithstanding anything else herein contained to the contrary, this lease shall be for a term of ten years from this date (called "primary term") and as long thereafter as oil, gas or other mineral is produced from said land, or as long as this lease is continued in effect, as otherwise provided herein.

3. The royalties to be paid by Lessee are: (a) on oil, one-eighth of that produced and saved from said land, the same to be delivered at the wells or to the credit of Lessor into the pipeline to which the wells may be connected; Lessee may from time to time purchase any royalty oil in its possession, paying the market price therefor prevailing for the field where produced on the date of purchase, and Lessee may sell any royalty oil in its possession and pay Lessor the price received by Lessee for such oil computed at the well; (b) on gas, including casinghead gas or other gaseous substance, produced from said land and sold or used off the premises or for the extraction of gasoline or other product therefrom, the market value at the well of one-eighth of the gas so sold or used, provided that on gas sold by Lessee the market value shall not exceed the amount received by Lessee for such gas computed at the mouth of the well, and on gas sold at the well the royalty shall be one-eighth of the amount realized by Lessee from such sale; and (c) on fissionable materials and all other minerals mined and marketed, one-tenth either in kind or value at the well or mine, at Lessee's election, except that on sulphur mined or marketed, the royalty shall be Two Dollars ($2.00) per long ton. If the price of any mineral or substance upon which royalty is payable hereunder is regulated by any governmental agency, the market value or market price of such mineral or substance for the purpose of computing royalty hereunder shall not be in excess of the price which Lessee may receive and retain. Lessee shall have free from royalty or other payment the use of water, other than water from Lessor's wells or tanks, and of oil, gas and coal produced from said land in all operations which Lessee may conduct hereunder, including water injection and secondary recovery operations, and the royalty on oil, gas and coal shall be computed after deducting any so used. If Lessee drills a well on land covered by this lease, which well is capable of producing oil or gas but such well is not being produced and this lease is not being maintained otherwise as provided herein, this lease shall not terminate, whether it be during or after the primary term, (unless released by Lessee) and it shall nevertheless be considered that oil or gas is being produced from the land covered by this lease. When the lease is continued in force in this manner, Lessee shall pay or tender (or make a bona fide attempt to pay or tender) as royalty to the parties who at the time of such payment would be entitled to receive royalty hereunder if the well were producing, or deposit to their credit in_____

Figure E.2—*Continued*

Bank at_____
(which bank and its successors are royalty owner or owner's agent, and shall continue as depository for all such sums which Lessee may pay hereunder regard-

less of changes in ownership of royalties) the sum of_____Dollars (S_____) for
each calendar month, or portion thereof, thereafter during which said well is situated on said land and this lease is not otherwise maintained, or this lease is not released by Lessee as to the land on which or the horizon, zone or formation in which the well is completed. The first payment of such sum shall be made on or before the first day of the calendar month after expiration of ninety (90) days from the date the lease is not otherwise maintained for all accruals to such date, and thereafter on or before the first day of each third calendar month for all accruals to each such date. Lessee's failure to pay or tender or to properly or timely pay or tender any such sum as royalty shall render Lessee liable for the amount due but it shall not operate to terminate this lease. The payment or tender of royalty under this paragraph on any well which is not being produced, hereinafter referred to as "shut-in-royalty", may be made by check or draft of Lessee mailed or delivered to the parties entitled thereto or to said bank on or before the date of payment.

4. The down cash payment is consideration for this lease according to its terms and shall not be allocated as rental for a period. Lessee may at any time, and from time to time, execute and deliver to Lessor, or to the depository bank, or file for record a release or releases of this lease as to any part or all of said land or of any mineral or subsurface interval or any depths thereunder and thereby be relieved of all obligations as to the released land, mineral, horizon, zone or formation. If this lease is released as to all minerals, horizons, zones and formations under a portion of said land, the shut-in royalty and other payments computed in accordance therewith shall thereupon be reduced in the proportion that the acreage released bears to the acreage which was covered by this lease immediately prior to such release.

5. If at the expiration of the primary term, oil, gas, or other mineral is not being produced on said land, but Lessee is then engaged in drilling or reworking operations thereon, or shall have completed a dry hole thereon within 60 days prior to the end of the primary term, the lease shall remain in force so long as operations on said well or for drilling or reworking of any additional well are prosecuted with no cessation of more than 60 consecutive days, and if they result in the production of oil, gas, or other mineral, so long thereafter as oil, gas, or other mineral is produced from said land. If, after the expiration of the primary term of this lease and after oil, gas or other mineral is produced from said land, the production thereof should cease from any cause, this lease shall not terminate if Lessee commences operations for drilling or reworking within 60 days after the cessation of such production, but shall remain in force and effect so long as Lessee continues drilling or reworking operations on said well or for drilling or reworking of any additional well with no cessation of more than 60 consecutive days, and if they result in the production of oil, gas, or other mineral, so long thereafter as oil, gas, or other mineral is produced from said land. In the event a well or wells producing oil or gas in paying quantities should be brought in on adjacent land and within 330 feet of and draining the leased premises, Lessee agrees to drill such offset well or wells as a reasonably prudent operator would drill under the same or similar circumstances.

6. Lessee shall have the right at any time during or after the expiration of this lease to remove all property and fixtures placed by Lessee on said land, including the right to draw and remove all casing. When necessary for utilization of the surface for some intended use by Lessor and upon request of Lessor or when deemed necessary by Lessee for protection of the pipeline, Lessee will bury pipelines below ordinary plow depth, and no well shall be drilled within two hundred (200) feet of any residence or barn now on said land without Lessor's consent.

7. The rights of either party hereunder may be assigned in whole or in part, and the provisions hereof shall extend to their heirs, successors and assigns: but no change or division in ownership of the land or royalties, however accomplished, shall operate to enlarge the obligations or diminish the rights of Lessee, including, but not limited to, the location and drilling of wells and the measurement of production; and no change or division in such ownership shall be binding on Lessee until forty-five (45) days after Lessee shall have been furnished by registered U. S. mail at Lessee's principal place of business with a certified copy of recorded instrument or instruments evidencing same. In the event of assignment hereof in whole or in part, liability for breach of any obligation hereunder shall rest exclusively upon the owner of this lease or of a portion thereof who commits such breach. If six or more parties become entitled to royalty hereunder, Lessee may withhold payment thereof unless and until furnished with a recordable instrument executed by all such parties designating an agent to receive payment for all.

8. Breach by Lessee of any obligation hereunder shall not work a forfeiture or termination of this lease nor cause a termination or reversion of the estate created hereby nor be grounds for cancellation hereof in whole or in part. In the event Lessor considers that operations are not at any time being conducted in compliance with this lease, Lessor shall notify Lessee in writing of the facts relied upon as constituting a breach hereof, and Lessee, if in default, shall have sixty (60) days after receipt of such notice in which to commence compliance with the obligations imposed by this lease. After discovery of oil, gas or other mineral in paying quantities on said premises, Lessee shall develop the acreage retained hereunder as a reasonably prudent operator but in discharging this obligation as to oil and gas it shall in no event be required to drill more than one well per forty (40) acres of the area retained hereunder plus a tolerance of 10% thereof and capable of producing oil in pay quantities and one well per 640 acres plus a tolerance of 10% of 640 acres of the area retained hereunder and capable of producing gas in paying quantities.

9. Lessor hereby warrants and agrees to defend the title to said land and agrees that Lessee at its option may discharge any tax, mortgage or other lien upon said land, either in whole or in part, and if Lessee does so, it shall be subrogated to such lien with right to enforce same and apply royalties accruing hereunder toward satisfying same. When required by state, federal or other law, Lessee may withhold taxes with respect to royalty and other payments hereunder and remit the amounts withheld to the applicable taxing authority for the credit of Lessor. Without impairment of Lessee's rights under the warranty in event of failure of title, if Lessor owns an interest in the oil, gas or other minerals on, in or under said land less than the entire fee simple estate, whether or not this lease purports to cover the whole or a fractional interest, the royalties and shut-in royalties to be paid Lessor shall be reduced in the proportion that his interest bears to the whole and undivided fee and in accordance with the nature of the estate of which Lessor is seized. Should any one or more of the parties named above as Lessor fail to execute this lease, it shall nevertheless be binding upon the party or parties executing same.

10. Should Lessee be prevented from complying with any express or implied covenant of this lease, from conducting drilling or reworking operations thereon or from producing oil, gas or other mineral therefrom by reason of scarcity or of inability to obtain or to use equipment or material, or by operation of force majeure, any federal or state law or any order, rule or regulation of governmental authority, then while so prevented, Lessee's obligation to comply with such covenant shall be suspended, and Lessee shall not be liable in damages for failure to comply therewith; and this lease shall be extended while and so long as Lessee is prevented by any such cause from conducting drilling or reworking operations on or from producing oil, gas or other mineral from the leased premises, and the time while Lessee is so prevented shall not be counted against Lessee, anything in this lease to the contrary notwithstanding.

11. Each singular pronoun herein shall include the plural whenever applicable.
IN WITNESS WHEREOF, this instrument is executed on the date first above written.

_____   _____

_____   _____

_____   _____   _____   _____
LESSOR   SOCIAL SECURITY NO.   LESSOR   SOCIAL SECURITY NO.

Figure E.2 – *Continued*

THE STATE OF TEXAS
COUNTY OF

BEFORE ME, the undersigned authority, on this day personally appeared_____
known to me to be the person whose name is subscribed to the foregoing instrument, and acknowledged to me that he executed the same for the purposes and consideration therein expressed.

GIVEN UNDER MY HAND AND SEAL OF OFFICE this the_____day of_____, 19____.

_____

Notary Public in and for_____County, Texas

THE STATE OF TEXAS
COUNTY OF

BEFORE ME, the undersigned authority, on this day personally appeared_____
and _____, known to me to be the persons whose names are subscribed to the foregoing instrument, and acknowledged to me that they executed the same for the purposes and consideration therein expressed.

GIVEN UNDER MY HAND AND SEAL OF OFFICE this the_____day of_____, 19____.

_____

Notary Public in and for_____County, Texas

No._____

Oil, Gas and Mineral Lease

FROM

TO

Dated_____, 19____

No. Acres_____

Term_____

This instrument was filed for record on the_____ day of_____, 19____, at_____ o'clock_____ M., and duly recorded in Book_____, Page_____, of the_____ records of this office.

_____ County Clerk

By_____, Deputy

When recorded return to

Figure E.3. Wyoming oil and gas lease with a unitization clause
(Courtesy of Exxon)

062-0152
Producers 88 — Revised
Wyoming (U)

OIL AND GAS LEASE

THIS AGREEMENT, made and entered into this _____ day of _____ , 19 _____ , by and between

_____

_____

of _____ , hereinafter called lessor (whether one or more), and

_____ of _____ , hereinafter called lessee;

WITNESSETH: that lessor, for and in consideration of _____ DOLLARS ($ _____)
in hand paid, receipt of which is hereby acknowledged, and of the agreements of lessee hereinafter set forth, hereby grants, demises, leases and lets exclusively unto said lessee the lands hereinafter described for the purpose of prospecting, exploring by geophysical and other methods, drilling, mining, operating for and producing oil or gas, or both, including, but not as a limitation, casinghead gas, casinghead gasoline, gas-condensate (distillate) and any substance, whether similar or dissimilar, produced in a gaseous state, together with the right to construct and maintain pipe lines, telephone and electric lines, tanks, powers, ponds, roadways, plants, equipment, and structures thereon to produce, save and take care of said oil and gas, and the exclusive right to inject air, gas, water, brine and other fluids from any source into the subsurface strata and any and all other rights and privileges necessary, incident to, or convenient for the economical operation of said land, alone or conjointly with neighboring land, for the production, saving and taking care of oil and gas and the injection of air, gas, water, brine, and other fluids into the subsurface strata, said lands being situated in the County of

_____ , State of Wyoming, and being described as follows, to-wit:

_____

_____

_____

_____

_____

_____

_____

_____

of Section _____ , Township _____ , Range _____ , it being the purpose and intent of lessor to lease,

and lessor does hereby lease, all of the lands or interests in lands owned by lessor which adjoin the lands above described or which lie in the section or sections herein

specified. For all purposes of this lease, said lands shall be deemed to contain _____ acres.

Subject to the other provisions herein contained, this lease shall remain in force for a term of ten (10) years from this date (herein called "primary term") and as long thereafter as oil and gas, or either of them, is produced from said leased premises or drilling operations are continuously prosecuted as hereinafter provided. "Drilling operations" includes operations for the drilling of a new well, the reworking, deepening or plugging back of a well or hole or other operations conducted in an effort to obtain or re-establish production of oil or gas; and drilling operations shall be considered to be "continuously prosecuted" if not more than 60 days shall elapse between the completion or abandonment of one well or hole and the commencement of drilling operations on another well or hole. If, at the expiration of the primary term of this lease, oil or gas is not being produced from the leased premises but lessee is then engaged in drilling operations, this lease shall continue in force so long as drilling operations are continuously prosecuted; and if production of oil or gas results from any such drilling operations, this lease shall continue in force so long as oil or gas shall be produced from the leased premises. If, after the expiration of the primary term of this lease, production on the leased premises should cease, this lease shall not terminate if lessee is then prosecuting drilling operations, or within 60 days after each such cessation of production commences drilling operations, and this lease shall remain in force so long as such operations are continuously prosecuted, and if production results therefrom, then as long thereafter as oil or gas is produced from the leased premises.

The royalties to be paid by lessee are: (a) on oil, one-eighth of that produced and saved from said land, the same to be delivered at the wells or to the credit of lessor into the pipeline to which the wells may be connected; lessee may from time to time purchase any royalty oil in its possession, paying the market price therefor prevailing for the field where produced on the date of purchase, and lessee may sell any royalty oil in its possession and pay lessor the price received by lessee for such oil computed at the well; (b) on gas, including casinghead gas or other gaseous substance, produced from said land and sold or used off the premises or for the extraction of gasoline or other product therefrom, the market value at the well of one-eighth of the gas so sold or used, provided that on gas sold by lessee the market value shall not exceed the amount received by lessee for such gas computed at the mouth of the well, and on gas sold at the well the royalty shall be one-eighth of the amount realized by lessee from such sale. If the price of any mineral or substance upon which royalty is payable hereunder is regulated by any governmental agency, the market value or market price of such mineral or substance for the purpose of computing royalty hereunder shall not be in excess of the price which lessee may receive and retain.

If no well be commenced on said land on or before one year from the date hereof, this lease shall (except as otherwise provided in this paragraph) terminate, unless lessee (or someone in his behalf), on or before such date, shall pay or tender to lessor, or to lessor's credit in the

_____ Bank at _____
(which bank and its successors shall continue as the depository regardless of changes in the ownership of said land or of the right to receive rentals), the sum of

_____ DOLLARS ($ _____), which shall
operate as a rental and cover the privilege of deferring the commencement of a well for 12 months from said date. In like manner and upon like payments or tenders, the commencement of a well may be further deferred for like periods of the same number of months successively during the primary term hereof. All payments or tenders may be made by cash, check or draft, mailed or delivered on or before the rental date, and the depositing of such cash, check or draft in any post office, addressed to the depository bank or lessor (at his last known address as shown by lessee's records) on or before the rental date, shall be deemed payment or tender as herein provided. Notwithstanding the death of lessor, payment or tender of rentals to such deceased or to his credit in the manner provided herein shall be binding on the heirs, devisees, executors, administrators and personal representatives of lessor and his successors in interest. If lessee shall, on or before any rental date, make a bona fide attempt to pay or deposit rental to a lessor entitled thereto under this lease according to lessee's records or to a lessor who, prior to such attempted payment or deposit, has given lessee notice, in accordance with the terms of this lease hereinafter set forth, of his right to receive rental, and if such payment or deposit shall be erroneous in any regard (whether deposited in the wrong depository, paid to persons other than the parties entitled thereto as shown by lessee's records, in an incorrect amount, or otherwise), lessee shall be unconditionally obligated to pay to such lessor the rental properly payable for the rental period involved, but this lease shall be maintained in the same manner as if such erroneous rental payment or deposit had been properly made, provided that the erroneous rental payment or deposit be corrected within 30 days after receipt by lessee of written notice from such lessor of such error accompanied by any documents and other evidence necessary to enable lessee to make proper payment. The consideration first recited herein, the down payment, covers not only the privilege granted to the date when said first rental is payable as aforesaid, but also lessee's option of extending that period as aforesaid, and any and all other rights conferred.

Should the first well drilled on the above described land be completed as a dry hole, then, and in that event, if a second well is not commenced on said land within 12 months from the expiration of the last rental period for which rental has been paid (it being understood that for the purpose of this paragraph the period of time extending from the date of this lease to the first rental date shall be considered as a rental period for which rental has been paid), this lease shall terminate as to both parties, unless lessee on or before the expiration of said 12 months shall resume the payment of rentals in the same amount and in the same manner as hereinbefore provided. Upon resumption of the payment of rentals, as above provided, the last preceding paragraph hereof, governing the payment of rentals and the effect thereof, shall continue in force just as though there had been no interruption in rental payments.

If a well capable of producing gas or gas and gas-condensate in paying quantities located on the leased premises (or on acreage pooled or consolidated with all or a portion of the leased premises into a unit for the drilling or operation of such well) is at any time shut in and no gas or gas-condensate therefrom is sold or used off the premises or for the manufacture of gasoline or other products, nevertheless such shut-in well shall be deemed to be a well on the leased premises producing gas in paying quantities and this lease will continue in force during all of the time or times while such well is so shut in, whether before or after the expiration of the primary term hereof. Lessee shall use reasonable diligence to market gas or gas and gas-condensate capable of being produced from such shut-in well but shall be under no obligation to market such

Figure E.3 — *Continued*

products under terms, conditions or circumstances which, in lessee's judgment exercised in good faith, are unsatisfactory. Lessee shall be obligated to pay or tender to lessor within 45 days after the expiration of each period of one year in length (annual period) during which such well is so shut in, as royalty, an amount equal to the annual delay rental herein provided applicable to the interest of lessor in acreage embraced in this lease as of the end of such annual period, or, if this lease does not provide for any delay rental, then the sum of $50.00; provided that, if gas or gas-condensate from such well is sold or used as aforesaid before the end of any such annual period, or if, at the end of any such annual period, this lease is being maintained in force and effect otherwise than by reason of such shut-in well, lessee shall not be obligated to pay or tender, for that particular annual period, said sum of money. Such payment shall be deemed a royalty under all provisions of this lease. Such payment may be made or tendered to lessor or to lessor's credit in the depository bank above designated. Royalty ownership as of the last day of each such annual period as shown by lessee's records shall govern the determination of the party or parties entitled to receive such payment.

If lessor owns a less interest in the land covered by this lease than the entire and undivided fee simple mineral estate therein, then whether or not such less interest is referred to or described herein, all rentals and royalties herein provided shall be paid lessor only in the proportion which his interest bears to the whole and undivided mineral fee.

If the estate of either party hereto is assigned or sublet, and the privilege of assigning or subletting in whole or in part is expressly allowed, the express and implied covenants hereof shall extend to the sublessees, successors and assigns of the parties; and in the event of an assignment or subletting by lessee, lessee shall be relieved and discharged as to the leasehold rights so assigned or sublet from any liability to lessor thereafter accruing upon any of the covenants or conditions of this lease, either express or implied. No change in the ownership of the land, rentals or royalties, however accomplished, shall operate to enlarge the obligations or diminish the rights of lessee or require separate measuring or installation of separate tanks by lessee. Notwithstanding any actual or constructive knowledge of or notice to lessee, no change in the ownership of said land or of the right to receive rentals or royalties hereunder, or of any interest therein, whether by reason of death, conveyance or any other matter, shall be binding on lessee (except at lessee's option in any particular case) until 90 days after lessee has been furnished written notice thereof, and the supporting information hereinafter referred to, by the party claiming as a result of such change in ownership or interest. Such notice shall be supported by original or certified copies of all documents and other instruments or proceedings necessary in lessee's opinion to establish the ownership of the claiming party. If this lease is assigned or sublet insofar as it covers only a part of the acreage embraced in the leased premises, the delay rentals hereinabove provided for shall be apportioned to the separate parts, rateably according to the surface acreage of each, and failure of the leasehold owner or sublessee of any separate part of the above described lands to make a rental payment with respect to such part shall in no event operate to terminate or affect this lease insofar as it covers any other part thereof.

Lessee may, at any time, execute and deliver to lessor or place of record a release covering all or any part of the acreage embraced in the leased premises or covering any one or more zones, formations or depths underlying all or any part of such acreage, and thereupon shall be relieved of all obligations thereafter to accrue with respect to the acreage, zones, formations or depths covered by such release. In event of a release of this lease as to all rights in only a part of the acreage embraced in the leased premises, thereafter the delay rentals hereinabove provided for shall be reduced proportionately on an acreage basis.

Lessee shall have the right to unitize all or any part of the above described lands with other lands in the same general area by entering into a unit agreement setting forth a plan of development or operation approved by the Secretary of the Interior, or other officer or representative of the United States having authority to approve such unit agreements, and, from time to time, with like approval, to modify, change or terminate any such agreement. In any of such events, the terms, conditions and provisions of this lease shall be deemed modified to conform to the terms, conditions and provisions of such approved unit agreement, and all drilling and development requirements of this lease, express or implied, shall be satisfied by compliance with the drilling and development requirements of such agreement, and this lease shall not terminate or expire during the life of such agreement except as may be otherwise provided in said agreement. In the event that said above described lands, or any part thereof, shall hereafter be operated under any such unit agreement whereby the production thereunder is allocated to different portions of the land covered by said agreement, then the production allocated to any particular tract of land pursuant to such agreement shall, for the purpose of computing royalties, be regarded as having been produced from the particular tract of land to which it is allocated and not from any other tract of land and any royalty payments on such production to be made hereunder to lessor shall be based solely upon the production so allocated. Nothing herein contained shall authorize or effect any transfer of any title to any leasehold, royalty or other interest unitized pursuant hereto. Lessee's execution of such unit agreement shall be binding as to both lessor and lessee and their respective interests. Lessee, following such execution, shall furnish lessor with a copy of such unit agreement by mail to lessor's last known address as shown by lessee's records and shall give lessor written notice of approval of the same in the same manner within a reasonable time after lessee is notified of such approval.

Lessee shall have the right to use, free of cost, oil, gas and water produced on said land for its operations thereon except water from wells of lessor. Lessee shall have the right at any time to remove all machinery and fixtures placed on said premises, including the right to draw and remove casing. No part of the surface of the leased premises shall, without the written consent of lessee, be let, granted or licensed by lessor to any other party for the location, construction or maintenance of structures, tanks, pits, reservoirs, equipment, or machinery to be used for the purpose of exploring, developing or operating adjacent lands for oil, gas or other minerals.

Lessee shall bury below plow depth its pipe lines on the leased premises when requested by a lessor owning an interest in the surface. No well shall be drilled nearer than 200 feet to any house or barn now on said premises without the written consent of the owner of the surface on which such house or barn is located. Lessee shall pay for damages to growing crops caused by its operations on said lands.

Lessor hereby warrants and agrees to defend the title to the lands herein described, but if the interest of lessor covered by this lease is expressly stated to be less than the entire fee or mineral estate, lessor's warranty shall be limited to the interest so stated. Lessee may purchase or lease the rights of any party claiming any interest in said land and exercise such rights as may be obtained thereby but lessee shall not suffer any forfeiture nor incur any liability to lessor by reason thereof. Lessee shall have the right at any time to pay for lessor, any mortgage, taxes or other lien on said lands, in the event of default of payment by lessor, and be subrogated to the rights of the holder thereof, and any such payments made by lessee for lessor may be deducted from any amounts of money which may become due lessor under this lease.

All express provisions and implied covenants of this lease shall be subject to all applicable laws, governmental orders, rules and regulations. This lease shall not be terminated in whole or in part, nor lessee held liable in damages, because of a temporary cessation of production or of drilling operations due to breakdown of equipment or due to the repairing of a well or wells, or because of failure to comply with any of the express provisions or implied covenants of this lease if such failure is the result of the exercise of governmental authority, war, armed hostilities, lack of market, act of God, strike, civil disturbance, fire, explosion, flood or any other cause reasonably beyond the control of lessee.

This lease and all provisions thereof shall be applicable to and binding upon the parties and their respective successors and assigns. Reference herein to lessor and lessee shall include reference to their respective successors and assigns. Should any one or more of the parties named above as lessors not execute this lease, it shall nevertheless be binding upon the party or parties executing the same.

Lessor hereby releases and waives all rights in the leased premises under and by virtue of the homestead exemption laws of the State of Wyoming insofar as the same may in any way affect the purposes for which this lease is made.

IN WITNESS WHEREOF, this lease is executed as of the day and year first above written.

_____   _____

_____   _____

_____   _____

_____   _____

Figure E.3—*Continued*

STATE OF_____ } SS.   (Individual—Wyo.)
COUNTY OF_____

On this day_____ day of _____, 19 ____, before me personally appeared _____ _____, to me known to be the person (or persons) described in and who executed the foregoing instrument, and acknowledged that he (or she or they) executed the same as his (or her or their) free act and deed.

My commission expires: _____
                                               Notary Public

_____

STATE OF_____ } SS.   (Individual—Wyo.)
COUNTY OF_____

On this_____ day of _____, 19 ____, before me personally appeared _____ _____, to me known to be the person (or persons) described in and who executed the foregoing instrument, and acknowledged that he (or she or they) executed the same as his (or her or their) free act and deed.

My commission expires: _____
                                               Notary Public

_____

STATE OF_____ } SS.   (Corporation—Wyo.)
COUNTY OF_____

On this_____ day of _____, 19 ____, before me appeared _____ _____, to me personally known, who, being by me duly sworn, did say that he is the _____ President of _____, a corporation, and that the seal affixed to the foregoing instrument is the corporate seal of said corporation and that said instrument was signed and sealed in behalf of said corporation by authority of its board of directors, and said _____ acknowledged said instrument to be the free act and deed of said corporation.

My commission expires: _____
                                               Notary Public

_____

STATE OF_____ } SS.   (Certificate of Recording)
COUNTY OF_____

This instrument was filed for record on the_____ day of _____, 19 ____ at _____ o'clock ___ M and recorded in Book _____ at Page _____ of the records of this office.

                                               By_____
_____
Register of Deeds   **Deputy**

AFTER RECORDING, RETURN TO: _____

Figure E.4. Michigan oil and gas lease with gas storage provision
(Courtesy of Exxon)

Producers 88—Revised
Michigan G
(1-61)

OIL AND GAS LEASE
(With Gas Storage Provisions)

THIS AGREEMENT, made and entered into this .... day of ...., 19........., by and between ....

....

whose address is ...., hereinafter called lessor (whether
　　　　　　　　　　　　Street Address　　　　　　　City　　　　　　State

one or more), and ....

whose address is ...., hereinafter called lessee; WITNESSETH THAT:

1. Lessor, for and in consideration of .... DOLLARS ($ ....) in hand paid, receipt of which is hereby acknowledged, and of the agreements of lessee hereinafter set forth, hereby grants, demises, leases and lets exclusively unto said lessee the lands hereinafter described for the purpose of prospecting, exploring by geophysical and other methods, drilling, mining, operating for and producing oil or gas, or both, including, but not as a limitation, casinghead gas, casinghead gasoline, gas-condensate (distillate) and any substance, whether similar or dissimilar, produced in a gaseous state, and for the purpose of storing any kind of gas as provided in Paragraph 6 hereof, together with the right to construct and maintain pipe lines, telephone and electric lines, tanks, powers, ponds, roadways, plants, equipment, and structures thereon to produce, save, store and take care of said oil and gas, and the exclusive right to inject air, gas, water, brine and other fluids from any source into the subsurface strata and any and all other rights and privileges necessary, incident to, or convenient for the economical operation of said land, alone or conjointly with neighboring land, for the production, saving, storing and taking care of oil and gas and the injection of air, gas, water, brine, and other fluids into the subsurface strata, said lands being situated in the Township of ...., County of

....,State of Michigan, and being described as follows, to-wit:

....

....

....

....

....

....

....

....

....

....

....

....

....

....

....

of Section ...., Township ...., Range...................., it being the purpose and intent of lessor to lease, and lessor does hereby lease, all strips or parcels of land owned by lessor which adjoin the lands above described or which lie in the section or sections herein specified. For all purposes of this lease, said lands shall be deemed to contain ....acres.

2. Subject to the other provisions herein contained, this lease shall remain in force for a term of .... years from this date (herein called "primary term") and as long thereafter as oil and gas, or either of them, is produced from the above described land or drilling operations are continuously prosecuted as hereinafter provided or said land is used for gas storage purposes as provided in Paragraph 6 hereof. "Drilling operations" includes operations for the drilling of a new well, the reworking, deepening or plugging back of a well or hole or other operations conducted in an effort to obtain or re-establish production of oil or gas; and drilling operations shall be considered to be "continuously prosecuted" if not more than 60 days shall elapse between the completion or abandonment of one well or hole and the commencement of drilling operations on another well or hole. If, at the expiration of the primary term of this lease, oil or gas is not being produced from the above described land and said land is not then being used for gas storage purposes but lessee is then engaged in drilling operations, this lease shall continue in force so long as drilling operations are continuously prosecuted; and if production of oil or gas results from any such drilling operations, this lease shall continue in force so long as oil or gas shall be produced or said land is used for gas storage purposes. If, after the expiration of the primary term of this lease, production from the above described land should cease and said land is not then being used for gas storage purposes, this lease shall not terminate if lessee is then prosecuting drilling operations, or within 60 days after each such cessation of production commences drilling operations, and this lease shall remain in force so long as such operations are continuously prosecuted, and if production results therefrom, then as long thereafter as oil or gas is produced from the above described land or said land is used for gas storage purposes.

3. In consideration of the premises, lessee covenants and agrees:

First. To deliver, free of cost, to lessor at the wells, or to the credit of lessor in the pipeline to which the wells may be connected, the equal one-eighth ($\frac{1}{8}$) part of all oil and other liquid hydrocarbons produced and saved from the leased premises, or, at lessee's option, to pay to lessor for such one-eighth ($\frac{1}{8}$) royalty the market price at the well for such oil and other liquid hydrocarbons of like grade and gravity prevailing on the day such oil and other liquid hydrocarbons are run from the lease stock tanks.

Second. To pay lessor one-eighth ($\frac{1}{8}$) of the proceeds received by lessee at the well for all gas (including all substances contained in such gas) produced from the leased premises and sold by lessee; if such gas is used by lessee off the leased premises or is stored or used by lessee for the manufacture of casinghead gasoline or other products, to pay to lessor one-eighth ($\frac{1}{8}$) of the prevailing market price at the well for the gas so used or stored.

Figure E.4—*Continued*

The provisions of this Paragraph 3 shall have no application whatever to, and no royalty shall be due on, any gas and associated hydrocarbons and substances which may be produced from any stratum or strata used by lessee for gas storage purposes.

4. If operations for drilling or gas storage are not commenced on said land on or before one year from the date hereof, this lease shall (except as otherwise provided in this paragraph) terminate, unless lessee (or someone in his behalf), on or before such date, shall pay or tender to lessor, or to lessor's credit in the .... Bank at .... (which bank and its successors shall continue as the depository regardless of changes in the ownership of said land or of the right to receive rentals), the sum of .... DOLLARS ($ ....), which shall operate as a delay rental and cover the privilege of deferring the commencement of such operations for 12 months from said date. In like manner and upon like payments or tenders, the commencement of such operations may be further deferred for like periods of the same number of months successively during the primary term hereof. All payments or tenders may be made by cash, check or draft, mailed or delivered on or before the delay rental date, and the depositing of such cash, check or draft in any post office, addressed to the depository bank or lessor (at his last known address as shown by lessee's records) on or before the delay rental date, shall be deemed payment or tender as herein provided. Notwithstanding the death of lessor, payment or tender of rentals to such deceased or to his credit in the manner provided herein shall be binding on the heirs, devisees, executors, administrators and personal representatives of lessor and his successors in interest. If lessee shall, on or before any delay rental date, make a bona fide attempt to pay or deposit delay rental to a lessor entitled thereto under this lease according to lessee's records or to a lessor who, prior to such attempted payment or deposit, has given lessee notice, in accordance with the terms of this lease hereinafter set forth, of his right to receive delay rental, and if such payment or deposit shall be erroneous in any regard (whether deposited in the wrong depository, paid to persons other than the parties entitled thereto as shown by lessee's records, in an incorrect amount, or otherwise), lessee shall be unconditionally obligated to pay to such lessor the delay rental properly payable for the delay rental period involved, but this lease shall be maintained in the same manner as if such erroneous payment or deposit had been properly made, provided that the erroneous payment or deposit be corrected within 30 days after receipt by lessee of written notice from such lessor of such error accompanied by any documents and other evidence necessary to enable lessee to make proper payment. The consideration first recited herein, the down payment, covers not only the privilege granted to the date when said first delay rental is payable as aforesaid, but also lessee's option of extending that period as aforesaid, and any and all other rights conferred.

5. Should the first well drilled on the above described land in an effort to secure production of oil or gas be completed as a dry hole, and the above lands are not at the time being used for gas storage purposes hereunder, then, and in that event, if additional operations for drilling or operations for gas storage are not commenced on said land within 12 months from the expiration of the last delay rental period for which rental has been paid (it being understood that for the purpose of this paragraph the period of time extending from the date of this lease to the first delay rental date shall be considered as a rental period for which delay rental has been paid), this lease shall terminate as to both parties, unless lessee on or before the expiration of said 12 months shall resume the payment of delay rentals in the same amount and in the same manner as hereinbefore provided. Upon resumption of the payment of delay rentals, as above provided, the last preceding paragraph hereof, governing the payment of delay rentals and the effect thereof, shall continue in force just as though there had been no interruption in delay rental payments.

6. Lessee shall have the exclusive right to employ any stratum or strata underlying said lands (except any stratum bearing potable water or workable coal) for the storage of any kind of gas, from whatever source obtained, and may for this purpose re-open and restore to operation any and all abandoned wells on the premises which may have penetrated such stratum or strata, or may drill new wells thereon for the purpose of introducing and storing any kind of gas in any such stratum or strata and recovering the same therefrom. It is understood that a well need not be drilled on said land to permit the storage of gas. Lessee shall be the sole judge as to whether gas is being stored within the leased premises and lessee's determination in respect thereto shall be final and conclusive. As full compensation for the storage rights herein granted and in lieu of all delay rental or royalty due or to become due on the production or removal of stored gas from the leased premises, lessee agrees to pay lessor an annual rental of $ .... commencing with the date of first utilization of any such stratum or strata for gas storage purposes and for as long thereafter as any such stratum or strata be so utilized, such annual rental to be paid within three months after the commencement of each annual period of utilization for storage purposes. Lessee further agrees to pay lessor as liquidated damages for the drilling, operation and maintenance of each well on the leased premises which is utilized for the storage of gas, as well as for the necessary or useful surface rights and privileges relating thereto, for the entire term of this agreement, the sum of $100.00 payable in one sum within three months after each well now existing or hereafter drilled upon the leased premises is so utilized. Lessee agrees to give lessor written notice of the use of the leased premises for gas storage purposes and of the use of any well drilled thereon for gas storage purposes. In the event any stratum or strata utilized for gas storage purposes contains an economically recoverable reserve of native gas, lessee agrees to compensate lessor for his royalty on such gas at the prevailing well-head market price in the vicinity at the time lessee gives notice of use of the premises for gas storage purposes for gas of comparable quality, the volume of such gas to be based on an estimate of such reserves by accepted geological methods. - - - The rights granted in this Paragraph 6 are separate and distinct from the other rights granted by this lease, and should lessee fail or make default in any of the covenants, conditions or obligations of lessee, express or implied, relating to gas storage rights, such failure or default shall not defeat or affect this lease insofar as it covers such other rights and, in like manner, should lessee fail or make default in any of the covenants, conditions or obligations of lessee, express or implied, relating to such other rights, such failure or default shall not defeat or affect this lease insofar as it covers the rights granted in this Paragraph 6.

7. If a well capable of producing gas other than stored gas in paying quantities located on the leased premises (or on acreage pooled or consolidated with all or a portion of the leased premises into a unit for the drilling or operation of such well) is at any time shut-in and no gas or gas-condensate therefrom is sold or used off the premises or for the manufacture of gasoline or other products, nevertheless such shut-in well shall be deemed to be a well on the leased premises producing gas in paying quantities and this lease will continue in force during all of the time or times while such well is so shut-in, whether before or after the expiration of the primary term hereof. Lessee shall use reasonable diligence to market gas or gas and gas-condensate capable of being produced from such shut-in well but shall be under no obligation to market such products under terms, conditions or circumstances which, in lessee's judgment exercised in good faith, are unsatisfactory. Lessee shall be obligated to pay or tender to lessor within 45 days after the expiration of each period of one year in length (annual period) during which such well is so shut-in, as royalty, an amount equal to the annual delay rental herein provided applicable to the interest of lessor in acreage embraced in this lease as of the end of such annual period, or, if this lease does not provide for any delay rental, then the sum of $50.00; provided that, if gas or gas-condensate from such well is sold or used as aforesaid before the end of any such annual period, or if, at the end of any such annual period, this lease is being maintained in force and effect otherwise than by reason of such shut-in well, lessee shall not be obligated to pay or tender, for that particular annual period, said sum of money. Such payment shall be deemed a royalty under all provisions of this lease. Such payment may be made or tendered to lessor or to lessor's credit in the depository bank above designated. Royalty ownership as of the last day of each such annual period as shown by lessee's records shall govern the determination of the party or parties entitled to receive such payment.

8. The respective amounts of all delay rentals, royalties and other payments hereunder are to be calculated in proportion to lessor's interest in the rights with respect to which each such payment is made; that is, in case lessor owns a less interest in any of the rights which are the subject of this lease than the full and entire interest therein, then the payments in respect to such rights which are herein provided for shall be paid lessor only in the proportion which lessor's interest in such rights bears to the full and entire interest in such rights.

Figure E.4—*Continued*

9. If the leased premises are now, or shall hereafter be, owned in severalty or in separate tracts, the premises nevertheless shall be developed and operated as one lease, and all rentals, royalties and payments provided for hereunder shall be treated as an entirety and shall be divided among, and paid to, such separate owners in the proportion that the acreage owned by each such separate owner bears to the entire leased acreage.

10. If the estate of either party hereto is assigned or sublet, and the privilege of assigning or subletting in whole or in part is expressly allowed, the express and implied covenants hereof shall extend to the sublessees, successors and assigns of the parties; and in the event of an assignment or subletting by lessee, lessee shall be relieved and discharged as to the leasehold rights so assigned or sublet from any liability to lessor thereafter accruing upon any of the covenants or conditions of this lease, either express or implied. No change in the ownership of said land or any interest therein or pertaining thereto, however accomplished, shall operate to enlarge the obligations or diminish the rights of lessee or require separate measuring or installation of separate tanks by lessee. Notwithstanding any actual or constructive knowledge of or notice to lessee, no change in ownership, whether by reason of death, conveyance or any other matter, shall be binding on lessee (except at lessee's option in any particular case) until 90 days after lessee has been furnished written notice thereof, and the supporting information hereinafter referred to, by the party claiming as a result of such change in ownership. Such notice shall be supported by original or certified copies of all documents and other instruments or proceedings necessary in lessee's opinion to establish the ownership of the claiming party. If this lease is assigned or sublet insofar as it covers only a part of the acreage embraced in the leased premises, the delay rentals hereinabove provided for shall be apportioned to the separate parts, ratably according to the surface acreage of each, and failure of the leasehold owner or sublessee of any separate part of the above described lands to make a rental payment with respect to such part shall in no event operate to terminate or affect this lease insofar as it covers any other part thereof.

11. Lessee may, at any time, execute and deliver to lessor or place of record a release covering all or any part of the acreage embraced in the leased premises or covering any one or more zones, formations or depths underlying all or any part of such acreage, and thereupon shall be relieved of all obligations thereafter to accrue with respect to the acreage, zones, formations or depths covered by such release. In event of a release of this lease as to all rights in only a part of the acreage embraced in the leased premises, thereafter the delay rentals hereinabove provided for shall be reduced proportionally on an acreage basis.

12. Lessee is granted the right, from time to time while this lease is in force, to pool into a separate drilling or production unit or units all or any part of the land covered by this lease with other land, lease or leases, or interests therein (whether such other interests are pooled by a voluntary agreement on the part of the owners thereof or by the exercise of a right to pool by the lessees thereof), when in lessee's judgment it is necessary or advisable in order to promote conservation, to properly develop or operate the land and interests to be pooled, or to obtain a multiple production allowable from any governmental agency having control over such matters. Any pooling hereunder may cover all oil and gas, or any one or more of the substances covered by this lease, and may cover one or more or all zones or formations underlying all or any portion or portions of the leased premises. Any unit formed by such pooling shall be of abutting or cornering tracts and shall not exceed 160 acres (plus a tolerance of 10%) for gas or gas-condensate and shall not exceed 40 acres (plus a tolerance of 10%) for any other substance covered by this lease; provided that if any governmental regulation or order shall prescribe a spacing pattern for the development of a field wherein the above described land, or a portion thereof, is located, or allocate a producing allowable based on acreage per well, then any such unit may embrace as much additional acreage as may be so prescribed or as may be permitted in such allocation of allowable. The area pooled and the zones or formations and substances pooled shall be set forth by lessee in a "declaration of pooling" filed for record in the county or counties in which the pooled area is located which declaration of pooling shall constitute a supplement to this lease. Such pooling shall be effective on the date such declaration is filed unless a later effective date is specified in such declaration. In lieu of the royalties elsewhere herein specified, except shut-in gas well royalties, lessor shall receive on production from an area so pooled only such portion of the royalties which, in the absence of such pooling, would be payable hereunder to lessor on production from the land covered by this lease which is placed in the pooled area as the amount of the surface acreage in the land covered by this lease which is placed in the pooled area bears to the amount of the surface acreage of the entire pooled area. Nothing herein contained shall authorize or effect any transfer of any title to any leasehold, royalty or other interest pooled pursuant hereto. The commencement of a well, the conduct of other drilling operations, the completion of a well or of a dry hole, or the operation of a producing well on the pooled area, shall be considered for all purposes (except for royalty purposes) the same as if said well were located on, or such drilling operations were conducted upon, the lands covered by this lease whether or not such well is located upon, or such drilling operations are conducted upon, said lands. Lessee may terminate any pooling effected pursuant hereto at any time the pooled unit is not producing and no drilling operations are being conducted thereon by executing and filing of record in the county or counties in which the pooled area is located a written declaration of the termination of such pooling, provided that the pooling of all interests not covered by this lease which comprise a part of such pooled unit be also terminated in some effective manner.

13. Lessee shall have the right to use, free of cost, oil, gas and water produced on said land for its operations thereon except water from wells of lessor. Lessee shall have the right at any time to remove all machinery and fixtures placed on said premises, including the right to draw and remove casing. No part of the surface of the leased premises shall, without the written consent of lessee, be let, granted or licensed by lessor to any other party for the location, construction or maintenance of structures, tanks, pits, reservoirs, equipment, or machinery to be used for the purpose of exploring, developing or operating adjacent lands for oil, gas or other minerals.

14. Lessee shall bury below plow depth its pipe lines on the leased premises when requested by a lessor owning an interest in the surface. No well shall be drilled nearer than 200 feet to any house or barn now on said premises without the written consent of the owner of the surface on which such house or barn is located. Lessee shall pay for damages to growing crops caused by its operations on said lands.

15. Lessor hereby warrants and agrees to defend the title to the lands herein described, but if the interest of lessor covered by this lease is expressly stated to be less than the entire fee or mineral estate, lessor's warranty shall be limited to the interest so stated. Lessee may purchase or lease the rights of any party claiming any interest in said land and exercise such rights as may be obtained thereby but lessee shall not suffer any forfeiture nor incur any liability to lessor by reason thereof. Lessee shall have the right at any time to pay for lessor, any mortgage, taxes or other lien on said lands, in the event of default of payment by lessor, and be subrogated to the rights of the holder thereof, and any such payments made by lessee for lessor may be deducted from any amounts of money which may become due lessor under this lease.

16. All express provisions and implied covenants of this lease shall be subject to all applicable laws, governmental orders, rules and regulations. This lease shall not be terminated in whole or in part, nor lessee held liable in damages, because of a temporary cessation of production or of drilling operations due to breakdown of equipment or due to the repairing of a well or wells, or because of failure to comply with any of the express provisions or implied covenants of this lease if such failure is the result of the exercise of governmental authority, war, armed hostilities, lack of market, act of God, strike, civil disturbance, fire, explosion, flood or any other cause reasonably beyond the control of lessee.

17. This lease and all provisions thereof shall be applicable to and binding upon the parties and their respective heirs, devisees, personal representatives, successors and assigns. Reference herein to lessor and lessee shall include reference to their respective heirs, devisees, personal representatives, successors and assigns. Should any one or more of the parties named above as lessors not execute this lease, it shall nevertheless be binding upon the party or parties executing the same.

Figure E.4—*Continued*

IN WITNESS WHEREOF, this lease is executed as of the day and year first above written.

WITNESS: LESSOR:

....

....(SEAL)

....

....(SEAL)

....

....(SEAL)

....

....(SEAL)

....

.... (SEAL)

STATE OF .... }
                                                                } SS.   **(Individual—Mich.)**
COUNTY OF .... }

On this .... day of ...., 19............, before me personally appeared

....

to me known to be the person....... described in and who executed the foregoing instrument, and acknowledged that ....

executed the same as .... free act and deed. Given under my hand and seal the day and year first above written.

My commission expires:..   ....
                                                                                        Notary Public

STATE OF .... }
                                                                } SS.   **(Individual—Mich.)**
COUNTY OF .... }

On this .... day of ...., 19... ...., before me personally appeared

....

to me known to be the person....... described in and who executed the foregoing instrument, and acknowledged that ....

executed the same as .... free act and deed. Given under my hand and seal the day and year first above written.

My commission expires:..   ....
                                                                                        Notary Public

STATE OF .... }
                                                                } SS.   **(Corporation—Mich.)**
COUNTY OF .... }

On this .... day of ...., 19............, before me appeared ....

...., to me personally known, who, being by me duly sworn, did say that he is

the .... President of ...., a corporation, and that the
seal affixed to said instrument is the corporate seal of said corporation and that said instrument was signed and sealed in behalf of said
corporation by authority of its Board of Directors, and the said ....
acknowledged the execution of the said instrument as the free act and deed of said corporation. Given under my hand and seal the day
and year first above written.

My commission expires:..   ....
                                                                                        Notary Public

Figure E.4—*Continued*

OIL AND GAS LEASE

FROM

TO

When Recorded
Return to

APPENDIX F
FILING OF LEGAL INSTRUMENTS FOR RECORD

Herewith are presented the recording procedures prescribed by statute for the 254 counties of Texas. With minor changes, the same procedures apply generally to every recording jurisdiction within the United States.

One major difference occurs in Louisiana. Louisiana recorders *keep* the filed original documents in permanent files in every case. Should one wish a true copy of the recorded instrument in his file, he must send a duplicate original to the recorder with the request that such duplicate be certified and returned.

In states where marginal entries are made in tract books, the recorder may retain record files of somewhat different nomenclature than here presented.

RECORDING DUTY OF COUNTY CLERK

Of all the various responsibilities assigned to the county clerk, the recording of legal instruments is perhaps the most traditional and basic. In terms of sheer volume, legal instruments constitute the major portion of paperwork flowing through the office, require the greatest amount of storage space, and usually take up a larger portion of the clerk's time than any other single duty.

While almost any paperwork passing through the county clerk's office can be considered a legal instrument, the discussion here will deal with those instruments that are merely filed for record and require no other action by the clerk.

Statutory authority for the county clerk to perform this function comes from the Texas Civil Statutes, which say in part:

County Clerks shall be the recorders for their respective counties; they shall provide and keep in their offices well-bound books in which they shall record all instruments of writing authorized or required to be recorded in the County Clerk's office....

Most of the confusion arising from this function of the clerk's office stems not from the complexity of the recording process itself but from the volume of work and from the myriad number of different instruments to be filed. Furthermore, the legislature quite often adds new instruments to the list of those required to be filed in the clerk's office, although on occasion it deletes filing requirements.

To fully appreciate the magnitude and importance of this responsibility, one must realize that the county clerk's office is viewed by all as an absolutely honest, impartial, and infallibly safe depository for any document. Almost literally, any citizen may file any instrument of writing to be kept safe and to be made part of the public record.

While this naturally leads to filing of some documents that defy categorization, instruments may be roughly divided into three areas of interest:

1. Instruments that prove ownership or interest in real or personal property. These also include instruments that facilitate or restrict transfer of property.
2. Instruments concerning identity of commercial activities.
3. Instruments concerning identity of persons.

The clerk's responsibility for maintenance of these records is threefold: accepting instruments for filing, recording instruments in a safe and permanent manner, and providing an index to all material so that records may be easily and completely retrieved.

While statutes require that many instruments must be filed with the clerk, it is never the clerk's responsibility to solicit or enforce such filing. On the other hand, the clerk cannot refuse to file an instrument so long as it is properly signed and acknowledged and the filing fee is paid.

Instruments filed for public record are just that—public record, and the clerk may not refuse access to these records to anyone so long as such exposure does not endanger the safekeeping of the records. Most clerks provide convenient working space for persons wishing to examine public records, and it is quite common practice to allow abstractors and others who make great use of the files to set up desks and office equipment in the records area if space permits.

The clerk is often called upon to make an attested or certified copy of an instrument as proof that the original document is a part of the public record. Such copies are often used to prove ownership of property, personal identity, or other important matters. The clerk, by affixing his seal and signature, is swearing that the copy is a true and exact replica of his files. The clerk cannot refuse to issue such a copy to anyone requesting such service for any public record so long as the fee for this service is paid. Exceptions to this rule are made only where disclosure of a public record would cause grave personal injury to an individual. Such exceptions are few and include the following types of records:

1. Illegitimate births
2. Statement of facts in mental cases
3. Juvenile records
4. Medical certificates for marriage licenses
5. Wills filed for safekeeping but not admitted to probate

In summary, the clerk is the trusted guardian of all instruments of public record and as such should do all that is possible to keep such records safe, maintain their integrity, and facilitate public access to the files.

INSTRUMENTS TO BE FILED IN THE CLERK'S OFFICE

As already stated, instruments are so varied that it is not possible to make a definitive listing of all possibilities. But for purposes of classification, a list of the most common instruments to be filed is presented in five categories of related records:

1. Deed records
2. Deeds of trust
3. Liens and abstracts
4. Licenses
5. Miscellaneous and obsolete records

Deed Records

The typical clerk's office will have more volumes of deed records than of any other kind. The reason is that deed records are composed of literally dozens of different types of instruments, related only in that they affect title to real estate. The relation of some instruments to real estate is quite obvious and, in other cases, quite tenuous. *Power of attorney,* for instance, does not seem related to real estate except that such power may include the right to dispose of property. A rule of thumb used by most clerks is that all instruments related to real estate that are not deeds of trust, mortgages, judgments, or liens should be filed in the deed records. The statutes specifically state that the above exceptions should be filed in volumes separate from the deed records. Interestingly, however, the law requires that the clerk record all releases of liens, mortgages, and judgments in the deed records. A listing of common deed records is presented below.

Master mortgage—deed of
trust records (need not
be acknowledged or proved)
Deed
General warranty deed
Special warranty deed

Gift deed
Partition deed
Guardian deed
Quitclaim deed
Trustee's deed
Right-of-way deed
Cemetery deed
Royalty deed
Affidavit (various types)
Appointment of trustee
Resignation of trustee
Transfer of lien
Conveyance of lien
Assignment of lien
Subordination of lien
Release (various types)
Partial release (various types)
Lease
Easement
Contract of sale
Bill of sale
Homestead designation
Agreement (various types)
Power of attorney
Revocation of power of attorney
Removal of disabilities—minor
Removal of disabilities—coveture
Certified copy of probate procedures
Certified copy of divorce decree (when
   real property is divided)
Oil leases
Gas leases
Extensions
Options
Rental division
Restrictions
Amended restrictions
Trust indentures

Deeds of Trust

Deeds of trust records are usually the second most numerous among the legal instruments. Deeds of trust in Texas are used as

mortgage or lien records on real estate or improvements to real estate. A modification to a deed of trust is recorded in the deed of trust books, but renewals, extensions, or releases of trust deeds are recorded in the deed records books.

Liens and Abstracts

A *lien* is an instrument stating that the property of one person is security for the cost of goods or services provided to that person by another. Liens may be agreed to by both parties, or they may be involuntarily filed by one party after the fact. Liens are usually recorded in separate books for each type of lien. Releases of liens are recorded in the deed records, except for release of federal and state tax liens, which are recorded in their respective lien books.

Abstracts of judgment are public notices that judgment against a person has been rendered in a court of law and that this judgment may be enforced against property. Abstracts of judgment should be recorded and indexed in a separate book, and the release of an abstract of judgment should be recorded in the deed records and noted on the original abstract instrument filed for record.

Bonds

Many businesses and occupations are required to file a bond with the clerk's office before engaging in public contact. The clerk simply files and records the original bond in the appropriate book.

Licenses

Occupations that require state licensing must have these licenses recorded in either the district clerk's or the county clerk's office. District clerks usually record doctor's certificates, and county clerks record most others.

Miscellaneous Records

Plats are maps showing legal descriptions and boundaries of subdivided land. A plat must be filed with the county clerk each time a legal boundary of a parcel is changed or divided. If such land is within a city limit, approval of the city council must be shown on the plat before it can be filed. For county land, the commissioner's court must approve the plat. Most cities maintain extraterritorial jurisdiction over county land within a certain distance of the city limits. If such land is divided, both legislative bodies must approve the plat.

At one time, plats were recorded in the deed records. Most clerks now use special plat books, and the clerk may wish to require that plats conform to a standard size for easy filing.

Other miscellaneous records include *lis pendens,* marks and brands, assumed names, condominium records, deputation records, field notes of surveyors, and others.

COUNTY CLERK'S RECORDING FEES

The Texas Civil Statutes outline fees that may be charged for recording instruments by the county clerk. The fees are set on a sliding-scale basis, depending on the length of the document and the number of parties to be indexed. The law leaves a great deal of latitude to the clerk in setting fees but is outlined generally as follows.

For filing or registering (including indexing) most simple non-real-estate records, the clerk is to charge $2.00. These records do not include notary bonds, marriage records, vital statistics records, financing statements, or records pertaining to the criminal, civil, and probate courts. Fees for these documents are set out separately.

The cost of filing real estate instruments varies with the length and complexity of the documents. To cut down on confusion about filing costs, many clerks have either predetermined the cost (based on accepted formulas) of standard and common instruments filed or have developed a flat-fee system that averages out the official costs. These standard fees are generally applied to the following instruments:

1. Deeds
2. Deeds of trust
3. Liens
4. Leases
5. All other instruments filed in deed records

The fee for issuing a certified copy of any record may be assessed on a per-page basis. The clerk is also entitled to a fee for administering each oath or issuing the clerk's certification on copies of documents, whether or not the clerk's seal is used. There is also a fee for approving and filing all non-court-related bonds.

Finally, the civil statutes provide that "for such other duties prescribed, authorized, and/or permitted by the Legislature for which no fee is set by this Act, reasonable fees shall be charged." This leaves the clerk free to set fees for recording such items as plats, abstracts, and miscellaneous items.

RECEIPT OF INSTRUMENTS

Instruments for recording are quite often brought to the clerk's office personally but may also be mailed in for processing. Before the recording process is started, several important preliminary steps must be taken:

1. The document must be examined to make sure that all parties to the instrument are clearly identifed as to name. In two-party documents, these parties will be the grantor(s) or grantee(s).

2. Each instrument for record must be acknowledged to by the grantor appearing before some officer authorized to take such acknowledgment. The grantor states that he has executed the instrument for the consideration and purposes therein stated, and the officer before whom this is sworn testifies to the fact and affixes his seal to the document. No instrument relating to a contract, agreement, or legal proceeding may be filed without this acknowledgment. Officers who may be authorized to acknowledge instruments are clerks of the district court, a judge or clerk of the county court, a notary public, and, in the case of foreign documents, a diplomatic official of the United States. For members of the armed forces, a commissioned officer may also fulfill this duty. (Authorizing officers vary from state to state.)

3. A correct address to which the recorded original document is to be returned must be checked for.

4. The appropriate recording fee is collected and a receipt for the amount collected is issued. The fee should also be entered into the clerk's accounting system, which may be a cash register, daily cash log, or other means of properly accounting for fees received.

After filing is completed, the clerk should filemark the instrument with the clerk's name and title, the date, and the exact time of filing. These constitute the clerk's endorsement that the instrument is filed for record and is very important, because legally the record becomes part of the public record at this time, regardless of when it is actually recorded and indexed.

Each instrument is assigned a unique number, which is stamped or written on the original document for the purpose of identification. The number should be assigned sequentially so that the clerk can tell in what order instruments have been processed.

CLERK'S REGISTER OF INSTRUMENTS FILED FOR RECORD

The clerk's register, an important volume required by statute, becomes the master list of all instruments that have been submitted for record, and each instrument is entered here immediately after receipt. Instruments are entered into the clerk's register in chronological sequence and should contain the information listed as follows:

1. Instrument number
2. Grantor(s) name(s) and address(es)
3. Grantee(s) name(s) and address(es)
4. By whom filed
5. Nature of, or type of instrument
6. Date of instrument
7. Date of filing
8. Date delivered
9. To whom delivered

NOTE: Items 8 and 9 are filled out after the recording process.

Clerks may desire to keep an alphabetical index to the clerk's register or to keep the register itself in alphabetical (then numerical) sequence for easy reference.

Some states may require statements as to identity of the person preparing the document and/or subscribing witnesses.

RECORDING OF INSTRUMENTS

The process of recording is really the transcribing of instruments for the clerk's files so that original documents may be returned to the owner. In a few cases, such as for bonds and assumed-name certificates, the original document will stay in the clerk's office, but these are exceptions. The procedure for recording is relatively simple.

1. Instruments for recording are separated by type (i.e., deed records, deeds of trust, etc.) and often put into numerical sequence.
2. The volume number of the book in which the instrument is to reside and the page number (of the volume) on which it will be recorded are now assigned and stamped or written on the original document in the same place as the filemark. Instruments of several pages in length will of course occupy several pages of the record.
3. The instrument is now transcribed into the permanent record manually, by photostatic process, or by microfilm. Each page of the permanent record is uniquely and sequentially numbered.
4. The permanent record is then compared to the original to ensure accuracy and legibility.
5. If indexing is to be done as a separate process or at a different time, the clerk may wish to make a takeoff sheet of index information so that return of the originals will not be delayed.
6. The instrument is now ready for indexing or return to the owner.

INDEXING OF INSTRUMENTS

For every type of instrument recorded in the permanent records, the clerk must also maintain a separate index volume so that individual documents may be referenced. All two-party instruments must be indexed as both direct index and reverse index, while one-party instruments (bonds, licenses, etc.) require only one index. The index is always in alphabetic sequence by last name of the parties. The indexing process is as follows:

1. The clerk starts with a takeoff sheet or with the original instruments sorted by type and arranged in grantor (direct) alphabetic sequence.
2. The clerk then locates the direct (grantor) index volume for the particular type of record to be indexed and opens it to the next blank index line devoted to the alphabetic sequence of the grantor's last name.
3. In the case of any records pertaining to real estate (deed records, deeds of trust, liens, etc.), the following information is recorded in the index:
   (a) Instrument number
   (b) Grantor's name
   (c) Grantee's name
   (d) Kind of instrument
   (e) Volume and page number of the permanent record
   (f) Enough of the legal description of the property to be meaningful.
   If there is more than one grantor, all names should be indexed in the same manner.
4. When all grantors have been indexed, the reverse (grantee) index volume is completed for each grantee mentioned in the instrument.
5. Once recorded and indexed, the instrument may be returned to its owner after completing the "to whom mailed" and "date mailed" portion of the clerk's register of instruments filed for record.

NOTE: Many clerks have adopted the following notation to show inclusion of other parties when indexing an instrument — *et vir,* and husband; *et ux,* and wife; *et al,* and others.

APPENDIX G
LEASE FILING SYSTEMS

No two offices arrange their files in exactly the same way. Some common procedures are discussed below, but individual companies, consultants, and brokers tailor such procedures to meet their own needs. There is also the complicating question of automation. More and more companies are putting their lease information into computerized storage systems. For some, the switch has been smooth and almost immediately productive, but for others it has been more difficult. Software (that is, computer programs) now exists for virtually all the procedures to be mentioned—and for a great many other storage, mapping, and computational functions. The available software can, however, cause problems for land support personnel who know their jobs very well but automated systems rather sketchily. Where both software and computer hardware are concerned, some companies have bought in haste and repented at leisure, struggling for months to make a computerized system actually work for them. Not a few have become discouraged and fallen back, temporarily at least, on their old paper filing systems. Other companies have adopted the new technology more slowly and cautiously, always keeping backup files on paper, especially for the payment of delay rentals. The change to an automated system can be frustrating if it is not undertaken with care. The fact that software exists and is enthusiastically described by salespersons does not mean that a given company can use it to advantage. (Preliminary research into particular computer packages should always include talking with satisfied users.) After this caution, it must also be said that computers, especially microcomputers, can be a blessing to companies large and small. They can reduce drudgery while increasing the speed of information retrieval and the accuracy of data manipulation.

TWO KINDS OF FILES

The two kinds of files kept by nearly all companies are files for individual leases and files for general prospect areas. The first are usually referred to as *lease files.* The second may be called *area files, legal files,* or *prospect files.* Both kinds commonly employ one or more methods of cross-referencing. Such cross-referencing, or cross-indexing, can be alphabetical, numerical, or a combination of the two. Numbers, though, are used with increasing frequency, since computer codes are so often numerical. For example, one widely used code represents the states by two-digit numbers and the counties within a state by five-digit numbers: 01 for Alabama and 01001 for Autauga County.

INDEXES FOR LEASE FILES

Individual leases are usually filed by lease number, by lessor name, or by geographical names or codes. Many lease files are cross-indexed so that the information in them can be found by using any of two or three different indicators, just as a book in a library appears in the catalog by a number, by author name, by title, and by subject.

When files are arranged in numerical order, lease numbers (often assigned sequentially as leases are acquired) will appear as the first entries on the tabs of paper file folders. Computerized files can be assigned numbers in a similar way for storage on tape or disc and later printout or display on a screen. What else appears on the tabs or on the electronic medium varies. Some companies prefix the lease number with the two-letter post office code for the state in which the lease is located: TX-200 for Texas lease #200. Some companies prefix with a *numerical* state and county code like the one mentioned earlier: 01-01001-200 for Autauga County, Alabama, lease #200. Some systems follow the lease number with the last name and first name of the lessor (assuming only one lessor is involved; where there are more, the first lessor's name may be used). For example, the tab might read: #200-Mulligan, Mike. When state prefixes are not used, the names of the county or parish and the state may complete the tab information: #200 — Mulligan, Mike — Autauga County, Alabama. Clearly, the whole lease file could be arranged alphabetically by lessor's last name. The information would simply appear on the tabs in a different order, with the lessor's name first and then any additional identifying codes.

So long as paper files are used, alphabetical codes — or whole names — are easier for people to read. Computers, on the other hand, "read" numbers with ease. Many land support personnel are adding numerical codes to their existing paper files with a view to one day acquiring software compatible with their present filing systems.

CONTENTS OF LEASE FILES

Assuming that a set of lease files is arranged in numerical order with *#200 — Mulligan, Mike — Autauga County, Alabama* on the tab of one paper folder, what goes inside the folder? The oil and gas lease, plus a summary of the most critical information to be pulled

from it. This summary is known as a *lease data sheet.* (See figure G.1. Computerized forms for lease data sheets can also be purchased.) Even if the lease is assigned to a third party, the assignor will keep the lease data sheet, or a copy of it, until the lease expires. In our sample form, the "rentals to be paid by-----" entry will change upon assignment of the lease. The timely payment of delay rentals is so important to the life of a lease, however, that the assignor usually keeps a watch on these payments and may, as we shall see, routinely remind assignees or partners of rental due dates.

Also included in the lease file, along with the lease and the lease data sheet, will be any other instruments or documents pertaining to the individual lease: assignments made after the lease date, the paid draft, title opinions and curative material, rental receipts, well commencement and completion notices, correspondence (usually in chronological order), a plat or map of the acreage, and anything else that the company normally uses — a notice of lease acquisition, for example, or invoices for professional services.

The precise order in which these items are placed in the folder varies from one office to another. How the items are ordered probably matters less than the fact that all files are consistently arranged in a way that new personnel can learn quickly. Finally, the advantages of computerized filing can be seen as lease files grow. Two hundred paper folders are manageable. Two thousand are considerably less so. As the numbers increase, office managers begin to read software advertisements with eager interest.

INDEXES FOR PROSPECT FILES

The files for prospects or areas of interest are often arranged by prospect name and number. A folder tab will show the prospect

Figure G.1. Lease data sheet
(Courtesy of K. Kunkel Resources)

RENTALS TO BE PAID BY _____   RENTAL DATE _____

                                                   LEASE NO. _____

GROSS   NET   RENTAL   NET
ACRES _____   ACRES _____   PER ACRE _____   RENTAL _____

DATE OF LEASE _____   TERM _____   EXPIRATION DATE _____

STATE _____   COUNTY _____   LEASED INTEREST _____

RECORDED: BOOK _____   PAGE _____   PROSPECT _____

LESSOR _____   LESSEE _____

RENTAL PAYMENT DETAIL (NAME AND ADDRESS)

DEPOSITORY

DESCRIPTION:

PARTNER OR CO-OWNER (Name, address, interest, proportionate share of rental)

Remarks:

RENTALS PAID

YEAR	198	198	198	198	198	198	198	199	199	199
DATE										
CHECK NO.										

name—Siamese Twin Creek—and the number assigned to that prospect—#1. The assigned number may be designed to convey more information: #8312, as the prospect is the twelfth taken in 1983. Or the number may be followed by the county or parish name, plus the name of the state in which the prospect is located: Siamese Twin Creek #1, Autauga County, Alabama. In selecting filing codes for prospects, the amount of information to be conveyed, the kinds of cross-referencing planned, and the possibility of switching to an automated system should all be considered.

Companies may prefer to group all the leases within a given prospect together, assigning sequential numbers to the leases and to the wells on each lease. The leases for each prospect can then be filed in numerical order and easily consulted as a group. For instance, if a hypothetical prospect had ten leases on it, they might be numbered from 001 to 010, leaving a third place in the system should the number of leases increase to require it. A glance at the prospect folder tab would tell how many leases had been acquired for the prospect:

Siamese Twin Creek   #1   001-010
(Prospect name)   (Prospect   (Lease
                    number)   numbers)

The wells drilled on each lease could also be numbered. The filing system in which the lease files were arranged would then be behind the general prospect folder, and the well files behind the relevant lease folder.

CONTENTS OF PROSPECT FILES

Prospect files contain correspondence about the area of interest as well as any supplemental agreements like support letters, operating agreements, and unitization agreements or orders. Since prospect files can

quickly become crowded with material, they are often subdivided. Separate files for agreements, for letters, for gas contracts, and so forth can always be created to keep the system orderly.

MANAGEMENT OF DELAY RENTALS

The prompt payment of rentals is very important to a petroleum company, since such payments keep leases alive. Many companies double or triple their reminders to themselves, using a calendar book that shows the rentals coming up month by month, a calendar form like the one in figure G.2, which can be regularly prepared from the calendar book and reviewed by the land department, a schedule of reminder notices to partner companies or companies that hold assigned leases, and so forth. Copies of lease data sheets are sometimes included in the rental calendar book as an added precaution against rental payments being missed.

From decision makers' reviews come rental payment or expiration recommendations that can be noted on the rental calendar form. On the basis of such recommendations, check preparation and receipt processing can go forward, and any special obligations like shut-in royalty payments or special conditions like seasonal limitations on drilling can be noted on the form, in the book, or in both places. When rental receipts (of the kind shown in figure G.3) come back signed by the landowners, they can be set up in a book or file of their own—or put into the appropriate lease files.

As noted, computer software is available to perform all these tasks. In addition, a computer can keep track of one more important set of figures—the total amounts spent on leased acreage. These totals include not only rentals and royalties but also lease bonuses

**Figure G.2. Calendar form for lease rentals
(Courtesy of K. Kunkel Resources)**

RENTAL CALENDAR

COUNTY/STATE	LEASE NO.	DESCRIPTION	EXPIRATION	RENTAL		RECOMMENDATION		
				DUE DATE	AMOUNT	PAY	DROP	RENEW

Figure G.3. Rental receipt form
(Courtesy of K. Kunkel Resources)

RENTAL RECEIPT

_____
NAME OF OWNER OF LEASE

_____
ADDRESS

_____   Date _____

_____

Gentlemen:

    We enclose herewith our check in the amount of _____ payable to yourselves to be deposited to the credit of the following parties:

    The above amount is in payment of delay rentals for the period from _____ to _____ due under that certain oil and gas lease executed _____ in favor of _____ _____, insofar as said lease covers and includes the following described tract of land located in _____ to-wit:

    PLEASE SIGN IN THE SPACE PROVIDED BELOW AND RETURN THE ORIGINAL AND ONE COPY OF THIS RENTAL RECEIPT TO US.

Yours very truly,

Receipt is hereby acknowledged of the above amount and the same has been credited according to your instructions.

Dated _____   _____

                                     _____

                      By _____

LEASE NO. _____   _____Title.

and contract expenses (for instance, for the services of independent professionals like attorneys or landmen). Companies need to know how much each leased acre has cost if they are to pay their taxes and budget for future acquisitions. An acreage/cost report (sometimes included on the lease data sheet) is an important piece of information and can be generated by a number of available computer programs.

APPENDIX H
CALCULATING INTERESTS

A division order lists all the interest owners in a given unit and expresses their net revenue interests as decimal figures. These figures should add up to 100%. They will include:

Royalty owners' revenue interests
Overriding royalty owners'
    revenue interests
Each working interest owner's net
    revenue interest
_____
Total: 100%.

To calculate the net revenue interest of the various kinds of owners, the formulas shown below are commonly used. The examples assume a drilling and spacing unit of 640 acres made up of individually owned and leased tracts.

1. *For a royalty owner:*
  (a) First, calculate the owner's net mineral acres by the formula—
    Net acres = fraction of ownership
          × total acres in the tract.

For example, if John Smith owns a $\frac{1}{8}$ mineral interest in one quarter of the 640-acre unit, he owns a $\frac{1}{8}$ interest in a 160-acre tract. His net mineral acres can be calculated as follows:

$\frac{1}{8}$ × 160 = 20 net mineral acres

If Mr. Smith's ownership were expressed as a percentage instead of a fraction, the formula would look like this:

0.125 × 160 = 20 net mineral acres.

  (b) Second, calculate the owner's net revenue interest in the unit by the formula—
    RI = royalty retained by owner
          × net acres owned
          ÷ total acres in unit.

In Mr. Smith's case, he leases his 20 net acres to the GAS Company while retaining a $\frac{3}{16}$ royalty interest. His net revenue interest will be—

$\frac{3}{16}$ × 20 ÷ 640 = 0.00585937.

(To turn the $\frac{3}{16}$ into a decimal number for easier calculation, consult the table at the end of this appendix.)

2. *For an overriding royalty owner:*
    Calculate the overriding royalty interest by the formula—
    ORRI = overriding royalty
          × net acres subject to override
          ÷ total acres in unit.

For example, if Ms. L. Consultant receives a $\frac{1}{16}$ overriding royalty on the $\frac{7}{8}$ working interest held by the GAS Company in another quarter of the 640-acre unit, her revenue interest will be:

$(\frac{1}{16} × \frac{7}{8})$ × 160
        ÷ 640 = 0.01367187.

3. *For a working interest owner:*
  (a) First, determine how many net acres are subject to each retained royalty interest. For example, the GAS Company has 160 acres subject to a $\frac{3}{16}$ royalty (Mr. Smith's) and another 160 acres subject to a $\frac{1}{8}$ royalty (which belongs to Mr. Jones).
  (b) Next, determine how many net acres are subject to overriding royalties. In this case, the GAS Company has 160 acres subject to Ms. Consultant's $\frac{1}{16}$ overriding royalty. (ORRI = 0.01367187.)

(c) Next, determine the gross working interest on each of the GAS Company's tracts. For example, 160 acres retain a $\frac{3}{16}$ royalty, so the GAS Company is left with a $\frac{13}{16}$ gross working interest in that tract. Its second tract retains a $\frac{1}{8}$ royalty, leaving the company with a $\frac{7}{8}$ gross working interest. Now use the formula—

WI = gross working interest
× net acreage ÷ total unit acreage.

For example,
$\frac{13}{16}$ × 160 ÷ 640 = 0.203125 WI on first tract and
$\frac{7}{8}$ × 160 ÷ 640 = 0.218750 WI on second tract.

(d) Now add the totals from (c) together.
0.203125 WI
0.218750 WI
_____
0.421875 total working interest

(e) Then add all the totals from (b) together. In this case, there is only one overriding royalty interest:
0.01367187.

(f) Finally, subtract the override total from the working interest total:
0.42187500
0.01367187
_____
0.40820313 working interest owner's net revenue interest.

To determine a working interest owner's working interest in the entire 640-acre unit, use the following formula:

WI = total net acres under lease
÷ total unit acres

For example, if the GAS Company has 320 net acres under lease in the 640-acre unit, its working interest in the unit will be:

320 ÷ 640 = 0.5 or 50% WI.

The total working interests of all the companies involved in the unit add up to 100%. In addition to the GAS Company, two other companies may share in the unit of 640 acres.

LITE Company	28%
PETRO Company	22%
GAS Company	50%
	100% total WI

TABLE H.1
Common and Decimal Fractions

	4ths	6ths	7ths	8ths	9ths	12ths	16ths	21sts	22nds	24ths	32nds	
1	.25	.166667	142857	.125	.111111	.083333	.0625	.047619	.045455	.041667	.03125	1
2	.50	.333333	.285714	.25	.222222	.166667	.125	.095238	.090909	.083333	.0625	2
3	.75	.50	.428571	.375	.333333	.25	.1875	.142857	.136364	.125	.09375	3
4	1.00	.666667	.571429	.50	.444444	.333333	.25	.190476	.181818	.166667	.125	4
5		.833333	.714286	.625	.555556	.416667	.3125	.238095	.227273	.208333	.15625	5
6		1.00	.857143	.75	.666667	.50	.375	.285714	.272727	.25	.1875	6
7			1.00	.875	.777776	.583333	.4375	.333333	.318182	.291667	.21875	7
8				1.00	.888889	.666667	.50	.380952	.363636	.333333	.25	8
9					1.00	.75	.5625	.428571	.409091	.375	.28125	9
10						.833333	.625	.47619	.454545	.416667	.3125	10
11						.916667	.6875	.52381	.50	.458333	.34375	11
12						1.00	.75	.571429	.545455	.50	.375	12
13							.8125	.619046	.590909	.541667	.40625	13
14							.875	.666667	.636364	.583333	.4375	14
15							.9375	.714286	.681818	.625	.46875	15
16							1.00	.761905	.727273	.666667	.50	16
17								.809524	.772727	.708333	.53125	17
18								.857143	.818182	.75	.5625	18
19								.904762	.863636	.791667	.59375	19
20								.952381	.909091	.833333	.625	20
21								1.00	.954545	.875	.65625	21
22									1.00	.916667	.6875	22
23										.958333	.71875	23
24										1.00	.75	24
25											.78125	25

TABLE H.1–*Continued*

	35ths	36ths	40ths	48ths	54ths	56ths	64ths	72nds	80ths	84ths	88ths	
1	.028571	.027778	.025	.020833	.018519	.017857	.015625	.013889	.0125	.011905	.011364	1
2	.067143	.055556	.05	.041667	.037037	.035714	.03125	.027778	.025	.02381	.022727	2
3	.085714	.083333	.075	.0625	.055556	.053571	.046875	.041667	.0375	.035714	.034091	3
4	.114286	.111111	.10	.083333	.074074	.071429	.0625	.055556	.05	.047619	.045455	4
5	.142857	.138889	.125	.104167	.092593	.089286	.078125	.069444	.0625	.059524	.056818	5
6	.171429	.166667	.15	.125	.111111	.107143	.09375	.083333	.075	.071429	.068182	6
7	.2	.194444	.175	.145833	.12963	.125	.109375	.097222	.0875	.083333	.079545	7
8	.228571	.222222	.20	.166667	.148148	.142857	.125	.111111	.10	.095238	.090909	8
9	.257143	.125	.225	.1875	.166667	.160714	.140625	.125	.1125	.107143	.102273	9
10	.285714	.277778	.25	.208333	.185185	.178571	.15625	.138889	.125	.119048	.113636	10
11	.314286	.305556	.275	.229167	.203704	.196429	.171875	.152778	.1375	.130952	.125	11
12	.342857	.333333	.30	.25	.222222	.214286	.1875	.166667	.15	.142857	.136364	12
13	.371429	.361111	.325	.270833	.240741	.232143	.203125	.180556	.1625	.154762	.147727	13
14	.4	.388889	.35	.291667	.259259	.25	.21875	.19444	.175	.166667	.159091	14
15	.428571	.416667	.375	.3125	.277778	.267857	.234375	.208333	.1875	.178571	.170455	15
16	.457143	.444444	.40	.333333	.296296	.285714	.25	.222222	.20	.190476	.181818	16
17	.485714	.472222	.425	.354167	.314815	.303571	.265625	.236111	.2125	.202381	.192182	17
18	.514286	.50	.45	.375	.333333	.321429	.28125	.25	.225	.214286	.204545	18
19	.542857	.527778	.475	.395833	.351852	.339286	.296875	.263889	.2375	.22619	.215909	19
20	.571429	.555556	.50	.416667	.37037	.357143	.3125	.277778	.25	.238095	.227273	20
21	.6	.583333	.525	.4375	.388889	.375	.328125	.291667	.2625	.25	.238636	21
22	.628571	.611111	.55	.458333	.407407	.392857	.34375	.305556	.275	.261905	.25	22
23	.657143	.638889	.575	.479167	.425926	.410714	.359375	.319444	.2875	.27381	.261364	23
24	.685714	.666667	.60	.50	.444444	.428571	.375	.333333	.30	.285714	.272727	24
25	.714286	.694444	.625	.520833	.462963	.446489	.390625	.347222	.3125	.297619	.284091	25

TABLE H.1—Continued

	256ths	280ths	288ths	320ths	336ths	352nds	360ths	384ths	448ths	480ths	512ths	
1	.003906	.003571	.003472	.003125	.002976	.002841	.002778	.002604	.002232	.002083	.001953	1
2	.007813	.007143	.006944	.00625	.005952	.005682	.005556	.005208	.004464	.004167	.003906	2
3	.011719	.010714	.010417	.009375	.008929	.008523	.008333	.007812	.006696	.00625	.005859	3
4	.015625	.014286	.013889	.0125	.011905	.011364	.011111	.010417	.008929	.008333	.007813	4
5	.019531	.017857	.017361	.015625	.014881	.014205	.013889	.013021	.011161	.010417	.009766	5
6	.023438	.021429	.020833	.01875	.017857	.017045	.016667	.015625	.013393	.0125	.011719	6
7	.027344	.025	.024306	.021875	.020833	.019886	.019444	.018229	.015625	.014583	.013672	7
8	.03125	.028571	.027778	.025	.02381	.022727	.022222	.020833	.017857	.016667	.015625	8
9	.035156	.032143	.03125	.028125	.026786	.025568	.025	.023437	.020089	.01875	.017578	9
10	.039063	.035714	.034722	.03125	.029762	.028409	.027778	.026042	.022321	.020833	.019531	10
11	.042969	.039286	.038194	.034375	.032738	.03125	.030556	.028646	.024554	.022917	.021484	11
12	.046875	.042857	.041667	.0375	.035714	.034091	.033333	.03125	.026786	.025	.023438	12
13	.050781	.046429	.045139	.040625	.03869	.036932	.036111	.033854	.029018	.027083	.025391	13
14	.054688	.05	.048611	.04375	.041667	.039773	.038889	.036458	.03125	.029167	.027344	14
15	.058594	.053571	.052083	.046875	.044643	.042614	.041667	.039062	.033482	.03125	.029297	15
16	.0625	.057143	.055556	.05	.047619	.045455	.044444	.041667	.035714	.033333	.03125	16
17	.066406	.060714	.059028	.053125	.050595	.048295	.047222	.044271	.037946	.035417	.033203	17
18	.070313	.064286	.0625	.05625	.053571	.051136	.05	.046875	.040179	.0375	.035156	18
19	.074219	.067857	.067857	.059375	.056548	.053977	.052778	.049479	.042411	.039583	.037109	19
20	.078125	.071429	.069444	.0625	.059524	.056818	.055556	.052083	.044643	.041667	.039063	20
21	.082031	.075	.072917	.065625	.0625	.059659	.058333	.054687	.046875	.04375	.041016	21
22	.085938	.078571	.076389	.06875	.065476	.0625	.061111	.057292	.049107	.045833	.042969	22
23	.089844	.082143	.079861	.071875	.068452	.065341	.063889	.059896	.051339	.047917	.044922	23
24	.09375	.085714	.083333	.075	.071429	.068182	.066667	.0625	.053571	.05	.046875	24
25	.097656	.089286	.086806	.078125	.074405	.071023	.069444	.065104	.055804	.052083	.048828	25

TABLE H.1—*Continued*

No.	1056ths	1024ths	960ths	896ths	864ths	800ths	768ths	676ths	640ths	600ths	576ths	No.
1	.000947	.000977	.001042	.001116	.001157	.00125	.001302	.001479	.001563	.001667	.001736	1
2	.001894	.001953	.002083	.002232	.002315	.0025	.002604	.002959	.003125	.003333	.003472	2
3	.002841	.00293	.003125	.003348	.003472	.00375	.003906	.004438	.004688	.005	.005208	3
4	.003788	.003906	.004167	.004464	.00463	.005	.005208	.005917	.00625	.006667	.006944	4
5	.004735	.004883	.005208	.00558	.005787	.00625	.00651	.007396	.007813	.008333	.008681	5
6	.005682	.005859	.00625	.006696	.006944	.0075	.007812	.008876	.009375	.01	.010417	6
7	.006629	.006836	.007292	.007812	.008102	.00875	.009115	.010355	.010938	.011667	.012153	7
8	.007576	.007813	.008333	.008929	.009259	.01	.010417	.011834	.0125	.013333	.013889	8
9	.008523	.008789	.009375	.010045	.010417	.01125	.011719	.013314	.014063	.015	.015625	9
10	.00947	.009766	.010417	.011161	.011574	.0125	.013021	.014793	.015625	.016667	.017361	10
11	.010417	.010742	.011458	.012277	.012731	.01375	.014323	.016272	.017188	.018333	.019097	11
12	.011364	.011719	.0125	.013393	.013889	.015	.015625	.017751	.01875	.02	.020833	12
13	.012311	.012695	.013542	.014509	.015046	.01625	.016927	.019231	.020313	.021667	.022569	13
14	.013258	.013672	.014583	.015625	.016204	.0175	.018229	.02071	.021875	.023333	.024306	14
15	.014205	.014648	.015625	.016741	.017361	.01875	.019531	.022189	.023438	.025	.026042	15
16	.015152	.015625	.016667	.017857	.018519	.02	.020833	.023669	.025	.026667	.027778	16
17	.016098	.016602	.017708	.018973	.019676	.02125	.022135	.025148	.026563	.028333	.029514	17
18	.017045	.017578	.01875	.020089	.020833	.0225	.023437	.026627	.028125	.03	.03125	18
19	.017992	.018555	.019792	.021205	.021991	.02375	.02474	.028107	.029688	.031667	.032986	19
20	.018939	.019531	.020833	.022321	.023148	.025	.026042	.029586	.03125	.033333	.034722	20
21	.019886	.020508	.021875	.023437	.024306	.02625	.027344	.031065	.032813	.035	.036458	21
22	.020833	.021484	.022917	.024554	.025463	.0275	.028646	.032544	.034375	.036667	.038194	22
23	.02178	.022461	.023958	.02567	.02662	.02875	.029948	.034024	.035938	.038333	.039931	23
24	.022727	.023438	.025	.026786	.027778	.03	.03125	.035503	.0375	.04	.041667	24
25	.023674	.024414	.026042	.027902	.028935	.03125	.032552	.036982	.039063	.041667	.043403	25

	1120ths	1152nds	1200ths	1280ths	1536ths	1680ths	1728ths	1920ths	2048ths	2304ths	2560ths
1	.000893	.000868	.000833	.000781	.000651	.000595	.000579	.000521	.000488	.000434	.000391
2	.001786	.001736	.001667	.001563	.001302	.00119	.001157	.001042	.000977	.000868	.000781
3	.002679	.002604	.0025	.002344	.001953	.001786	.001736	.001562	.001465	.001302	.001172
4	.003571	.003472	.003333	.003125	.002604	.002381	.002315	.002083	.001953	.001736	.001563
5	.004464	.00434	.004167	.003906	.003255	.002976	.002894	.002604	.002441	.00217	.001953
6	.005357	.005208	.005	.004688	.003906	.003571	.003472	.003125	.00293	.002604	.002344
7	.00625	.006076	.005833	.005469	.004557	.004167	.004051	.003646	.003418	.003038	.002734
8	.007143	.006944	.006667	.00625	.005208	.004762	.00463	.004167	.003906	.003472	.003125
9	.008036	.007812	.0075	.007031	.005859	.005357	.005208	.004687	.004395	.003906	.003516
10	.008929	.008681	.008333	.007813	.00651	.005952	.005787	.005208	.004883	.00434	.003906
11	.009821	.009549	.009167	.008594	.007161	.006548	.006366	.005729	.005371	.004774	.004297
12	.010714	.010417	.01	.009375	.007812	.007143	.006944	.00625	.005859	.005208	.004608
13	.011607	.011285	.010833	.010156	.008464	.007738	.007523	.006771	.006348	.005642	.005078
14	.0125	.012153	.011667	.010938	.009115	.008333	.008102	.007292	.006836	.006076	.005469
15	.013393	.013021	.0125	.011719	.009766	.008929	.008681	.007812	.007324	.00651	.005859
16	.014286	.013889	.013333	.0125	.010417	.009524	.009259	.008333	.007813	.006944	.00625
17	.015179	.014757	.014167	.013281	.011068	.010119	.009838	.008854	.008301	.007378	.006641
18	.016071	.015625	.015	.014063	.011719	.010714	.010417	.009375	.008789	.007812	.007031
19	.016964	.016493	.015833	.014844	.01237	.011310	.010995	.009896	.009277	.008247	.007422
20	.017857	.017361	.016667	.015625	.013021	.011905	.011574	.010417	.009766	.008681	.007813
21	.01875	.018229	.0175	.016406	.013672	.0125	.012153	.010937	.010254	.009115	.008203
22	.019643	.019097	.018333	.017188	.014323	.013095	.012731	.011458	.010742	.009549	.008594
23	.020536	.019965	.019167	.017969	.014974	.01369	.01331	.011979	.01123	.009983	.008984
24	.021429	.020833	.02	.01875	.015625	.014286	.013889	.0125	.011719	.010417	.009375
25	.022321	.021701	.020833	.019531	.016276	.014881	.014468	.013021	.012207	.010851	.009766

TABLE H.1 – Continued

	2592nds	2688ths	2880ths	3136ths	3200ths	3456ths	3584ths	3840ths	3888ths	4000ths	4224ths	
1	.000386	.000372	.000347	.000319	.000313	.000289	.000279	.00026	.000257	.00025	.000237	1
2	.000772	.000744	.000694	.000638	.000625	.000579	.000558	.00052	.000514	.0005	.000473	2
3	.001157	.001116	.001042	.000957	.000938	.000868	.000837	.000781	.000772	.00075	.00071	3
4	.001543	.001488	.001389	.001276	.00125	.001157	.001116	.001042	.001029	.001	.000947	4
5	.001929	.00186	.001736	.001594	.001563	.001447	.001395	.001302	.001286	.00125	.001184	4
6	.002315	.002232	.002083	.001913	.001875	.001736	.001674	.001563	.001543	.0015	.00142	6
7	.002701	.002604	.002431	.002232	.002188	.002025	.001953	.001823	.0018	.00175	.001657	7
8	.003086	.002976	.002778	.002551	.0025	.002315	.002232	.002083	.002058	.002	.001894	8
9	.003472	.003348	.003125	.00287	.002813	.002604	.002511	.002344	.002315	.00225	.002131	9
10	.003858	.00372	.003472	.003189	.003125	.002894	.00279	.002604	.002572	.0025	.002367	10
11	.004244	.004092	.003819	.003508	.003438	.003183	.003069	.002865	.002829	.00275	.002604	11
12	.00463	.004464	.004167	.003827	.00375	.003472	.003348	.003125	.003086	.003	.002841	12
13	.005015	.004836	.004514	.004146	.004063	.003762	.003627	.003385	.003344	.00325	.003078	13
14	.005401	.005208	.004861	.004464	.004375	.004051	.003906	.003646	.003601	.0035	.003314	14
15	.005787	.00558	.005208	.004783	.004688	.00434	.004185	.003906	.003858	.00375	.003551	15
16	.006173	.005952	.005556	.005102	.005	.00463	.004464	.004167	.004115	.004	.003788	16
17	.006559	.006324	.005903	.005421	.005313	.004919	.004743	.004427	.004372	.00425	.004025	17
18	.006944	.006696	.00625	.00574	.005625	.005208	.005022	.004688	.00468	.0045	.004261	18
19	.00733	.007068	.006597	.006059	.005938	.005498	.005301	.004948	.004887	.00475	.004498	19
20	.007716	.00744	.006944	.006378	.00625	.005787	.00558	.005208	.005144	.005	.004735	20
21	.008102	.007813	.007292	.006696	.006563	.006076	.005859	.005469	.005401	.00525	.004972	21
22	.008488	.008185	.007639	.007015	.006875	.006366	.006138	.005729	.005658	.0055	.005208	22
23	.008873	.008557	.007986	.007334	.007188	.006655	.006417	.00599	.005916	.00575	.005445	23
24	.009259	.008929	.008333	.007653	.0075	.006944	.006696	.00625	.006173	.006	.005682	24
25	.009645	.009301	.008681	.007972	.007813	.007234	.006975	.00651	.00643	.00625	.005919	25

TABLE H.1—_Continued_

	9600ths	12960ths	17280ths	18432nds	24576ths	25600ths	46080ths	49152nds	53760ths	57600ths	90720ths	
1	.000104	.000077	.000058	.000054	.000041	.000039	.000022	.00002	.00019	.000017	.000011	1
2	.000308	.000154	.000116	.000109	.000081	.000078	.000043	.000041	.000037	.000035	.000022	2
3	.000313	.000231	.000174	.000163	.000122	.000117	.000065	.000061	.0056	.000052	.000033	3
4	.000417	.000309	.000231	.000217	.000163	.000156	.000087	.000081	.000074	.000069	.000044	4
5	.000521	.000386	.000289	.000271	.000203	.000195	.000109	.000102	.000093	.000087	.000055	5
6	.000625	.000463	.000347	.000326	.000244	.000234	.00013	.000122	.000112	.000104	.000066	6
7	.000729	.00054	.000405	.00038	.000285	.000273	.000152	.000142	.00013	.000122	.000077	7
8	.000833	.000617	.000463	.000434	.000326	.000313	.000174	.000163	.000149	.000139	.000088	8
9	.000938	.00-694	.000521	.000488	.000366	.000352	.000195	.000183	.000167	.000156	.000099	9
10	.001042	.000772	.000579	.000543	.000407	.000391	.000217	.000203	.000186	.000174	.0011	10
11	.001146	.000849	.000637	.000597	.000448	.00043	.000239	.000224	.000205	.000191	.000121	11
12	.00125	.000926	.000694	.000651	.000488	.000469	.00026	.000244	.000223	.000208	.000132	12
13	.001354	.001003	.000753	.000705	.000529	.000508	.000282	.000264	.000242	.000226	.000143	13
14	.001458	.00108	.00081	.00076	.00057	.000547	.000304	.000285	.0026	.000243	.000154	14
15	.001562	.001157	.000868	.000814	.00051	.000586	.000326	.000305	.000279	.00026	.000165	15
16	.001667	.001235	.000926	.000868	.000651	.000625	.000347	.000326	.000298	.000278	.000176	16
17	.001771	.001312	.000984	.000922	.000692	.000664	.000369	.000346	.000316	.000295	.000187	17
18	.001875	.001389	.001042	.000977	.000732	.000703	.000391	.000366	.000335	.000313	.000198	18
19	.001979	.001400	.0011	.001031	.000773	.000742	.000412	.000387	.000353	.00033	.000209	19
20	.002083	.001543	.001157	.001085	.000814	.000781	.000434	.000407	.000372	.000347	.00022	20
21	.002188	.00162	.001215	.001139	.000854	.00082	.000456	.000427	.000391	.000365	.000231	21
22	.002292	.001698	.001273	.001194	.000895	.00859	.000477	.000448	.000409	.000382	.000243	22
23	.002396	.001775	.001331	.001248	.000936	.000898	.000499	.000468	.000438	.000399	.000254	23
24	.0025	.001862	.001389	.001302	.000977	.000938	.000521	.000488	.000446	.000417	.000265	24
25	.002604	.001929	.001447	.001356	.01017	.000977	.000543	.000509	.000465	.000434	.000276	25

GLOSSARY

A

abandon *v:* to cease producing oil and gas from a well when it becomes unprofitable. Any well may be abandoned after it has proven nonproductive. Several steps are involved in abandoning a well: part of the casing may be removed and salvaged; one or more cement plugs are placed in the borehole to prevent migration of fluids between the different formations penetrated by the borehole; and the well is abandoned. In most oil-producing states, it is necessary to secure permission from official agencies before a well may be abandoned.

absolute ownership *n:* the theory that minerals such as oil and gas are fully owned in place before they are extracted and reduced to possession. Despite this theory, title to oil and gas may be lost by legitimate drainage and by the rule of capture. Also called ownership in place.

abstract-based title opinion *n:* a title opinion based upon a complete abstract of title, plus other relevant documents. Compare *stand-up title opinion.*

abstract company *n:* a private company in the business of preparing abstracts of title and performing related services. Also called abstract plant.

abstract of title *n:* a collection of all of the recorded instruments affecting title to a tract of land. Compare *base abstract.*

abstract plant *n:* See *abstract company.*

acknowledgment *n:* a declaration or an avowal of any act or fact made by a signatory party to a document to a notary public or other public official authorized to take an acknowledgment to give it legal effect.

acquired land *n:* land owned by the United States, acquired by deed or otherwise. Such land has never been in the public domain or has been in the public domain at one time and been disposed of, later being reacquired by purchase, condemnation, or donation.

acreage contribution *n:* acreage owned in the vicinity of a test being drilled by another party and contributed to the driller of the well in return for information obtained from its drilling. The assignment is usually made on completion of the well.

administrator *n:* person appointed by the court to administer the estate of someone who dies without leaving a will, that is, who dies intestate.

adverse possession *n:* a method of asserting and gaining title to property against other claimants, including the record owner. The claim through adverse possession must include certain acts (as required by statute) over an uninterrupted interval of time. It must also be, in most states, "open" and "notorious" and "hostile."

AFE *abbr:* authority for expenditure.

affiant *n:* the person who makes a sworn statement.

affidavit *n:* a written affirmation of fact made and sworn to before a notary public or other authorized official. The official signs a certificate called a jurat stating that the affidavit was signed and sworn to before him.

allotted land *n:* Indian land designated for use by a specific individual, although the title is still held by the United States. In the case of the Five Civilized Tribes, the title is held by the allottee, but leasing, operations, and so forth are subject to the control of the United States.

AMI *abbr:* area of mutual interest.

anniversary date *n:* the date, usually 1 year from the effective date of the lease, by which rentals must be paid to maintain the lease in effect in the absence of drilling or production.

APO *abbr:* after payout. Commonly used in land departments.

area of mutual interest *n:* an area usually outlined on a plat attached to a farmout agreement or described in an exhibit, allowing both parties the first right of refusal on leases acquired by either party after the agreement is executed.

arpent *n:* a French unit of measurement, equal to 191.833 feet.

assignment *n:* a transfer of rights and interests in real or personal property or rights under a contract — for example, the transfer of an oil and gas lease from the original lessee to another party.

assignment clause *n:* a clause in any instrument that allows either party to the instrument to assign all or part of his interest to others.

attest *v:* to verify or witness, by a designated company official, the signature of the signing company officer and the affixing of the official company or corporation seal. The title of the company official executing the instrument and the title of the company official attesting it should appear under the signatures.

authority for expenditure *n:* an estimate of costs prepared by a lease operator and sent to nonoperators for their approval before work is undertaken. Normally used in connection with well drilling operations.

B

back-in *n:* an option right reserved by the granting company of a farmout to convert an overriding royalty to a working interest once the conditions for such back-in have been met. Compare *election at casing point.*

base abstract *n:* an abstract of title that contains full and complete copies of all recorded instruments from the sovereignty of the soil to the date the same is completed as set forth in the abstractor's certificate.

bequeath *v:* to make a gift of personal property by means of a will. Compare *devise.*

bonus consideration *n:* a cash payment by the lessee for the execution of an oil and gas lease by the mineral owner, expressed as dollars per acre. Occasionally, an oil payment or overriding royalty may be reserved as a bonus by a lessor, this being in addition to regular royalty.

bottomhole letter *n:* a contract providing for the payment of money or other considerations upon the completion of a well to a specified depth, regardless of whether the well is a producer of oil or gas or is a dry hole.

BPO *abbr:* before payout. Commonly used in land departments.

C

carried interest *n:* an interest in oil and gas properties that belongs, for example, to a working interest owner or unleased landowner who agrees to a joint operation without being willing to pay a share of the costs of the operation. An interest may be carried until the well pays out, at which point it may stop or may continue for the life of production.

carved-out interest *n:* an interest in oil and gas created out of a greater interest and assigned by the owner. Examples are the grant of an overriding royalty interest out of a working interest and the grant of an oil payment out of a working interest.

case law *n:* See *common law.*

casing point *n:* 1. the depth in a well at which casing is set, generally the depth at which the casing shoe rests. 2. the objective depth in a drilling contract, either a specified depth or the depth at which a specific zone is penetrated. When the depth is reached, the operator makes a decision with respect to running and setting a production string of casing. Under some farmout and letter agreements some owners are carried to casing point.

certified copy *n:* a copy made from records in a recorder's or county clerk's office, certified to by the recorder or county clerk as being the exact copy of the paper on file or of record.

cessation of production clause *n:* in an oil and gas lease, a clause that provides the lessee with the right to begin new operations within a stated time period should production cease.

chain of title *n:* recorded transfers (links) in title from patent to present.

checkerboard farmout *n:* an agreement for the acquisition of mineral rights (i.e., oil and gas leases) in a checkerboard pattern of cornering alternate tracts, usually beginning, in the case of farmouts, with the drill site tract.

civil law *n:* See *statute law.*

cloud on a title *n:* a claim or encumbrance that, if upheld by a court, would impair the owner's title to the property.

commercial quantity *n:* an amount of oil and gas production large enough to enable the operator to realize a profit, however small. To keep a lease in force, production must be in quantities sufficient to yield a return in excess of operating costs, even though drilling and equipment costs may never be recovered.

common law *n:* a system of law based on court decisions, or judicial precedent, rather than on legislated statutes or executive decrees. Common law began in England and was later used in English colonies. It is still applied in most of the United States; Louisiana operates under the Napoleonic code. Also called case law.

community property *n:* property held jointly by husband and wife, usually property acquired after marriage.

competitive leasing *n:* a procedure, based on competitive bidding, used to acquire oil and gas leases to federal lands within areas designated by U.S.G.S. as known geologic structures (KGS) or on offshore federal lands.

completed well *n:* a well on which drilling and completion operations have been finished. The well may be completed as a dry hole, a well capable of producing oil or gas, a disposal well for salt water, or another type of special-purpose well.

consideration *n:* a promise or an act of legal value bargained for and received in return for a promise; an essential element of a contract. In oil and gas leases, consideration may be payment in money or in kind; it must often be "serious" consideration. Compare *bonus consideration.*

construction *n:* in contract law, the interpretation given by a court of competent jurisdiction — for example, an interpretation of a possibly ambiguous instrument or statute.

continuous development clause *n:* in an oil and gas lease, a clause designed to keep drilling operations going steadily after the primary term has expired. In some clauses, designated intervals between completion of one well and commencement of the drilling of another may require the operator to develop the leased land up to its allowable density.

contract *n:* a written agreement that can be enforced by law, listing the terms under which the acts required are to be performed. A drilling contract covers such factors as the cost of drilling the well (whether by foot or by day), the distribution of expenses between operator and contractor, and the type of equipment to be used.

convey *v:* to transfer title to property from one party to another, usually by means of a written instrument.

co-owners *n:* See *cotenants.*

correlative rights *n pl:* rights afforded the owner of each property in a pool to produce without waste his just and equitable share of the oil and gas in such pool.

cotenants *n:* persons who hold possessory interests, from title or a lease, in the same piece of land. Also called co-owners or tenants in common.

coverall clause *n:* See *Mother Hubbard clause.*

cure a title *v:* to remedy defects and omissions that, in the opinion of the examining attorney, could make the present owner's claim to property questionable. To cure a title, a title examiner may require additional facts not evident in the material examined. The curative material is usually obtained in recordable form.

curtesy rights *n:* the rights of a husband to a life interest in all his wife's inheritable lands. These rights come into effect upon the death of the wife, provided that the couple have had children capable of inheriting. Effective in some states.

D

damage clause *n:* in an oil and gas lease, the clause specifying that the lessee will be liable to the surface owner for damage to growing crops and other listed items.

deed of trust *n:* an instrument used to transfer legal title to property as security for the repayment of a loan or the fulfillment of some other obligation. Compare *mortgage.*

delay rental *n:* a sum of money payable to the lessor by the lessee for the privilege of deferring the commencement of drilling operations and keeping the lease valid. May be made monthly, quarterly, or annually.

descent and distribution laws *n:* the laws in a state that determine the disposition of property among heirs in the absence of a will.

depletion allowance *n:* a reduction in U.S. taxes for owners of an economic interest in minerals in place to compensate for the exhaustion of an irreplaceable capital asset. This economic interest includes mineral interest, working interest in a lease, royalty, overriding royalty, production payment interest, and net profits interest.

determinable fee *n:* an interest in property that will end at the happening or nonhappening of a particular event. In some states, an oil and gas lease is considered a determinable fee in real estate.

development well *n:* a well drilled in proven territory in a field to complete a pattern of production.

devise *v:* to make a gift of real property (for example, land) by means of a will. Compare *bequeath.*

disclaimer *n:* complete denial and renunciation of any claim to title to property. Surface tenants, for example, often sign disclaimers (in the form of tenant consent agreements) relating to the mineral estate and title of land leased for oil and gas exploration.

divided interest *n:* a fractional interest in minerals that, when conveyed, gives the new owner a 100 percent interest in the designated fraction of the described tract. For example a divided interest in an 80-acre tract results in a 100 percent interest in 20 specific, describable acres out of that tract. Compare *undivided interest.*

division order *n:* a contract of sale of oil or gas to a purchaser who is directed to pay for the oil or gas products according to the proportions set out in the division order. The purchaser may require execution thereof by all owners of interest in the property.

division order opinion *n:* a statement of opinion by a title examiner on the state of the title to land, mineral, royalty, or working interests in a producing tract of land. This opinion, usually in letter form, forms the basis of payment to all affected owners and must recite all the owners' interests. Compare *title opinion, drill site opinion.*

dower property *n:* in some states, that part of an estate to which a wife is entitled (for her lifetime) upon the death of her husband.

draft *n:* a written order drawn on a solvent bank that authorizes payment of a specified sum of money for a specific purpose to a named person. A draft may or may not be negotiable depending upon how it is drawn up. Also called bank draft.

drilling and delay rental clause *n:* in an oil and gas lease, the clause that allows the lease to expire after a given period of time (often 1 year from the date of the lease) unless drilling begins or delay rental is paid. Also called "unless" clause.

drilling and spacing unit *n:* a unit of the size required or permitted by statutory law or by regulations of a state conservation body for drilling an oil or gas well. Also called a proration unit.

drilling block *n:* a lease or a number of leases of adjoining tracts of land that constitute a unit of acreage sufficient to justify the expense of drilling a wildcat.

drill site opinion *n:* the written statement of opinion by a title examiner on the status of the title to a drill site, usually in letter form. Compare *title opinion, division order opinion.*

dry hole *n:* any well that does not produce oil or gas in commercial quantities. A dry hole may flow water, gas, or even oil, but not in amounts large enough to justify production.

dry hole clause *n:* in an oil and gas lease, a clause that allows the operator to keep the lease if he drills a dry hole. He has a specified period of time in which to drill a subsequent well or begin paying delay rentals again.

dry hole letter *n:* a form of support agreement in which the contributing company agrees to pay so much per foot drilled by another company in return for information gained from the drilling. The contribution is paid only if the well is a dry hole in all formations encountered in drilling.

E

election at casing point *n:* a decision taken to exercise or not to exercise an option to participate in the completion attempt on a well, including the costs of running completion production casing and all related completion costs. The decision is made when the operator is ready to run casing and complete the well and so ratifies the party owning the election.

encumbrance *n:* a claim or charge upon property, for example, a mortgage or lien for unpaid taxes.

equity *n:* those maxims and general principles that developed in England to moderate the common law and allow remedy for injury. In the broadest sense, justice.

escheat *n:* the reversion of property to the state in the event that the owner thereof dies without leaving a will and has no heirs to whom the property may pass by lawful descent. Also called unclaimed property statute.

estate *n:* the nature and extent of a person's ownership or right or interest in land or other property.

estoppel *n:* a bar, a prevention. Estoppel occurs when a person is prevented, by the proceedings of some duly constituted authority or by his own action, from denying the truth of a fact or from doing something contrary to his own previous assertion or act.

et al *abbr:* and others (Lat. *et alii*). Commonly used in oil and gas leases.

et ux *abbr:* and wife (Lat. *et uxor*). Commonly used in oil and gas leases.

et vir *abbr:* and husband (Lat. *et vir,* and man). Commonly used in oil and gas leases.

examination of title *n:* a thorough inspection of the recorded documents pertaining to a tract's history of ownership. Title examinations are performed by attorneys who look for gaps in the chain of title, ambiguities, or any doubtful points that would cast a cloud on the present owner's claim to the property. The examiner will then set forth in a written opinion the facts and instruments that, in his judgment, are necessary to make the title merchantable or legally defensible.

execution *n:* the completion of a legal instrument by the required actions—for example, by signing and delivering the instrument. Execution includes the actual delivery of the signed document to the named grantee, lessee, or assignee.

executive rights *n:* in regard to mineral rights and interests, the right to execute oil and gas leases. Executive rights may not include the right to bonus or rentals.

executor *n:* the person named in a will to carry out its provisions.

exhibit *n:* See *rider.*

exploration well *n:* a well drilled either in search of a new, as yet undiscovered, pool of oil or gas (a wildcat well) or to greatly extend the limits of a known pool. It involves a relatively high degree of risk. Exploratory wells may be classified as (1) wildcat, drilled in an unproven area; (2) field extension or step-out, drilled in an unproven area to extend the proved limits of a field; or (3) deep test, drilled within a field area but to unproven deeper zones.

F

farm-in *n:* an agreement identical to a farmout, with the operator as the third party. The operator takes the farm-in. See *farmout.*

farm in *v:* to accept, as an operator, a farmout. See *farmout.*

farmout *n:* an agreement whereby the owner of a lease who does not wish to drill at the time agrees to assign the leasehold interest, or some part of it, to a third party who does wish to drill, conditional upon the third party's drilling a well within the expiration date of the primary term of the lease. The assignment may include the entire interest together with dry hole money, or partial interest or entire interest with or without an override. If an override is retained, the owner of the lease may retain an option to convert such overriding royalty retained to an agreed-upon working interest. A farmout is distinguished from a joint operating agreement by the fact that the party farming out does not incur any of the drilling costs. The primary characteristic of a farmout is the obligation of the third party to drill one or more wells on the farmout acreage as a condition prerequisite to completion of the transfer of title to such third party.

farm out *v:* for a lessee, to agree to assign a leasehold interest to a third party, subject to stipulated conditions. See *farmout.*

federal lease *n:* an oil and gas lease on federal land issued under the Mineral Leasing Act. Federal leases usually provide step-scale or sliding-scale royalty; a flat discovery royalty of one-eighth may also be specified.

fee *n:* an estate in real property, completely owned, which the owner can sell or devise to his heirs. Often used as a term for distinguishing private lands (fee lands) from federal or state lands.

fee in surface *n:* an estate in the surface of land, created when the owner separates or severs his mineral interests from the surface of the land.

fee simple *n:* a freehold estate on which there are no restrictions or limitations as to the heirs who may inherit.

fee simple absolute *n:* an estate limited absolutely to a person, his heirs and assigns forever, without limitation or condition.

fee tail *n:* a freehold estate in which there is a fixed line of inheritable succession limited to the issue of the body of the grantee or devisee and in which the regular and general succession of heirs at law is cut off.

fee tail female *n:* an estate limited by a deed or will that conveys ownership to a person and the female heirs of his or her body. Male heirs are not capable of inheriting the estate.

fee tail male *n:* an estate limited by a deed or will that conveys ownership to a person and the male heirs of his or her body only. Female heirs are not capable of inheriting the estate.

fiduciary *n:* a person who serves, with or without bond, to act for the benefit of another in all matters connected with a specified undertaking. Fiduciary obligations exist, for example, between trustees and the beneficiaries of the trust.

file for record *v:* to send an instrument to the county clerk for recording.

forced pooling *n:* pooling of leased tracts undertaken without the willing cooperation of all the parties. Forced pooling may occur as the result of an order from a state regulatory agency, an order sought by one or more of the parties affected.

forced unitization *n:* See *statutory unitization.*

force majeure clause *n:* in an oil and gas lease, the clause that usually contains a statement that the lease is subject to state and federal laws. It also excuses the lessee from timely performance of his obligations should certain events beyond the lessee's power to control occur. *Force majeure* means a force or event that cannot be anticipated or controlled.

four-corner rule *n:* a rule of interpretation holding that an instrument such as an oil and gas lease must be interpreted from within the four corners of the instrument. Interpretation is made without any aid from knowledge of the circumstances under which the instrument came into being; the instrument is construed as a whole, without reference to any one part more than another.

Freestone rider *n:* See *Pugh clause.*

G

good title *n:* See *merchantable title.*

grantee *n:* a person to whom property is conveyed. Compare *grantor.*

granting clause *n:* clause in an oil and gas lease that specifies the rights and interests granted by the lessor to the lessee. Such rights usually involve searching and drilling for, then producing oil and gas.

grantor *n:* a person who conveys property. Compare *grantee.*

guardian *n:* person appointed by a court of competent jurisdiction for the purpose of managing property and rights for another person who is considered incapable of managing for himself—for example, a minor child, an insane person, or a mental incompetent.

H

habendum clause *n:* in an oil and gas lease, the clause that fixes the duration of the lessee's interest in both a primary and a secondary term. Also called term clause.

HBP *abbr:* held by production. Commonly used in land departments.

hectare *n:* an internationally used unit of measurement equal to 2.47 acres.

hereditaments *n:* whatever can be inherited. Of the two kinds of hereditaments, corporeal and incorporeal, the first usually includes tangible things and the second includes rights connected with land. Land itself would be a corporeal hereditament, and the right to rent would be an incorporeal hereditament.

homestead property *n:* property such as land, house, outbuildings, and tools, which cannot be seized to pay general debts.

I

implied covenant *n:* an obligation or benefit not specified in an oil and gas lease but held by the courts to be implicit in such lease. For example, one implied convenant is an obligation on the part of the lessee to drill an initial well.

incompetent *n:* a person judged by the court to be incapable of managing his own affairs by reason of insanity, imbecility, or feeblemindedness (referred to as *non compos mentis*).

independent *n:* a nonintegrated oil company or individual whose operations are in the field of petroleum production, excluding transportation, refining, and marketing.

interest *n:* pertaining to real estate, a right or a claim to property.

intestate *adj:* without leaving a will. A person may be said to have died intestate.

J

joint operating agreement *n:* a contract by which two or more co-owners of the operating rights in a tract of land join together to share the costs of exploration and possible development.

joint tenants *n pl:* two or more persons who are granted lands or tenements to hold in fee simple, fee tail, for life, for years, or at will, whose joint title is created by one and the same deed or will. The survivor receives the whole on the death of the other.

joint venture *n:* a business undertaking, usually of more limited scope and length than a partnership, in which control, profits, losses, and liability are all shared.

judicial determination *n:* See *judicial transfer*.

judicial transfer *n:* transfer by the court of an interest or of interests in real property. When ownership of land is concerned, a judicial transfer usually involves the appointment of a receiver by the court. The receiver can then act, for example, to execute an oil and gas lease on the property. The situation may arise when the landowner is missing or unknown, after foreclosures, or after tax sales. Also called judicial determination.

L

landman *n:* a person in the petroleum industry who negotiates with landowners for oil and gas leases, options, minerals, and royalties and with producers for joint operations relative to production in a field; also called a leaseman.

lease *n:* 1. a legal document executed between a landowner, as lessor, and a company or individual, as lessee, that grants the right to exploit the premises for minerals or other products; the instrument that creates a leasehold or working interest in minerals. 2. the area where production wells, stock tanks, separators, LACT units, and other production equipment are located.

lease bonus *n:* usually the cash consideration that is paid by the lessee for the execution of an oil and gas lease by a landowner. It is usually based on a per acre basis.

lease broker *n:* an independent landman who may work with several operators or companies.

leasehold *n:* the estate in real property created by a lease. A leasehold is held by a lessee, usually for a fixed period of time.

leasehold interest *n:* all or a fractional part of the interest of a lessee (grantee) under an oil and gas lease. Such interest includes the right on the part of the lessee to search for, drill, and produce oil and gas from a lease tract subject to royalty payments. The term usually refers to the remaining leasehold or working interest exclusive of any nonoperating interests created and assigned therefrom, such as overriding royalty interests and production payments. Also called working interest, operating interest.

lease purchase agreement *n:* an agreement between companies for the purchase by one company of a block of the other's leases. Also used between lease brokers and companies.

legal effect clause *n:* in an oil and gas lease, the clause that binds the parties and declares the lease effective for the lessor when he signs the instrument.

lessee *n:* the recipient of a lease (such as an oil and gas lease).

lessor *n:* the conveyer of a lease (such as an oil and gas lease).

life tenant *n:* someone who holds the exclusive right to possess and use property during his lifetime but who cannot devise or bequeath the property. Compare *remainderman*.

lis pendens *n:* notice that a suit has been filed in a court of law and that the property owned by the defendant may be liable to judgment.

location *n:* well site.

location damages *n pl:* compensation paid to the surface owner for actual and potential damage to the surface and crops in the drilling and operation of a well.

M

marketable title *n:* See *merchantable title*.

merchantable title *n:* a title, free from material defects or grave doubts and reasonably free from litigation, which can be sold or successfully defended in court; such a title as a court of equity will compel the vendee to accept as sufficient. Also called marketable title or good title.

metes and bounds *n pl:* a method of describing a piece of land that measures the boundaries by beginning at a well-marked reference point and following the boundaries of the land all the way around to the beginning point again. The description relies heavily on reference to natural or artificial but permanent objects (such as roads and streams).

mineral acre *n:* the full mineral interest and rights in 1 acre of land.

mineral deed *n:* the legal instrument that conveys minerals in place together with the rights to search for and produce minerals.

mineral estate *n:* rights and interests in the minerals found on or beneath the surface of land, created when the owner severs or separates his interests in the property.

mineral owner *n:* owner of the rights and interests in a mineral estate (where interests in a landed estate have been severed). Compare *surface owner*.

minimum royalty *n:* a royalty payment amount to be made regardless of the rate of production. The excess of such payments over regular royalty is chargeable against future production, if any, accruing to the royalty interest.

mining partnership *n:* a form of joint venture very similar to an oil and gas joint operating agreement. Profits, losses, operations, and ownership are all shared, and the partners are jointly as well as severally (separately) liable.

mortgage *n:* an estate created by a conveyance absolute in its form, but intended to secure the performance of some act such as the payment of money and to become void if the act is performed in agreement with the terms. Compare *deed of trust.*

Mother Hubbard clause *n:* a clause in an oil and gas lease that includes in the lease lands which may be owned by the lessor and inadvertently omitted from the legal description. These are usually oddly shaped bits owned by the lessor and adjoining the described tract. Also called coverall clause.

N

net revenue interest *n:* the portion of oil and gas production money out of which operating and development costs are paid (i.e., the portion remaining after deduction of royalty interests).

net working interest *n:* the share of production remaining to the working interest owners after all royalties, overriding royalties, production payments, and other reservations or assignments have been deducted.

nonabsolute ownership *n:* the legal view of minerals like oil and gas that says that such minerals cannot be owned in place. The landowner, as in Louisiana, owns the surface of his land along with the rights to explore, drill, and reduce subsurface minerals to possession. Also called nonownership, nonownership in place.

nonconsent/consent *n:* a provision in a joint operating agreement that allows parties who consent to later operations to penalize parties who do not consent. The penalty can be arranged in various ways but, to be effective, the penalty assumes the productiveness of the proposed operation.

nonownership *n:* See *nonabsolute ownership.*

nonownership in place *n:* See *nonabsolute ownership.*

nonparticipating royalty owner *n:* a person who owns a severed portion of a royalty interest but who does not execute leases, participate in bonuses or rentals, or have rights of exploration and production.

O

OCS *abbr:* Outer Continental Shelf.

offset drilling rule *n:* rule applied by the courts (especially in states that have adopted nonabsolute ownership views of oil and gas). It states that a landowner whose property is being drained by wells on neighboring tracts can protect himself only by drilling wells of his own and producing oil or gas as quickly as he can. Compare *rule of capture.*

offset well *n:* a well drilled on a tract of land next to another owner's tract on which there is a producing well.

oil payment *n:* a nonoperating interest in oil and gas from one or more leases, providing to its owner a fractional share of the oil and gas produced, free of the costs of production, and terminating when a specified dollar amount or volume of production has been realized. Oil payments may be created and reserved when a lease or royalty interest is assigned, or may be carved out of a leasehold or royalty interest and assigned to another party.

operating agreement *n:* See *joint operating agreement.*

Outer Continental Shelf *n:* the land seaward from areas subject to state mineral ownership to a depth of roughly 8,000 feet, beyond which mineral exploration and development are not, at present, feasible. Boundaries of the Outer Continental Shelf are set by law; for example, the state of Louisiana owns 3 miles seaward from the shoreline. Generally, the term is used to describe federally controlled areas.

overconvey *v:* in regard to land, to convey (intentionally or from ignorance) a larger fraction of interest in property than the owner actually has a right to convey.

overriding royalty *n:* an interest carved out of the lessee's working interest, entitling its owner to a fraction of production free of any production or operating expense, but not free of production or severance tax levied on production. An overriding royalty may be created by grant or by reservation. Commonly, an override is reserved by the assignor in a farmout agreement or other assignment. An override's duration corresponds to that of the lease from which it was created.

ownership in place *n:* See *absolute ownership.*

P

paid-up lease *n:* an oil and gas lease that, when first acquired, is paid up through the primary term. All delay rentals are paid along with the cash bonus, and no further action is required during the primary term.

parol evidence *n:* evidence given verbally rather than in writing.

patent *n:* in the case of land, an instrument by means of which a government transfers a fee simple estate to another party.

paying quantity *n:* See *commercial quantity.*

payout *n:* the point at which the operator of a well has recovered his costs of drilling, completing, and operating such a well and can begin to show a profit.

plat *n:* a map of a particular tract, group of tracts, or area of land.

pooling *n:* the combining of small or irregular tracts into a unit large enough to meet state spacing regulations for drilling. Compare *unitization.*

pooling and unitization clause *n:* in an oil and gas lease, the clause that permits the lessee to pool or unitize the leased tract.

potential *n:* the maximum volume of oil or gas that a well is capable of producing, calculated from well test data.

power of attorney *n:* a legal instrument that authorizes one person to act for another, generally or specifically. It ends upon the death of either of the parties unless specific language allows it to survive.

preferential right of purchase *n:* a prior right of purchase reserved to buy an oil and gas interest by meeting the terms of a proposed sale of the interest to any other party.

primary term *n:* the specified duration of an oil and gas lease, for example, 3 years. Compare *secondary term.*

Producers 88 *n:* any of a wide variety of lease forms used in the midcontinent and Gulf regions.

production payment *n:* a cost-free percentage of the working interest that ends when a specified amount of money or number of barrels has been reached.

proportionate reduction clause *n:* in an oil and gas lease, the clause that allows for proportionate reductions in rentals and royalties should the lessor's interests be less than the entire fee simple estate.

proration *n:* a system, enforced by a state or federal agency or by agreement between operators, that limits the amount of petroleum that can be produced from a well or a field within a given period of time.

proration unit *n:* See *drilling and spacing unit.*

prospect *n:* lease or other right in a particular geographical area believed to lie on a geologic structural or stratigraphic trap. Additional geological and geophysical work may be required before a test well is drilled thereon.

public domain land *n:* all land and water originally (and still) owned by the United States.

Pugh clause *n:* in an oil and gas lease, a clause that releases nonproducing acreage (horizontal release) or zones (vertical release) at the end of the primary term or some other specified period. Under such clause, unproductive or untested zones and acreage that are outside a producng pooled unit must be released if drilling or exploration does not occur by the end of the specified time. Also sometimes called a Freestone rider.

Q

quitclaim deed *n:* a deed that relinquishes to someone else any rights or interests that a person may have in property. The grantor of the quitclaim deed warrants nothing, merely conveys whatever rights, if any, he may have.

R

range *n:* the name given to the east-west lines of the rectangular survey system. Compare *township.*

range line *n:* an east-west line of the rectangular survey system.

ratification *n:* approval and confirmation of a contract or other legal instrument, usually by means of a second written instrument.

reassignment obligation *n:* a part of a farmout agreement or other assignment that stipulates an obligation to reassign earned acreage back to the farmor or assignor before the farmee or assignee allows the lease to expire on the acreage.

recording *n:* the act by which a legal instrument is entered in a book of public record, usually in the county clerk's office. Such recording amounts to legal notice to all persons of the rights or claims specified in the instrument.

rectangular survey system *n:* the method of measuring land adopted by the United States in 1785. Under this system the land is measured in squares called congressional townships, which are approximately 6 miles wide and approximately 6 miles long. The squares are marked off by means of parallel north-south lines called township lines and parallel east-west lines called range lines.

reform *v:* to rewrite a contract, guided by principles of equity. Parties who believe, for example, that the written form of an oil and gas lease does not express what was in fact intended or agreed upon may sue in hope that the court will agree with them and reform the lease to express the intended facts or circumstances.

release *n:* a statement filed by the lessee of an oil and gas lease indicating that the lease has been relinquished.

remainderman *n:* someone who holds a future interest in property and who will come into possession when the present possessory interest ends (as upon the death of a life tenant).

reversionary interest *n:* a future interest created by law when an estate is, for example, leased. The reversion is not conveyed but is retained to take effect later in favor of the grantor or his heirs. See *term minerals.*

rider *n:* a separately listed provision in a lease. Also called an exhibit or allonge.

right-of-way *n:* the legal right of passage over public land and privately owned property; also the way or area over which the right exists. The width of a right-of-way varies according to contract specifications and individual easements, but it is generally between 50 and 100 feet.

royalty *n:* the part of oil, gas, and minerals or their cash value paid by the lessee to the lessor or to one who has acquired possession of the royalty rights, based on a percentage of the gross production from the property free and clear of all costs except taxes.

royalty clause *n:* in an oil and gas lease, the clause that establishes the percentage of production paid to the lessor.

royalty deed *n:* the legal instrument that conveys a share of oil or gas production. Unlike a mineral deed, a royalty deed does not create a severance of the estate.

rule of capture *n:* rule applied by the courts (especially in states that have adopted nonabsolute ownership views of oil and gas) that gives title to oil and gas produced from a tract of land to the party reducing it to possession. The rule has been modified a great deal by state regulatory agencies. Compare *offset drilling rule.*

run sheet *n:* a landman's list and brief description of all the documents in the history of ownership of a given tract of land. Compare *takeoff.* See *chain of title.*

S

secondary term *n:* the term, usually in a phrase like "so long thereafter as oil or gas is produced in paying quantities," that extends a lease beyond its primary term. Compare *primary term.*

section *n:* a unit of land measurement in the rectangular survey system. Each 6-mile square, or township, is divided into 36 sections. A section is usually 1 square mile, or 640 acres. It may be larger or smaller depending on its position in the township.

seismic option agreement *n:* an agreement that permits seismic exploration of land for a specified price per acre. The company gathering seismic information can, by the terms of the agreement, eventually lease selected acreage, again for an agreed-upon price.

sever *v:* separate, disjoin.

severance *n:* the separation of a mineral or royalty interest from other interests in that land given by grant or reservation.

shut in *v:* 1. to close the valves on a well so that it stops producing. 2. to close in a well in which a kick has occurred.

shut-in royalty *n:* payment to royalty owners in lieu of production, rentals, or other consideration on a shut-in gas well that is capable of producing but does not have a market.

shut-in royalty clause *n:* clause in a lease specifying the payments that must be made on a gas well capable of producing but shut in for lack of a market or pending connection with a pipeline.

shut-in well *n:* usually, a gas well shut in for lack of a market or pending connection with a pipeline.

sight draft *n:* a draft or order for payment that must be picked up on the day that it arrives at the drawer's bank. For example, if a lessee pays a lessor a cash bonus by means of a sight draft, the lessee must pick up that draft on the same day that it arrives at his bank from the lessor's bank.

simultaneous filing *n:* a noncompetitive procedure—basically a drawing—used to grant oil and gas leases on federal lands that have not been leased before.

sovereign *n:* in the case of land, the government that holds and is capable of transferring title.

stand-up title opinion *n:* prepared in the absence of an abstract of title, a stand-up opinion is written by a title examiner who works from a run sheet that he checks at the county courthouse before deciding whether or not he needs additional facts. Compare *abstract-based title opinion.*

statute law *n:* the descendant of Roman law which, through the French Napoleonic Code, came to be the basis of law in Louisiana. Law enacted by a legislative body. Also called civil law.

statutory unitization *n:* unitization that proceeds without the willing cooperation of all the affected parties. The unitization is authorized by order of a state regulatory agency in accordance with state statute. Also called forced unitization.

subordination *n:* in the case of an oil and gas lease, a supplementary agreement that resolves the priority of rights to the leased property and subordinates an earlier instrument (for example, a mortgage) to the oil and gas lease.

support agreement *n:* an agreement between petroleum companies, in which one contributes money or acreage to another's drilling operation in return for information gained from the drilling.

surface estate *n:* rights and interests in the surface of land, created when the owner severs or separates his interests in the property.

surface owner *n:* owner of the rights and interests in a surface estate (where interests in a landed estate have been severed). Compare *mineral owner.*

surrender clause *n:* in an oil and gas lease, the clause that specifies the procedure to be followed should the lessee wish to surrender all or part of his leased interests.

T

takeoff *n:* usually prepared by an abstract company, a takeoff lists and briefly describes the documents relevant to the title of a given piece of property. It costs much less to prepare than an abstract of title and is similar to a landman's run sheet.

tenants in common *n:* See *cotenants.*

term clause *n:* See *habendum clause.*

term minerals *n pl:* severed minerals acquired for a certain time and, generally, as long thereafter as production continues.

tight hole *n:* a well about which information is restricted for security or competitive reasons and such information given only to those authorized to receive it.

title *n:* a term standing for those facts that, if proved, will enable a person to regain or retain possession of property.

title opinion *n:* the written opinion of a title examiner on the status of the title to a given piece of property. Compare *drill site opinion, division order opinion.*

top lease *n:* a lease acquired while a mineral lease to the same property is still in effect. The top lease replaces (by a different company) the existing lease when it expires or is terminated.

township *n:* 1. the north-south lines of the rectangular survey system. 2. the square, 6 miles on each side, that is the major unit of land in the rectangular survey scheme of measurement. Compare *range.*

township line *n:* a north-south line of the rectangular survey system.

transfer order *n:* an agreement regarding change of production ownership, indemnifying the pipeline company, or purchaser.

tribal land *n:* land within an Indian reservation or owned by an Indian tribe, group, or band.

trust *n:* a right in property held by one party for the benefit of another. The trustee holds the legal interest or title, and the beneficiary holds the equitable interest or title and receives the benefits.

trustee *n:* person who holds the legal title to property in trust for the benefit of another. With the title go specified powers and duties relating to the property.

turnkey contract *n:* a drilling contract that calls for the payment of a stipulated amount to the drilling contractor on completion of the well. In a turnkey contract, the contractor furnishes all material and labor and controls the entire drilling operation, independent of supervision by the operator. A turnkey contract does not as a rule include the completion of a well as a producer.

U

undivided interest *n:* a fractional interest in minerals that, when conveyed, gives the new owner that fractional interest in the described tract. For example, a ¼ undivided interest in an 80-acre tract amounts to a ¼ interest in the entire 80 acres, or 20 net undivided mineral acres. Compare *divided interest.*

unitization *n:* the combining of leased tracts on a field-wide or reservoir-wide scale so that many tracts may be treated as one to facilitate operations like secondary recovery. Compare *pooling.*

"unless" clause *n:* See *drilling and delay rental clause.*

V

vara *n:* a Spanish unit of measurement, equal to 33⅓ inches.

voluntary pooling *n:* pooling of leased tracts willingly undertaken by all the parties involved, both working interest owners and royalty owners.

voluntary unitization *n:* unitization that is accomplished with the willing cooperation of the affected parties, both working interest owners and royalty owners.

W

warranty clause *n:* in an oil and gas lease, the clause that assures title to the leased property by an express covenant to that effect.

warranty deed *n:* a deed in which the grantor stipulates by express covenant that the title to property is as it is represented to be and that the grantee's possession shall be undisturbed. Defects in title may include those that may have existed before the grantor obtained the title as well as any that have arisen during his ownership.

well density *n:* the ratio between the number of wells drilled in a field and the acreage. Under a 40-acre spacing pattern, the well density is one well per 40 acres.

well spacing *n:* the regulation of the number and location of wells over an oil or gas reservoir as a conservation measure. Compare well density.

windfall profit tax *n:* a federal excise tax on crude oil, which has a different rate for oil in a number of categories, for example, newly discovered oil, stripper oil, stripper oil produced by independents, and so on. The tax rate is determined at a percentage—for instance, at 25 percent—of the difference between a base price and a market price. There are a variety of exceptions and exemptions; interested parties should query the IRS or a tax accountant.

working interest *n:* the interest in oil and gas that includes reponsibility for all drilling, developing, and operating costs. Also called operating interest or leasehold interest.

BIBLIOGRAPHY

American Petroleum Institute. *Energy Security for the United States: Progress, Pitfalls, Potential.* Washington, D. C.: 1982.

American Petroleum Institute. *More Oil and Gas from Government Lands.* Washington, D. C.: n.d.

Berger, Bill D., and Kenneth E. Anderson. *Modern Petroleum: A Basic Primer of the Industry.* 2d ed. Tulsa: PennWell Publishing Co., 1981.

Boatright, Mody C. *Folklore of the Oil Industry.* Dallas: Southern Methodist University Press, 1963.

Boignon, Howard L., and Christine L. Murphy. "Liabilities of Nonoperating Mineral Interest Owners." *University of Colorado Law Review* 51, no. 1 (Fall 1979): 153-207.

Brown, Earl A., Jr. "Elemental Principles of the Modern Oil and Gas Lease." *Montana Law Journal* 17 (Fall 1955): 39ff.

Fiske, Terry Noble. "Mining Partnership." In *Proceedings of the Twenty-Sixth Annual Institute on Oil and Gas Law and Taxation of the Southwest Legal Foundation.* Edited by Armine Carol Ernst. New York: Matthew Bender, 1975.

Fundamentals of Petroleum. 2d ed. Austin: Petroleum Extension Service, 1981.

Gifis, Steven H. *Law Dictionary.* Woodbury, N.Y.: Barron's Educational Series, 1975.

Hamm, W. Jeff. "Operating Agreements and Farmouts." MS from Oil and Gas Lawyers Association and American Association of Petroleum Landmen.

Hankinson, R. L., and R. L. Hankinson, Jr. *Landman's Encyclopedia.* 2d ed. Houston: Gulf Publishing Co., 1981.

Harper, John T. "Division Orders — Their Use and Effect after the Middleton Case." In *Advanced Oil, Gas and Mineral Law Course of the State Bar of Texas.* Austin, 1981.

Houghton, James L., ed. *Miller's Oil and Gas Federal Income Taxation.* Chicago: Commerce Clearing House, 1981.

Jones, Charlotte. "An Overview of the Terminology and Procedures of Oil and Gas Land Work." Dallas: Skilldex, 1981. Pamphlet.

Kenney, Bruce A. "Construction and Negotiation of Oil and Gas Leases." *Law Notes* 15, no. 4 (Fall 1979).

Kresge, David T., Thomas A. Morehouse, and George W. Rogers. *Issues in Alaska Development.* Institute of Social and Economic Research of the University of Alaska. Seattle: University of Washington Press, 1977.

Langenkamp, R. D. *Handbook of Oil Industry Terms and Phrases.* 2d ed. Tulsa: Petroleum Publishing Co., 1977.

Leecraft, Jodie, ed. *A Dictionary of Petroleum Terms.* 3d ed. Austin: Petroleum Extension Service, 1983.

Lowe, John S., ed. *Fundamentals of Oil and Gas Leasing.* Rev. ed. Tulsa: IED Exploration, 1982.

McCray, Arthur W., and Frank W. Cole. *Oil Well Drilling Technology.* Norman: University of Oklahoma Press, 1959.

McDonald, Ben F., Jr. "Oil and Gas Leases for the General Practitioner." In *Advanced Oil, Gas and Mineral Law Course of the State Bar of Texas.* Austin, 1980.

_____. *"The Modern Oil and Gas Lease." In Advanced Oil, Gas and Mineral Law Course of the State Bar of Texas.* Austin, 1981.

Martin, Robert M., Jr. "Some Problems Created by Severed Mineral Interests." In *Advanced Oil, Gas and Mineral Law Course of the State Bar of Texas.* Austin, 1981.

Mecredy, Henry E., Jr. "Push a Button—Get a Map!" *TIPRO Reporter* (Spring 1982): 16–23, 64–67, 101.

Mosburg, Lewis G., Jr., ed. *Basics of Structuring Exploration Deals.* Oklahoma City: IED Exploration, 1980.

_____, ed. *Land Support Personnel—Phase One.* Fort Worth: Institutes for Energy Development, 1980.

_____, ed. *The Landman's Role in Unitization: Voluntary and Compulsory, Single Well and Fieldwide.* Fort Worth: Institutes for Energy Development, 1978.

Mosburg, Lewis G., Jr., and Robert A. Seaton, eds. *Canadian Petroleum Land Operations.* Fort Worth: Institutes for Energy Development, 1977.

Moses, Leslie. *The AAPL Guide for Landmen: From Lease to Release.* Rev. ed. 1980.

Prindle, David F. *Petroleum Politics and the Texas Railroad Commission.* Austin: The University of Texas Press, 1981.

Rogers, George W., ed. *Change in Alaska: People, Petroleum, and Politics.* Seattle: University of Washington Press, 1970.

Scott, John R. "How to Prepare an Oil and Gas Farmout Agreement." *Baylor Law Review* 33 (1981): 63ff.

Smith, Ernest E., III. "Conveyancing Problems." In *Advanced Oil, Gas and Mineral Law Course of the State Bar of Texas.* Austin, 1981.

Stafford, James L. *Look Before You Lease: A Layman's Guide to Oil and Gas Leasing.* Ada, Oklahoma: ROAR Press, 1981.

Sullivan, Brian R. "Playing Around with the Rules." *TIPRO Reporter* (Spring 1982): 43–45, 63.

Sullivan, Robert E. *Handbook of Oil and Gas Law.* Englewood Cliffs, N. J.: Prentice-Hall, 1955.

INDEX